# Introduction to Chemical Thermodynamics

# INTRODUCTION TO CHEMICAL THERMODYNAMICS

**IRVING M. KLOTZ**
*Morrison Professor of Chemistry*
*Northwestern University*

*With advice and suggestions from*

**Thomas Fraser Young**
*University of Chicago*

W. A. Benjamin, Inc.
New York Amsterdam 1964

**INTRODUCTION TO CHEMICAL THERMODYNAMICS**



Library of Congress Catalog Card Number 64-13922
Manufactured in the United States of America

*The manuscript was put into production June 13, 1963, and this volume was published March 30, 1964*

*The publisher is pleased to acknowledge the assistance of Edith Feinstein, who copyedited the manuscript; Russell F. Peterson, who produced the illustrations; and William Prokos, who designed the cover and dust jacket*

**W. A. BENJAMIN, INC.**
**New York, New York**

# Preface

The heart of chemical thermodynamics lies in the three basic principles of thermodynamics. The concepts involved in these principles and the important computational techniques used can be developed in a reasonably short period if one limits considerations to simple systems of constant composition. It is the aim of this short volume to provide a self-teaching text which can guide a student to an understanding of the basic concepts of thermodynamics and which can train him in some of the most useful chemical applications, particularly free energy calculations.* The only essential prerequisite for the use of this volume is familiarity with elementary calculus.

This book should be most useful to undergraduates in chemistry seeking an introductory and yet rigorous exposition of the elements of chemical thermodynamics. With the increasing use of energy concepts and calculations in modern biology and geology, biochemists, biologists, and geologists also should find here the essential background for understanding the ideas and computational procedures used. Finally engineers, who are well-acquainted with the foundations of thermodynamics, may find here an insight into the forms into which physical chemists have molded the fundamental concepts.

It is my hope that after a reader has worked through this volume he will have a sound grounding in fundamentals and will be able to read with comprehension any source of advanced or special topics in macroscopic chemical thermodynamics.

IRVING M. KLOTZ

*Evanston, Illinois*
*September* 1963

* All footnote references to chapters beyond 12 refer to the author's revised edition, *Basic Chemical Thermodynamics*, Benjamin, New York, 1964.

# Contents

# Answers to Selected Problems

## CHAPTER 2

1. 1 liter-atm = (a) $1.013 \times 10^9$ ergs
   (b) 24.25 cal
2. (a) 1 $ft^3$-atm = 689 cal
   (b) 1 volt-faraday = 23,050 cal
3. (a) $b, -\frac{b}{l}, 2, -1, \frac{b}{d}, 2, l$

   (b) $l - \frac{b^2}{l}, \frac{1}{2}, l - b$

   (c) $\frac{2(l-b)}{l}, \frac{l}{2}, \frac{l}{2(l-b)}, \frac{l+b}{2}$

9. (a) $\Delta V_{AC} = R\frac{(P_1T_2 - P_2T_1)}{P_1P_2} = \Delta V_{AB+BC}$

   (c) $\Delta W = -RT_1 \ln\frac{P_2}{P_1} + R\frac{(T_2 - T_1)}{(P_2 - P_1)} P_1 \ln\frac{P_2}{P_1}$

   $\Delta W_{AB+BC} = R(T_2 - T_1) - RT_1 \ln\frac{P_2}{P_1}$

10. (a) $dL$ exact, by reciprocity test
    (b) $DW$ inexact, by reciprocity test
11. (a) $\left(\frac{\partial V}{\partial T}\right)_S = -\frac{C_v}{T}\frac{V}{R}$
    (b) Yes, by reciprocity test

16. (a) homogeneous, degree 3
    (b) homogeneous, degree 1
    (c) homogeneous, degree $\frac{1}{2}$
    (d) homogeneous, degree 0
    (e) nonhomogeneous

# CHAPTER 3

1. $0°K = -272.4°C$

# CHAPTER 4

1. (a) $H_{182.5°K} - H_{0°K} = 3445$ cal/mole
   (b) $\Delta H = 6799$ cal/mole
2. (a) $C_v = 4.3223 \times 10^{-4}\, T^3$
   (b) $H_{15.14°K} - H_{0°K} = 5.68$ cal mole$^{-1}$ deg$^{-1}$
   $H_{182.5°K} - H_{0°K} = 3445$ cal/mole
3. $Q_P - Q_V =$ (a) $-$ 890 cal/mole
   (b) 0
   (c) $-$ 2680 cal/mole $N_2$
5. (a) $\left(\frac{\partial E}{\partial V}\right)_P = \frac{PC_v}{R}$ (b) $\left(\frac{\partial E}{\partial P}\right)_V = \frac{VC_v}{R}$
6. Water at 4°C

# CHAPTER 5

1. $-$ 67,140 cal/mole; $-$ 66,356 cal/mole
2. (a) Fumaric, 193.83 kcal mole$^{-1}$
   Maleic, $-$ 188.28 kcal mole$^{-1}$
   (b) 5.55 kcal mole$^{-1}$
3. $\epsilon_{S—S} = 66$ kcal mole$^{-1}$
4. $\epsilon_{N—F} = 66.4$ kcal mole$^{-1}$
5. $\epsilon_{N=N} = 94$ kcal mole$^{-1}$
8. $\epsilon_{C—C} = 79.2$ kcal mole$^{-1}$
9. (a) $\epsilon_{S—S} = 50.2$ kcal mole$^{-1}$
   (b) $\epsilon_{S—Cl} = 60$ kcal mole$^{-1}$
   (c) $\Delta H = -8700$ cal/mole
10. $\Delta H° = -66{,}947 - 3.280T + 3.540 \times 10^{-3}\, T^2 - 9.623 \times 10^{-7} T^3$
11. (a) $-$ 1850 cal mole$^{-1}$
    (b) $-$ 1990 cal mole$^{-1}$
12. 210 kcal
13. 1420°K

## CHAPTER 6

1. (a) $W = P(V_2 - V_1)$

   (b) $W = nRT \ln \dfrac{V_2}{V_1}$

   (c) $W = RT\left(\ln \dfrac{\text{v}_2 - b}{\text{v}_1 - b}\right) + \dfrac{a}{\text{v}_2} - \dfrac{a}{\text{v}_1}$ for 1 mole of gas

   (d) $W = -RT \ln \dfrac{P_2}{P_1} + \dfrac{C}{2}(P_2^2 - P_1^2)$

   (e) $W = -RT \ln \dfrac{P_2}{P_1}$

3. (b) $W = -RT \ln \dfrac{P_2}{P_1}$; $\Delta E = 0$

   $Q = -RT \ln \dfrac{P_2}{P_1}$; $\Delta H = B(P_2 - P_1)$

4. (a) $T(\text{v} - B)^{R/C_v} = \text{constant}$
   (b) $\Delta H = C_p(T_2 - T_1) + B(P_2 - P_1)$
   (c) $\Delta H = B(P_2 - P_1)$

5. (b) $C_v = C_p - V\left(\dfrac{\partial P}{\partial T}\right)_V$

6. $W = -1.5\,RT_1\left[\left(\dfrac{V_1}{V_2}\right)^{2/3} - 1\right]$

7. $n = 2.00$ moles

12. (b) 330 meters $\text{sec}^{-1}$

13. $\beta = \dfrac{R\text{v}^2(\text{v} - b)}{RT\text{v}^3 - 2a(\text{v} - b)^2}$

## CHAPTER 7

1. (a) $V = 33.97$ liters; $P = 0.09919$ atm; $T = 207.0$ and $108.4°\text{K}$
   (b)

| | | $W$, liter-atm | $Q$, liter-atm | $\Delta E$, liter-atm | $\Delta H$, liter-atm | $\Delta S$, liter-atm $\text{deg}^{-1}$ |
|---|---|---|---|---|---|---|
| (1) | A | 15.54 | 15.54 | 0.00 | 0.00 | 0.0569 |
| | B | 22.41 | 56.03 | 33.62 | 56.03 | 0.1425 |
| | Sum | 37.95 | 71.57 | 33.62 | 56.03 | 0.1994 |
| (2) | A | 31.07 | 31.07 | 0.00 | 0.00 | 0.1139 |
| | B | 0.00 | 33.62 | 33.62 | 56.03 | 0.0855 |
| | Sum | 31.07 | 64.69 | 33.62 | 56.03 | 0.1994 |

| | | $W$, liter-atm | $Q$, liter-atm | $\Delta E$, liter-atm | $\Delta H$, liter-atm | $\Delta S$, liter-atm deg$^{-1}$ |
|---|---|---|---|---|---|---|
| (3) | A | 8.14 | 0.00 | − 8.14 | − 13.56 | 0.00 |
| | B | 27.84 | 69.60 | 41.76 | 69.60 | 0.1995 |
| | Sum | 35.98 | 69.60 | 33.62 | 56.04 | 0.1995 |
| (4) | A | 20.28 | 0.00 | − 20.28 | − 33.80 | 0.00 |
| | B | 0.00 | 53.91 | 53.91 | 89.83 | 0.1992 |
| | Sum | 20.28 | 53.91 | 33.63 | 56.03 | 0.1992 |

4. (b) $\left(\frac{\partial E}{\partial V}\right)_P = C_v \frac{P}{R}$

   (c) $S = \int C_v \, d \ln T + R \ln (V - B) + S_0$

13. (a) $3.33 \times 10^{-3}$ eu; (b) $-3.33 \times 10^{-3}$ eu;
   (c) $5.0 \times 10^{-3}$ eu; (d) − 1.50 cal

# CHAPTER 8

5.

| | $W$, cal/mole | $Q$, cal/mole | $\Delta E$ | $\Delta H$ | $\Delta S$, cal/mole-deg | $\Delta G$, cal/mole | $\Delta A$, cal/mole |
|---|---|---|---|---|---|---|---|
| (a) | 1250 | 1250 | 0 | 0 | 4.58 | − 1250 | − 1250 |
| (b) | 0 | 0 | 0 | 0 | 0 | 0 | 0 |
| (c) | 0 | 0 | 0 | 0 | 4.58 | − 1250 | − 1250 |
| (d) | 0 | 0 | 0 | 0 | 4.58 | − 1250 | − 1250 |

6. $W = -740$ cal/mole; $Q = -9710$ cal/mole
   $\Delta E = -8970$ cal/mole; $\Delta H = -9710$ cal/mole
   $\Delta S = -26.0$ cal mole$^{-1}$ deg$^{-1}$; $\Delta G = 0$
   $\Delta A = +740$ cal/mole

7. $\Delta G^\circ = 66{,}947 + 0.77T + 7.554T \log T - 3.590 \times 10^{-3}T^2 + 4.812 \times 10^{-7}T^3$

8. $\Delta G = \Delta H_0 - \Delta a T \ln T - \frac{\Delta b}{2} T^2 + \frac{\Delta c}{2}\left(\frac{1}{T}\right) + IT$

13. (a) $W = -74.24$ ergs
   (b) $Q = 39.56$ ergs
   (c) $\Delta E = 113.80$ ergs $= \Delta H$; $\Delta S = 0.14$ erg deg$^{-1}$; $\Delta A = 74.24$ ergs
   (d) $\Delta G = -74.24$ ergs
   (e) $Q = -113.80$ ergs $= \Delta H = \Delta E$; $\Delta S = -0.14$ erg deg$^{-1}$; $\Delta A = -74.24$ ergs

15. (a) 690 cal given to bath
    (b) 1620 cal absorbed from bath

## CHAPTER 9

1. (a) None
   (b) 1
   (c) 2
   (d) 1, 2
   (e) 1
   (f) 2
   (g) 1
2. (a) $\Delta G^\circ = 0$
   (b) $\Delta G^\circ = 2050$ cal mole$^{-1}$
3. (a) $\Delta G = -1760$ cal mole$^{-1}$
5. 12.8 cal mole$^{-1}$
7. (a) $\Delta H = 615$ cal mole$^{-1}$; $\Delta S = 2.45$ eu
   (b) $\Delta H = 591$ cal mole$^{-1}$; $\Delta S = 1.39$ eu
8. $\Delta H = 8560$ cal mole$^{-1}$
11. $\log P = \text{constant} - \dfrac{\Delta H_0}{2.3RT} + \dfrac{\Delta a}{R} \log T + \dfrac{\Delta b}{4.6R} T$

## CHAPTER 10

1. (a) $\Delta G^\circ = -4.814\,RT + 2059\,R$
   (b) and (c): $\Delta S^\circ = 9.58$ cal mole$^{-1}$ deg$^{-1}$; $\Delta H = 4090$ cal mole$^{-1}$
   (d) $\Delta C_p^\circ = 0$
2. $\Delta H^\circ = -48.32$ kcal mole$^{-1}$; $\Delta S^\circ = -95.21$ gibbs mole$^{-1}$; $\Delta C_p^\circ = 0$
3. (c) $\Delta H^\circ = 5.9 \pm 0.6$ kcal mole$^{-1}$; $\Delta S^\circ = 4.9 \pm 1.0$ gibbs mole$^{-1}$
4. (b)

| $t$, °C | $\Delta G^\circ$, cal mole$^{-1}$ | $\Delta S^\circ$, cal mole$^{-1}$ deg$^{-1}$ | $\Delta H$, cal mole$^{-1}$ |
|---|---|---|---|
| 0 | − 5451.4 | − 10.98 | − 8,450.7 |
| 25 | − 5129.6 | − 14.83 | − 9,551.3 |
| 60 | − 4525.5 | − 19.38 | − 10,982.1 |

   (c) $\Delta G^\circ = -4525.8$ cal/mole
   $\Delta H^\circ = -10{,}972.1$ cal/mole
   $\Delta S^\circ = -19.349$ cal mole$^{-1}$ deg$^{-1}$

## CHAPTER 11

4. Yes, since $\Delta G^\circ = -31{,}869$ cal mole$^{-1}$
5. $\Delta H = 433$ cal mole$^{-1}$
8. No. Residual entropy at 0°K = 1.51 gibbs mole$^{-1}$

10. II has 1.484 eu residual entropy at 0°K
11. (a) 0.0234 volt

| (b) | | (c) |
|---|---|---|
| $W_{net}$ = | 1077 cal | 0 |
| $Q$ = | 477 cal | − 600 |
| $\Delta E$ = | − 600 cal | − 600 |
| $\Delta H$ = | − 600 cal | − 600 |
| $\Delta S$ = | 1.6 eu | 1.6 |
| $\Delta G$ = | − 1077 cal | − 1077 |

12. (a) Quinone, − 44.65 kcal mole$^{-1}$; hydroquinone, − 87.51 kcal mole$^{-1}$
    (b) − 42.86 kcal mole$^{-1}$
    (c) $\Delta S^\circ = -37.99$ eu; $\Delta G^\circ = -31.83$ kcal mole$^{-1}$
    (d) 0.690 volt

# CHAPTER 12

1. (a) $\Delta H^\circ = -44{,}888$ cal mole$^{-1}$
   (b) $\left(\frac{\partial H}{\partial P}\right)_T = \frac{9}{128}\frac{RT_c}{P_c} - \frac{162}{128}\frac{R}{P_c}\frac{T_c^3}{T^2}$
   (c) $\Delta H = -9.8$ cal
   (d) $\Delta H^\circ_{298} = -53{,}627$ cal
   (e) $S^\circ_{298} = 78.42$ cal mole$^{-1}$ deg$^{-1}$
   (f) $\Delta S^\circ_{298} = -180.79$ cal mole$^{-1}$ deg$^{-1}$
   (g) $\Delta S = 29.30$ cal mole$^{-1}$ deg$^{-1}$
   (h) $\Delta S = -5.56$ eu
   (i) $\Delta S^\circ_{298} = -157.06$ eu
   (j) $\Delta Gf^\circ_{298} = 297$ cal mole$^{-1}$
   (k) $\Delta Gf^\circ_{298} = 1941$ cal mole$^{-1}$
   (l) $\Delta Gf^\circ_{298} = 2092$ cal mole$^{-1}$
   (m) $S^\circ_{298} = 101.5$ eu, cf. 102.16 eu
   (n) $S^\circ_{298} = 78.9$ eu

# Chemical Thermodynamics

# 1 Introduction

## 1-1 OBJECTIVES OF CHEMICAL THERMODYNAMICS

An alert young chemist with only an elementary background in science might be surprised that a subject named "thermodynamics" has any pertinence to chemical change. *Thermodynamics* as a term implies literally a field concerned with mechanical action produced by heat. And indeed the origin of thermodynamics as a unified body of concepts and derived consequences does lie in the analysis by Carnot, in 1824, of the performance of heat engines. His famous memoir[1] on this subject is in fact entitled "Reflections on the Motive Power of Heat."

Although Carnot's primary objective was an evaluation of the mechanical efficiency of a steam engine, his analysis introduced certain broad concepts whose significance goes far beyond engineering problems. One of these conceptions is *reversible process*, which provides for thermodynamics the corresponding idealization that "frictionless motion" contributes to mechanics. The idea of "reversibility" has applicability much beyond ideal heat engines. Furthermore, it introduces continuity into the visualization of the process being considered, and hence invites the introduction of the differential calculus. It was Clapeyron[2] who actually expounded Carnot's ideas in

[1] S. Carnot, *Reflexions sur la puissance motrice du feu*, Bachelier, Paris, 1824. Carnot used the term "motive power" in the same sense that we use "work."

[2] E. Clapeyron, *J. Ecole Polytech.* (*Paris*), **14**, 153 (1834).

the notation of the calculus and who thereby derived the vapor pressure equation associated with his name, as well as the performance characteristics of ideal engines.

A second conception introduced by Carnot arose from the analogy he drew between the motive power of a heat engine and of a water wheel. In the heat engine one needs two temperature levels (a boiler and a condenser, respectively) corresponding to the two levels in height of a waterfall. In a waterfall, furthermore, the quantity of water discharged by the wheel at the bottom level is the same as originally entered at the top level. Carnot postulated, therefore, a corresponding "thermal quantity"[3] which was conserved as it was carried by the heat engine from a high temperature to a low one. On this basis he was able to answer in a very general way a long-standing question, whether steam was uniquely suited for a heat engine, by showing that in the ideal engine any other substance would be just as efficient. Shortly after the concept of energy was clarified and generalized into the first law of thermodynamics, particularly by Helmholtz, Mayer, and Joule, the "thermal quantity" of Carnot was reformulated by Clausius[4] into the concept of entropy. This conception then provided an alternative basis for the enunciation of another general principle, the second law of thermodynamics, applicable to all types of macroscopic natural phenomena instead of just to heat engines.

Consequently, during the latter part of the nineteenth century the scope of thermodynamics was greatly widened. It became apparent, for example, that the same concepts that allow one to predict the maximum efficiency of a heat engine also permit the computation of the maximum yield in a chemical reaction to equilibrium, or the change in vapor pressure of a liquid on addition of a solute, or the maximum voltage of a battery. For these and other phenomena of chemical concern, thermal and work quantities, although controlling factors, are only of indirect interest. Accordingly, a more sophisticated formulation of thermodynamic principles was established, particularly by J. Willard Gibbs,[5] which emphasized the nature and

[3] Since Carnot wrote his memoir some thirty years before the term "entropy" was invented and before the generalized conception of energy was established, we cannot be certain what he conceived to be the thermal quantity conserved in the cyclical operation of an ideal heat engine. Nevertheless, from an examination of the careful way in which he used his terms "calorique" and "chaleur," as well as from a study of his posthumously published notes, it seems very likely that by "calorique" he meant the quantity now termed "entropy." For a discussion of this subject see H. L. Callendar, *Proc. Phys. Soc.* (*London*) **23**, 153 (1911), and V. K. LaMer, *Am. J. Phys.*, **23**, 95 (1955).

[4] R. Clausius, *Pogg. Ann.*, **79**, 368, 500 (1850), and later papers.

[5] J. W. Gibbs, *Trans. Conn. Acad. Sci.*, **3**, 228 (1876). See also *The Collected Works of J. Willard Gibbs*, Yale Univ. Press, New Haven, 1928; reprinted 1948.

use of a number of special energy functions to describe the state of a system. These have proved to be much more convenient and powerful in prescribing the rules that govern chemical and physical transitions. In a sense, therefore, the name *energetics* is more descriptive than *thermodynamics* in so far as applications to chemistry are concerned. More commonly, however, one affixes an adjective, *chemical,* to *thermodynamics* to indicate the change in emphasis, and the modification of the literal and original meaning of "thermodynamics."

In practice, the primary objective of chemical thermodynamics is the establishment of a criterion for the determination of the feasibility or spontaneity of a given transformation. This transformation may be either physical or chemical. For example, one may be interested in a criterion for determining the possibility of a spontaneous transformation from one phase to another, as from one crystalline form to another, or one may wish to know whether a reaction suggested for the preparation of some substance has a reasonable chance of success or is utterly hopeless. Using the energy functions, based on the two fundamental (empirical) laws, chemical thermodynamics has developed a variety of further theoretical concepts and mathematical functions which provide a basis for answering these questions.

Having determined that a reaction is feasible, the chemist wishes to know further the maximum yields he may hope to obtain in a particular chemical transformation. Thermodynamic methods provide a basis for the formulation of the mathematical relations that are necessary to estimate such equilibrium yields.

Although the analysis of problems of chemical transformations is probably the main objective of chemical thermodynamics, the theory is capable also of application to many other problems encountered in chemical operations. As an illustration, the study of phase equilibria, for ideal and nonideal systems, is basic to the intelligent use of the techniques of extraction, fractional distillation, and crystallization. Similarly, one may be interested in the energy changes—either in the form of heat or of work—which may accompany a chemical or physical transformation. Thermodynamic concepts and methods provide a powerful approach to the solution of these and related chemical problems.

## 1-2 LIMITATIONS OF CLASSICAL THERMODYNAMICS

Although our descriptions of chemical changes are permeated with the terms and language of molecular theory, we should be aware that classical thermodynamics deals only with the properties of matter in bulk (e.g., pressure, temperature, volume, electromotive force, magnetic susceptibility, heat capacity). Its fundamental principles can be formulated without any recognition of the existence or properties of molecules; it is a phenomenological science.[6] Although in a formal sense this feature may seem an advantage, for classical thermodynamics does not require any modification as our knowledge and concepts of molecular structure change, it is also a distinct handicap; from a classical thermodynamic study one cannot obtain information at the molecular level. To obtain such information one must first apply the laws of mechanics to molecules and then formulate, by suitable statistical averaging methods, the rules of macroscopic behavior that would be expected from an assembly of a large number of such molecules. The collection of new concepts and procedures for this type of analysis constitute the subject of *statistical mechanics*.

There are also limitations of a more functional nature. Although the theory of thermodynamics provides the foundation for the solution of many chemical problems, the answers obtained are generally not definitive. In the language of the mathematician, we might say that classical thermodynamics is capable of formulating necessary conditions but not sufficient conditions. Thus, a thermodynamic analysis may rule out a given reaction for the synthesis of some substance by indicating that such a transformation cannot proceed spontaneously under any set of available conditions. In such a case we have a definitive answer. On the other hand, if the analysis indicates that a reaction may proceed spontaneously, no statement can be made from classical thermodynamics alone that it will do so in any finite time. For example, benzene is unstable with respect to its elements, according to thermodynamic calculations. In other words, according to thermodynamic theory, benzene *may* decompose spontaneously into carbon and hydrogen even at room temperature. Yet every chemist is aware of the practical stability of benzene standing in a room. This is not a contradiction of the theory, because thermodynamics claims no ability to predict the *time* required for a reaction. Much experience has indicated that when suitable catalysts are available, substances which apparently are very stable can be made to undergo transformations that thermodynamic calculation indicates are theoretically spontaneous.

An analogous situation is encountered in considerations of the *extent* to which a given chemical reaction may proceed. No statement can be made about the actual yield obtainable under a given set of conditions; only the maximum yield, the equilibrium yield, may be predicted. This limitation, too, is a consequence of the inability of classical thermodynamics to make any statement about the rate of a reaction. There is no relation between the kinetics of a reaction and the thermodynamic energy changes accompanying

[6] Classical thermodynamics is not unique in this respect. Classical mechanics likewise is concerned with the behavior of macroscopic systems, in this case the time course of the positions of a body, without regard of the molecular nature of the body.

the reaction. The problem of kinetics is one which classical thermodynamic analysis has been unable to solve. Only since the introduction of statistical methods and the concepts of the kinetic-molecular theory has a promising approach been made.

Similarly, in connection with the *work* obtainable from a chemical or physical transformation, only limiting values may be calculated. Thermodynamic functions predict the work which may be obtained if the reaction is carried out with infinite slowness, in a so-called "reversible" manner. However, it is impossible to specify the actual work obtained in a real or natural process in which the time interval is finite, except for the statement that the real work will be less than the quantity obtainable in a reversible situation.

Thus classical thermodynamic methods can treat only limiting cases.[7] Nevertheless, such a restriction is not nearly as severe as it may seem at first glance, since in many cases it is possible to approach equilibrium conditions very closely, and the thermodynamic quantities coincide with actual values, within experimental error. In other situations, thermodynamic analysis may rule out certain reactions under *any* conditions, and a great deal of time and effort may be saved. Even in their most constrained applications, thermodynamic methods, by limiting solutions within certain boundary values, can reduce materially the amount of experimental work necessary to yield a definitive answer to a particular problem.

[7] Classical thermodynamics also encounters difficulties in treating fluctuation phenomena, such as Brownian motion or the "shot effect" or certain turbidity phenomena. These difficulties are different in character from the limitations inherent in the framework of the analytical method. We recognize now that all such phenomena are expressions of local microscopic fluctuations in behavior of a relatively few molecules which deviate randomly from the average behavior of the entire assembly. Such random fluctuations make it impossible to assign, in this submicroscopic region, a definite value to such properties as temperature or pressure. Classical thermodynamics, however, is predicated on the assumption that a definite and reproducible value can always be measured for such properties. Hence it can only deal with systems where the number of molecules is so large that random fluctuations are not observable.

# 2 | Mathematical Apparatus[1]

Ordinary language is deficient in varying degrees for the expression of the ideas and findings of science. An exact science must be founded on precise definitions, which are difficult to obtain by verbalization. Mathematics, on the other hand, offers a precise mode of expression. Mathematics also provides a rigorous logical procedure and a device for the development in a succinct form of a long and often complicated argument. A long train of abstract thought can be condensed with full preservation of continuity into brief mathematical notation, and we can readily proceed with further steps in reasoning without carrying in our minds the otherwise overwhelming burden of all previous steps in the sequence. Mathematics, therefore, is the language of thermodynamics.

Most branches of theoretical science can be expounded at various levels of sophistication. The most elegant and formal approach to thermodynamics, that of Caratheodory,[2] depends on a familiarity with a special type of

[1] For convenience in writing, the author has assembled in this single chapter all the mathematical methods to be described in this textbook. In actual classroom presentations, however, the author discusses only the first third of this chapter at this point. The remaining portions are introduced as they are needed further along in the course.

[2] C. Caratheodory, *Math. Ann.*, **67**, 355 (1909); P. Frank, *Thermodynamics*, Brown Univ., Providence, R. I., 1945; J. T. Edsall and J. Wyman, *Biophysical Chemistry*, Vol. 1, Academic, New York, 1958; J. G. Kirkwood and I. Oppenheim, *Chemical Thermodynamics*, McGraw-Hill, New York, 1961.

differential equation (Pfaff equation), with which the usual student of chemistry is unacquainted. An introductory presentation follows best along historical lines of development, for which only the elementary principles of calculus are necessary. Nevertheless, since many concepts and derivations can be presented in a much more satisfying and precise manner if based on the use of exact differentials and of Euler's theorem, we shall introduce these propositions also, after a review of some elementary principles.

## 2-1 VARIABLES OF THERMODYNAMICS

### Extensive and Intensive Quantities

It is convenient to distinguish two kinds of thermodynamic variable, *extensive* and *intensive*. The values of extensive variables are proportional to the quantity of matter which is under consideration. Volume and heat capacity are typical examples of such variables. Intensive variables, on the other hand, are independent of the amount of matter under consideration, and are exemplified by quantities such as temperature, pressure, viscosity, concentration, and molal heat capacity.

***Table 2-1***

*Some definitions and units*[a]

| | | |
|---|---|---|
| 1 absolute volt | = | 0.99967 international volt |
| 1 absolute ampere | = | 1.00017 international amperes |
| 1 absolute coulomb | = | 1.00017 international coulombs |
| 1 absolute joule | = | 0.99984 international joule |
| 1 (defined) calorie | = | 4.1840 absolute joules |
| | = | 4.1833 international joules |
| | = | 0.041292 liter-atmosphere |
| absolute temperature at 0°C | = | 273.15°K[b] |
| $R$, gas constant | = | 8.3143 absolute joules $deg^{-1}$ $mole^{-1}$ |
| | = | 1.9872 cal $deg^{-1}$ $mole^{-1}$ |
| | = | 0.082053 liter-atm $deg^{-1}$ $mole^{-1}$ |
| 2.30258 $R$ | = | 4.57565 cal $deg^{-1}$ $mole^{-1}$ |
| $R$ (298.15) ln $x$ | = | 1364.21 $\log_{10} x$ cal $mole^{-1}$ |
| $N$, Avogadro's number | = | $6.023 \times 10^{23}$ molecules $mole^{-1}$ |
| $\mathscr{F}$, the Faraday constant | = | 96,487 abs coul (gram-equivalent)$^{-1}$ |
| | = | 23,061 cal (abs volt)$^{-1}$(gram-equivalent)$^{-1}$ |

[a] F. D. Rossini, F. T. Gucker, Jr., H. L. Johnston, L. Pauling, and G. W. Vinal, *J. Am. Chem. Soc.*, **74**, 2699 (1952); *Natl. Bur. Std.* (*U.S.*) *Tech. News.*, **47**, 175 (1963).

[b] By international agreement for the thermodynamic temperature scale. See H. F. Stimson, *Am. J. Phys.*, **23**, 614 (1955). Many standard reference tables still use 273.16°, however.

In general, both extensive and intensive variables are handled by the same mathematical techniques. Nevertheless, as we shall see later, extensive and intensive variables differ in their degree of homogeneity.

It is perhaps pertinent to point out also that some variables encountered in thermodynamic problems are neither extensive nor intensive. An example is the square root of the volume. The appearance of such variables produces no formal difficulties, however.

### Units and Conversion Factors

The numerical value which is assigned to a particular variable in a given problem depends, of course, on the units in which it is expressed. Critical evaluations of conversion factors between units are available in standard reference works. The authoritative values, chosen by the Committee on Physical Chemistry of the National Research Council, for the units and constants which occur in thermodynamic calculations are assembled in Table 2-1. In accordance with international agreement, units of energy should be expressed, as of January 1, 1948, in terms of the *absolute* joule.

## 2-2 THEORETICAL METHODS

### Partial Differentiation

Since the state of a given thermodynamic system is generally a function of more than one independent variable, it is necessary to consider the mathematical techniques of handling these polyvariable relations. Since many thermodynamic problems involve only two independent variables and since the extension to more variables is generally obvious, we shall limit our illustrations to functions of two variables.

***Equation for the total differential.*** Let us consider a specific example such as the volume of a pure substance. This volume is a function of the temperature and pressure of the substance, and the relation may be written in general notation as

$$V = f(P,T) \tag{2-1}$$

Utilizing the principles of calculus,[3] we may write for the total differential

$$dV = \left(\frac{\partial V}{\partial P}\right)_T dP + \left(\frac{\partial V}{\partial T}\right)_P dT \tag{2-2}$$

[3] W. A. Granville, P. F. Smith, and W. R. Longley, *Elements of the Differential and Integral Calculus*, Ginn, Boston, 1941; G. B. Thomas, Jr., *Calculus and Analytic Geometry*, 3rd ed., Addison-Wesley, Reading, Mass., 1960; J. W. Mellor, *Higher Mathematics for Students of Chemistry and Physics*, Dover, New York, 1946, pp. 68–75.

For the special case of one mole of an ideal gas, Eq. (2-1) is

$$V = \frac{RT}{P} = R(T)\left(\frac{1}{P}\right) \tag{2-3}$$

Since the partial derivatives are given by the expressions

$$\left(\frac{\partial V}{\partial P}\right)_T = -\frac{RT}{P^2} \tag{2-4}$$

and

$$\left(\frac{\partial V}{\partial T}\right)_P = \frac{R}{P} \tag{2-5}$$

the total differential for the special case of the ideal gas may be obtained by substitution into Eq. (2-2) and is given by the relation

$$dV = -\frac{RT}{P^2}\,dP + \frac{R}{P}\,dT \tag{2-6}$$

We shall have frequent occasion to make use of this expression.

***Transformation formulas.*** It frequently happens in thermodynamic problems that a given partial derivative, for example $(\partial V/\partial T)_P$, is necessary for the solution of an equation or numerical problem, but that there is no convenient experimental method of evaluating this derivative. If an expression were available which related this derivative to other partial derivatives which are known or readily obtainable, we could solve our problem without difficulty. For this purpose we must be able to transform a partial derivative into some alternative form.

We shall illustrate a procedure for obtaining such transformation formulas with the example of the preceding section, the volume function.

a. We can obtain the first transformation formula readily[4] by rearranging Eq. (2-2) to find $dV/dT$ and imposing the restriction that $V$ shall be constant. Keeping in mind, then, that $dV = 0$, we may obtain

$$\frac{dV}{dT} = 0 = \left(\frac{\partial V}{\partial P}\right)_T \frac{dP}{dT} + \left(\frac{\partial V}{\partial T}\right)_P \tag{2-7}$$

If we now indicate explicitly for the second factor of the first term on the right-hand side that $V$ is constant, and if we rearrange terms, we obtain

$$\left(\frac{\partial V}{\partial T}\right)_P = -\left(\frac{\partial V}{\partial P}\right)_T \left(\frac{\partial P}{\partial T}\right)_V \tag{2-8}$$

[4] For a rigorous derivation of these transformation formulas, see H. Margenau and G. M. Murphy, *The Mathematics of Physics and Chemistry*, Van Nostrand, Princeton, N.J., 1st ed., 1943, pp. 6–8; 2nd ed., 1956, pp. 6–8.

Thus if in some situation we needed $(\partial V/\partial T)_P$ but had no method of direct evaluation, we could establish its value if $(\partial V/\partial P)_T$ and $(\partial P/\partial T)_V$ were available.

It may be desirable to verify the validity of Eq. (2-8) for an ideal gas by evaluating both sides explicitly and showing that the equality holds. The values of the partial derivatives can be determined readily by reference to Eq. (2-3), and the following deductions can be made:

$$\frac{R}{P} = -\left(-\frac{RT}{P^2}\right)\left(\frac{R}{V}\right) = \frac{R^2T}{P^2V} = \frac{RT}{PV}\frac{R}{P} = \frac{R}{P} \tag{2-9}$$

b. The second transformation formula is obtained by finding $dV/dP$ from Eq. (2-2). Then again $V$ is held constant. After suitable rearrangement we obtain

$$\left(\frac{\partial V}{\partial P}\right)_T = -\left(\frac{\partial V}{\partial T}\right)_P\left(\frac{\partial T}{\partial P}\right)_V \tag{2-10}$$

c. A third formula is obtainable by rearranging Eq. (2-10) to

$$\left(\frac{\partial V}{\partial T}\right)_P = -\frac{(\partial V/\partial P)_T}{(\partial T/\partial P)_V} \tag{2-11}$$

and setting the right-hand side of this expression equal to the right-hand side of Eq. (2-8):

$$-\left(\frac{\partial V}{\partial P}\right)_T\left(\frac{\partial P}{\partial T}\right)_V = -\left(\frac{\partial V}{\partial P}\right)_T\frac{1}{(\partial T/\partial P)_V} \tag{2-12}$$

Therefore

$$\left(\frac{\partial P}{\partial T}\right)_V = \frac{1}{(\partial T/\partial P)_V} \tag{2-13}$$

Thus, within limits, the derivatives may be handled formally as if they were fractions.

d. Another important relation must be obtained for use in a problem in which a new but not independent variable is introduced. For example, we might consider the energy, $E$, of a pure substance as a function of pressure and temperature:

$$E = g(P,T) \tag{2-14}$$

We may then wish to evaluate the partial derivative $(\partial V/\partial P)_E$, that is, the change of volume with change in pressure at constant energy. A suitable expression for this derivative in terms of other partial derivatives may be obtained readily from Eq. (2-2) by finding $dV/dP$ and putting in explicitly the restriction that $E$ is to be held constant. The result obtained is the relation

$$\left(\frac{\partial V}{\partial P}\right)_E = \left(\frac{\partial V}{\partial P}\right)_T + \left(\frac{\partial V}{\partial T}\right)_P \left(\frac{\partial T}{\partial P}\right)_E \tag{2-15}$$

e. A fifth transformation formula, for use in certain situations where a new variable $x(P,T)$ is to be introduced, is obtained conveniently (although not rigorously) as follows:

$$\left(\frac{\partial V}{\partial T}\right)_P = \left(\frac{\partial V}{\partial T}\frac{\partial x}{\partial x}\right)_P = \left(\frac{\partial V}{\partial x}\frac{\partial x}{\partial T}\right)_P$$

$$= \left(\frac{\partial V}{\partial x}\right)_P \left(\frac{\partial x}{\partial T}\right)_P \tag{2-16}$$

These illustrations, based on the example of the volume function, are typical of the type of transformation which is required so frequently in thermodynamic manipulations. Great facility in their use may be acquired by solution of the appropriate exercises at the end of this chapter.

## Exact Differentials

Many thermodynamic relations can be derived with such ease by use of the properties of the exact differential that it is highly desirable for the student to become familiar with this type of function. As an introduction to the characteristics of exact differentials, we shall consider the properties of certain simple functions used in connection with a gravitational field.

***Example of the gravitational field.*** Let us compare the change in potential energy and the work done, respectively, in moving a large boulder up a hill, that is, against the force of gravity. From our familiarity with elementary physics, it is easy to see that these two quantities, $\Delta E$ and $W$, differ in the following respects.

a. The change in potential energy depends only on the initial and final heights of the stone, whereas the work done (as well as the heat generated) depends upon the path used. That is, the quantity of work expended if we use a pulley and tackle to raise the boulder directly will be much less than if we have to bring the object up the hill by pushing it over a long, muddy, and tortuous road. On the other hand, the change in potential energy is the same for both paths, so long as they have the same starting point and the same end point. Independence of the path is a characteristic of an exact differential; dependence, of an inexact differential. Therefore

$$dE = \text{exact differential}$$
$$dW = DW = \text{inexact differential}$$

In general we shall use the capital letter $D$ to indicate inexactness.

b. There is an explicit expression for the potential energy, $E$, and this function can be differentiated to give $dE$, whereas no explicit expression leading to $DW$ can be obtained. The function for the potential energy, $E$, is a particularly simple one for the gravitational field, in that two of the space coordinates drop out and only the height, $h$, remains:

$$E = \text{constant} + mgh \tag{2-17}$$

The symbols $m$ and $g$ have the usual significance, mass and acceleration due to gravity, respectively. This characteristic, the existence of a function which leads to the differential expression, is another property of the exact differential, in this case $dE$, as contrasted to $DW$.

c. A third difference between $\Delta E$ and $W$ lies in the values obtained if one uses a cyclic path, as in moving the boulder up the hill and then back down again to the initial point. For such a cyclic or closed path, the net change in potential energy is zero, since the final and initial points are identical. This fact may be represented by the equation

$$\oint dE = 0 \tag{2-18}$$

where $\oint$ denotes the integral around a closed path. On the other hand, the value of $W$ is not fixed at all. It depends upon the path used. If one uses each of the same two paths described above to bring the stone uphill and then, in each case, allows the stone to fall freely through the air back to its starting point, the net works done in the two cyclic paths are neither zero nor equal.

***General formulation.*** With the gravitational example as a guide to the nature of exact differentials, we may set up the properties of these functions in general terms for use in thermodynamic analysis. To understand the notation which is generally adopted, we shall rewrite Eq. (2-2) in the following form, which makes explicit recognition of the fact that the partial derivatives and the total differential are functions (indicated by $M$ and $N$) of the independent variables $P$ and $T$:

$$dV(P,T) = M(P,T)\,dP + N(P,T)\,dT \tag{2-19}$$

It is obvious, then, that a formulation for a general case with two independent variables, $x$ and $y$, could take the form

$$dL(x,y) = M(x,y)\,dx + N(x,y)\,dy \tag{2-20}$$

Using this expression, we may summarize the characteristics of an exact differential as follows.

a. A (linear) differential expression, containing two variables, of the form of Eq. (2-20), is an exact differential if there exists a function $f(x,y)$ such that

$$df(x,y) = dL(x,y) \tag{2-21}$$

b. If $dL$ is an exact differential, the line integral[3] (that is, the integral over some path), $\int dL(x,y)$, depends only on the initial and final states and not on the path between them.

c. If $dL$ is an exact differential, the line integral over a closed path is zero:

$$\oint dL(x,y) = 0 \tag{2-22}$$

It is this characteristic which is most frequently used in testing thermodynamic functions for exactness. If the differential of a thermodynamic function, $dJ$, *is exact*, then $J$ *is called a thermodynamic property*.

***Reciprocity characteristic.*** A common test of exactness of a differential expression $dL(x,y)$ is to see whether the following relation holds:

$$\left(\frac{\partial}{\partial y} M(x,y)\right)_x = \left(\frac{\partial}{\partial x} N(x,y)\right)_y \tag{2-23}$$

We can see readily that this relation must be true if $dL$ is exact, since in that case there exists a function $f(x,y)$ such that

$$df(x,y) = \left(\frac{\partial f}{\partial x}\right)_y dx + \left(\frac{\partial f}{\partial y}\right)_x dy = dL(x,y) \tag{2-24}$$

But for the function $f(x,y)$ we know from the principles of calculus that

$$\frac{\partial}{\partial y}\left(\frac{\partial f}{\partial x}\right)_y = \frac{\partial^2 f}{\partial y\, \partial x} = \frac{\partial}{\partial x}\left(\frac{\partial f}{\partial y}\right)_x \tag{2-25}$$

Since it follows from Eqs. (2-24) and (2-20) that

$$M(x,y) = \left(\frac{\partial f}{\partial x}\right)_y \tag{2-26}$$

and

$$N(x,y) = \left(\frac{\partial f}{\partial y}\right)_x \tag{2-27}$$

it is obvious that if $dL$ is exact,

$$\frac{\partial}{\partial y} M(x,y) = \frac{\partial}{\partial x} N(x,y) \tag{2-23}$$ [5]

To apply this criterion of exactness to a simple example, let us assume

[5] We have demonstrated that Eq. (2-23) is a necessary condition for exactness, which is adequate for our purposes. For a proof of mathematical sufficiency also, see A. J. Rutgers, *Physical Chemistry*, Interscience, New York, 1954, p. 177, or F. T. Wall, *Chemical Thermodynamics*, W. H. Freeman, San Francisco, 1958, p. 397.

that we know only the expression for the total differential of the volume of an ideal gas, Eq. (2-6), and do not know whether this differential is exact or not. Applying the procedure of (2-23) to Eq. (2-6), we obtain

$$\frac{\partial}{\partial P}\left(\frac{R}{P}\right) = -\frac{R}{P^2} = \frac{\partial}{\partial T}\left(-\frac{RT}{P^2}\right) \tag{2-28}$$

Thus we would know that the volume of an ideal gas is a thermodynamic property, even if we had not been aware previously of an explicit function for $V$.

## Homogeneous Functions

In connection with the development of the thermodynamic concept of partial molal quantities it will be desirable to be familiar with a mathematical transformation known as *Euler's theorem.* Since this theorem is stated with reference to "homogeneous" functions, we shall consider briefly the nature of these functions.

***Definition.*** Let us consider, as a simple example, the function

$$u = ax^2 + bxy + cy^2 \tag{2-29}$$

If we replace the variables $x$ and $y$ by $\lambda x$ and $\lambda y$, where $\lambda$ is a parameter, it is obvious that

$$\begin{aligned} u^* &= a(\lambda x)^2 + b(\lambda x)(\lambda y) + c(\lambda y)^2 \\ &= \lambda^2 ax^2 + \lambda^2 bxy + \lambda^2 cy^2 \\ &= \lambda^2(ax^2 + bxy + cy^2) \\ &= \lambda^2 u \end{aligned} \tag{2-30}$$

The net result of multiplying each independent variable by the parameter $\lambda$ has been merely to multiply the function by $\lambda^2$. Since the $\lambda$ can be factored out, the function is called *homogeneous*; since the exponent of the factor $\lambda^2$ is 2, the function is of the second degree.

We turn now to an example of experimental significance. If we mix certain quantities of benzene and toluene, the total volume, $V$, will be given by the expression[6]

$$V = v_b n_b + v_t n_t \tag{2-31}$$

where $n_b$ is the number of moles of benzene, $v_b$ is the volume of 1 mole of pure benzene, $n_t$ is the number of moles of toluene, and $v_t$ is the volume of

[6] For simplicity an ideal solution has been used in this illustration. However, Eq. (2-32) is true of all solutions if partial molal volumes are used instead of mole volumes of the pure components. See Chapter 13.

1 mole of pure toluene. Suppose, now, that we increase the quantity of each of the independent variables, $n_b$ and $n_t$, by the same factor, say 2. We know from experience that the volume of the mixture will be doubled. Similarly, if the factor were $\lambda$, the volume of the new mixture would be $\lambda$ times that of the original. In terms of Eq. (2-31) we can see also that if we replace $n_b$ by $\lambda n_b$ and $n_t$ by $\lambda n_t$, the new volume $V^*$ will be given by

$$\begin{aligned} V^* &= v_b \lambda n_b + v_t \lambda n \\ &= \lambda(v_b n_b + v_t n_t) \\ &= \lambda V \end{aligned} \qquad (2\text{-}32)^6$$

The volume function then is homogeneous of the first degree since the parameter $\lambda$ which factors out occurs to the first power.

Proceeding to a general definition, we may say that a function $f(x,y,z,\ldots)$ is homogeneous of degree $n$ if upon replacement of each independent variable by an arbitrary parameter, $\lambda$, times the variable, the function is merely multiplied by $\lambda^n$, that is, if

$$f(\lambda x,\lambda y,\lambda z,\ldots) = \lambda^n f(x,y,z,\ldots) \qquad (2\text{-}33)$$

***Euler's theorem.*** We shall state and prove Euler's theorem only for a function of two variables, $f(x,y)$. The extension to more variables will be obvious.

The statement of the theorem may be made as follows: If $f(x,y)$ is a homogeneous function of degree $n$, then

$$x\left(\frac{\partial f}{\partial x}\right)_y + y\left(\frac{\partial f}{\partial y}\right)_x = nf(x,y) \qquad (2\text{-}34)$$

The proof may be carried out by the following steps. Let us represent the variables $x^*$ and $y^*$ by

$$x^* = \lambda x \qquad (2\text{-}35)$$

and

$$y^* = \lambda y \qquad (2\text{-}36)$$

Then since $f(x,y)$ is homogeneous,

$$f^* = f(x^*,y^*) = f(\lambda x,\lambda y) = \lambda^n f(x,y) \qquad (2\text{-}37)$$

The total differential, $df^*$, is given by

$$df^* = \frac{\partial f^*}{\partial x^*}\,dx^* + \frac{\partial f^*}{\partial y^*}\,dy^* \qquad (2\text{-}38)$$

Hence

$$\frac{df^*}{d\lambda} = \frac{\partial f^*}{\partial x^*}\frac{dx^*}{d\lambda} + \frac{df^*}{dy^*}\frac{dy^*}{d\lambda} \qquad (2\text{-}39)$$

From Eqs. (2-35) and (2-36) it is clear that

$$\frac{dx^*}{d\lambda} = x \tag{2-40}$$

and

$$\frac{dy^*}{d\lambda} = y \tag{2-41}$$

Consequently, Eq. (2-39) may be transformed into

$$\frac{df^*}{d\lambda} = \frac{\partial f^*}{\partial x^*} x + \frac{\partial f^*}{\partial y^*} y \tag{2-42}$$

Making use of the equalities in (2-37), we can obtain

$$\frac{df^*}{d\lambda} = \frac{df(x^*,y^*)}{d\lambda} = \frac{d[\lambda^n f(x,y)]}{d\lambda}$$

$$= n\lambda^{n-1} f(x,y) \tag{2-43}$$

Equating (2-42) and (2-43), we obtain

$$x \frac{\partial f^*}{\partial x^*} + y \frac{\partial f^*}{\partial y^*} = n\lambda^{n-1} f(x,y) \tag{2-44}$$

Since $\lambda$ is an arbitrary parameter, Eq. (2-44) must hold for any particular value. It must be true, then, for $\lambda = 1$. In such an instance, Eq. (2-44) reduces to

$$x \frac{\partial f}{\partial x} + y \frac{\partial f}{\partial y} = nf(x,y) \tag{2-34}$$

This equation is Euler's theorem.

As one example of the application of Euler's theorem, we may refer again to the volume of a two-component system. Evidently the total volume is a function of the number of moles of each component:

$$V = f(n_1,n_2) \tag{2-45}$$

As we have seen previously, the volume function is known from experience to be homogeneous of the first degree; that is, if we double the number of moles of each component, we also double the total volume. Applying Euler's theorem, then, we obtain the relation

$$n_1 \frac{\partial V}{\partial n_1} + n_2 \frac{\partial V}{\partial n_2} = V \tag{2-46}$$

Although the significance of Eq. (2-46) may not be clear at this point, when we discuss partial molal quantities it will become apparent that this expression is basic to the entire subsequent development.

## 2-3 PRACTICAL TECHNIQUES

Throughout all our discussions we shall emphasize the application of thermodynamic methods to chemical problems. Successful solutions of such problems depend upon a familiarity with practical graphical and analytical techniques, as well as with the theoretical methods of mathematics. We shall consider these techniques at this point, therefore, so that they may be available for use as we approach specific problems.

### Graphical Methods

Experimental data of thermodynamic importance may be represented either graphically or in terms of an analytical equation. Often these data do not fit into a simple pattern which can be transcribed into a convenient equation. Consequently, graphical techniques, particularly for differentiation and integration, have assumed an important position among methods of treating thermodynamic data.

***Graphical differentiation.*** Numerous procedures have been developed for graphical differentiation. A particularly convenient one,[7] which we may call the *chord-area method*, may be illustrated by the following example.

***Table 2-2***

*Standard potentials*[a] *for reaction:*
$\frac{1}{2} H_2 + AgCl = Ag + HCl$

| $t$, °C | $\mathscr{E}^\circ$, volt |
|---|---|
| 0 | 0.23634 |
| 5 | 0.23392 |
| 10 | 0.23126 |
| 15 | 0.22847 |
| 20 | 0.22551 |
| 25 | 0.22239 |
| 30 | 0.21912 |
| 35 | 0.21563 |
| 40 | 0.21200 |
| 45 | 0.20821 |
| 50 | 0.20437 |
| 55 | 0.20035 |
| 60 | 0.19620 |

[a] H. S. Harned and R. W. Ehlers, *J. Am. Chem. Soc.*, **55**, 2179 (1933).

[7] T. R. Running, *Graphical Mathematics*, Wiley, New York, 1927, pp. 65–66.

Let us consider a set of experimental determinations of the standard potential, $\mathscr{E}^\circ$, at a series of temperatures, such as is listed in Table 2-2. A graph of these data (Figure 2-1) shows that the slope varies slowly but uniformly over the entire range of temperature. For thermodynamic purposes, such as in the calculation of the heat of reaction in the transformation

$$\tfrac{1}{2}H_2 + AgCl = Ag + HCl$$

it is necessary to calculate precise values of the slope, $\partial\mathscr{E}^\circ/\partial t$. It is clear from Figure 2-1 that if we choose a sufficiently small interval of temperature, then the slope will be given approximately by $\Delta\mathscr{E}^\circ/\Delta t$. In the example we are considering, an interval of 5° is sufficiently small for the average slope within this region to be given by $\Delta\mathscr{E}^\circ/\Delta t$. We proceed then to tabulate values of $\Delta\mathscr{E}^\circ/\Delta t$ from 0° on, as is illustrated in Table 2-3 for the first few data. Note that values of $\Delta\mathscr{E}^\circ$ are placed between the values of $\mathscr{E}^\circ$ to which they refer, and the temperature intervals, 5°, are indicated between their extremities. Similarly, since $\Delta\mathscr{E}^\circ/\Delta t$ is an average value (for example $-0.000484$) within a particular region (such as 0 to 5°), values in the fifth column are also placed between the initial and final temperatures to which they refer.

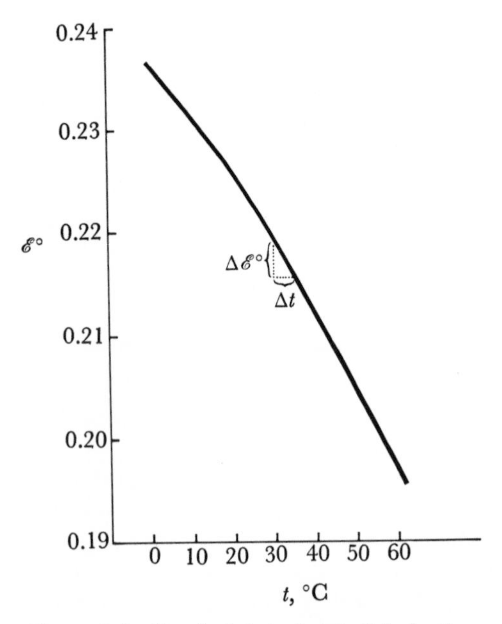


***Figure 2-1*** *Standard electrode potentials for the reaction* $\tfrac{1}{2}H_2(g) + AgCl(s) = Ag(s) + HCl(aq)$.

***Table 2-3***

*Tabulation for graphical differentiation*

| *1* | *2* | *3* | *4* | *5* | *6* |
|---|---|---|---|---|---|
| $t$ | $\mathscr{E}^\circ$ | $\Delta\mathscr{E}^\circ$ | $\Delta t$ | $\Delta\mathscr{E}^\circ/\Delta t$ | $\partial\mathscr{E}^\circ/\partial t$ |
| 0 | 0.23634 | | | | −0.000476 |
| | | −0.00242 | 5 | −0.000484 | |
| 5 | 0.23392 | | | | −0.000509 |
| | | −0.00266 | 5 | −0.000532 | |
| 10 | 0.23126 | | | | −0.000543 |
| | | −0.00279 | 5 | −0.000558 | |
| 15 | 0.22847 | | | | −0.000576 |
| | | −0.00296 | 5 | −0.000592 | |
| 20 | 0.22551 | | | | −0.000610 |

Having these *average* values of the slope, we now wish to determine the *specific* values at any given temperature. Since $\Delta\mathscr{E}^\circ/\Delta t$ is an average value, we shall draw it as a chord starting at the initial temperature of the interval and terminating at the final temperature. A graph of these chords over the entire temperature region from 0 to 60°C is illustrated in Figure 2-2. To find the slope, $\partial\mathscr{E}^\circ/\partial t$, a curve is drawn through these chords in such a manner that the sum of the areas of the triangles, such as $a$, of which the chords form the upper sides, shall be equal to the sum of the areas of the triangles, such as $a'$, of which the chords form the lower sides. This smooth curve gives $\partial\mathscr{E}^\circ/\partial t$ as a function of the temperature. Some values at various temperatures have been entered in column *6* of Table 2-3.

In the example given above, the chords have been taken for equal intervals, since the curve changes slope only gradually and the data are given at rounded temperatures at equal intervals. In many cases, the intervals will not be equal, nor will they occur at rounded numbers. Nevertheless, the chord-area method of differentiation may be used in substantially the same manner, although a little more care is necessary to avoid numerical errors in calculations.

***Graphical integration.*** The procedure for integration is rather closely analogous to that for differentiation. Again we shall cite an example of use in thermodynamic problems, the integration of heat-capacity data. Let us consider the heat-capacity data for solid $n$-heptane listed in Table 2-4. A graph of these data (Figure 2-3) shows a curve for which it may not be convenient to use an analytical equation. Nevertheless, in connection with determinations of certain thermodynamic functions it may be desirable to

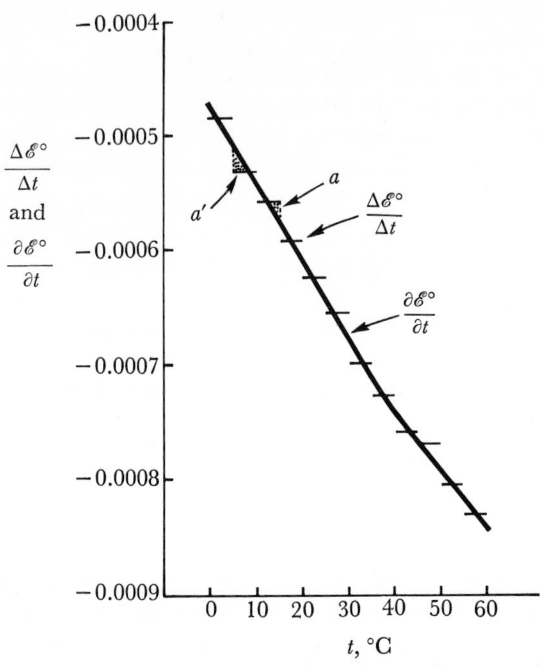


***Figure 2-2*** *Chord-area plot of slopes of curve of Figure 2-1.*

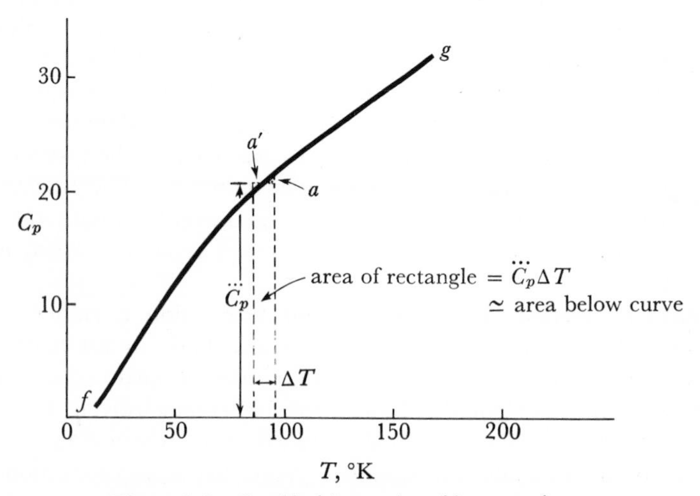


***Figure 2-3*** *Graphical integration of heat-capacity curve.*

evaluate the integral $\int C_p \, dT$. It is most convenient, therefore, to use a graphical method.

Once again we consider small intervals of the independent variable, $T$, as is indicated in Figure 2-3. At the mid-point of this interval we have an average value of the heat capacity, $\dddot{C}_p$, indicated by the broken horizontal line in the figure. It is clear that the area of the rectangle below this broken line is $\dddot{C}_p \, \Delta T$. If the interval chosen is so small that the section of the curve which has been cut is practically linear, then it is also evident that the area below this section of the curve is essentially the same as that of the rectangle, since the area $a'$ is practically equal to $a$. Hence it follows that the area under the curve between the limits $f$ and $g$ is given very closely by the sum of the areas of the rectangles taken over sufficiently short temperature intervals. Since the area under the curve corresponds to the integral $\int C_p \, dT$, it follows that

$$\sum_f^g \dddot{C}_p \, \Delta T = \int_f^g C_p \, dT \tag{2-47}$$

Since the first few data in Table 2-4 are given at closely successive temperatures, we may use these values to form the temperature intervals. (In

***Table 2-4***

*Heat capacities of solid n-heptane*[a]

| $T$, °K | $C_p$ cal mole$^{-1}$ deg$^{-1}$ | $T$, °K | $C_p$ cal mole$^{-1}$ deg$^{-1}$ |
|---|---|---|---|
| 15.14 | 1.500 | 53.18 | 12.80 |
| 17.52 | 2.110 | 65.25 | 15.69 |
| 19.74 | 2.730 | 71.86 | 17.04 |
| 21.80 | 3.403 | 79.18 | 18.53 |
| 24.00 | 4.112 | 86.56 | 19.83 |
| 26.68 | 4.935 | 96.20 | 21.58 |
| 30.44 | 6.078 | 106.25 | 23.22 |
| 34.34 | 7.370 | 118.55 | 25.09 |
| 38.43 | 8.731 | 134.28 | 27.15 |
| 42.96 | 10.02 | 151.11 | 29.54 |
| 47.87 | 11.36 | 167.38 | 31.96 |

[a] R. R. Wenner, *Thermochemical Calculations*, McGraw-Hill, New York, 1941, p. 356.

many cases it is more convenient to use intervals of equal size within a given region.) For $\ddot{C}_p$ between any two temperatures we may take the arithmetic mean between the listed experimental values. The values of $\Delta T$ and $\ddot{C}_p$ are then tabulated conveniently as in columns *3* and *4* of Table 2-5. Column *5* lists the area for the given interval. Finally, to obtain the area between any two of the temperatures listed in column *1*, the sums of the areas of the intervals from 15.14°K are tabulated in column *6*.

It is evident that if we wish to obtain the value of the integral at some temperature not listed in Table 2-5, we may plot the figures in column *6* as a function of $T$ and read off values of the integral at the desired upper limit.

## Analytical Methods

In many cases it is possible to summarize data in terms of a convenient algebraic expression. Such an equation is highly desirable, whenever it can be used with sufficient precision, because it is a very concise summary of much information. We shall consider two common methods of fitting an algebraic expression to a set of experimental data. In each case we shall use a simple quadratic equation as an example. The extension to power series with terms of higher or lower degree will be obvious. Methods of fitting other types of equation to experimental data are described in appropriate mathematical treatises.[8]

The two approaches we shall consider are the method of averages and

***Table 2-5***

*Tabulation for graphical integration*

| *1* $T$, °K | *2* $C_p$ | *3* $\Delta T$ | *4* $\ddot{C}_p$ | *5* $\ddot{C}_p \, \Delta T$ | *6* $\Sigma \ddot{C}_p \, \Delta T$ |
|---|---|---|---|---|---|
| 15.14 | 1.500 | | | | 0.00 |
| | | 2.38 | 1.805 | 4.30 | |
| 17.52 | 2.110 | | | | 4.30 |
| | | 2.22 | 2.420 | 5.37 | |
| 19.74 | 2.730 | | | | 9.67 |
| | | 2.06 | 3.067 | 6.32 | |
| 21.80 | 3.403 | | | | 15.99 |
| | | 2.20 | 3.758 | 8.27 | |
| 24.00 | 4.112 | | | | 24.26 |

[8] A. G. Worthing and J. Geffner, *Treatment of Experimental Data*, Wiley, New York, 1943.

the method of least squares. In both cases we shall assume that we have a series of data, such as equilibrium constants as a function of pressure, to which we wish to fit a quadratic equation,

$$y = a + bx + cx^2 \tag{2-48}$$

Assuming that a quadratic equation can be used, we wish to obtain the best values of the constants, $a$, $b$, and $c$. The two methods differ as to the criterion of a "best" equation. In both, however, it is assumed implicitly that all of the error lies in the dependent variable, $y$, and none in the independent variable, $x$.[9]

***The method of averages.*** Let us suppose that we have a series of numerical values of equilibrium constants and corresponding pressures such as are given in Table 2-6 and that we wish to obtain a quadratic expression for $K_p$ as a function of the total pressure, $P$. Let us define the residual, $r$, as the difference between the experimentally determined $K_p$ and the value which may be calculated from the analytical expression; that is,

$$r = K_p - (a + bP + cP^2) \tag{2-49}$$

There will be a value of $r$ for each of the six experiments listed in Table 2-6. In obtaining an equation by the method of averages, we assume that the best values of the constants, $a$, $b$, and $c$ are those for which the sum of all (six) residuals is zero. Using this assumption,

$$\sum r = 0 \tag{2-50}$$

***Table 2-6***

*Equilibrium constants for reaction*[a]

$\frac{1}{2}N_2(g) + \frac{3}{2}H_2(g) = NH_3(g)$

| $P$, atm | $K_p$ at 500°C |
|---|---|
| 10 | 0.00381 |
| 30 | 0.00386 |
| 50 | 0.00388 |
| 100 | 0.00402 |
| 300 | 0.00498 |
| 600 | 0.00651 |

[a] A. T. Larson and R. L. Dodge, *J. Am. Chem. Soc.*, **45**, 2918 (1923); **46**, 367 (1924).

[9] The theory has also been developed for the case where a significant error may appear in $x$. See Worthing and Geffner, *op. cit.*, pp. 258–260.

we obtain the following condition for evaluating the constants:

$$\begin{aligned}\sum r &= [K_{p_1} - (a + bP_1 + cP_1^2)] + [K_{p_2} - (a + bP_2 + cP_2^2)] + \cdots \\ &= [K_{p_1} + K_{p_2} + \cdots] - [a + a + \cdots] - b[P_1 + P_2 + \cdots] \\ &\qquad - c[P_1^2 + P_2^2 + \cdots] \\ &= 0 = \sum_{i=1}^{n} K_{p_i} - na - b\sum_{i=1}^{n} P_i - c\sum_{i=1}^{n} P_i^2 \end{aligned} \tag{2-51}$$

where $n$ represents the number of experimental measurements. Rearrangement of the last expression gives

$$\sum K_{p_i} = na + b\sum P_i + c\sum P_i^2 \tag{2-52}$$

We now have one condition but three unknowns, $a$, $b$, and $c$. To fix three unknowns, it is necessary to have expressions for three restrictions. The three equations may be obtained if we divide the data into three equal (or nearly equal) groups and carry out the summations indicated in Eq. (2-52). With the data listed in Table 2-6, we might obtain the following set of relations:

$$\begin{aligned} 0.00381 &= a + b(10) + c(100) \\ 0.00386 &= a + b(30) + c(900) \\ \sum = 0.00767 &= 2a + 40b + 1000c \end{aligned} \tag{2-53}$$

$$\begin{aligned} 0.00388 &= a + b(50) + c(2500) \\ 0.00402 &= a + b(100) + c(10{,}000) \\ \sum = 0.00790 &= 2a + 150b + 12{,}500c \end{aligned} \tag{2-54}$$

$$\begin{aligned} 0.00498 &= a + b(300) + c(90{,}000) \\ 0.00651 &= a + b(600) + c(360{,}000) \\ \sum = 0.01149 &= 2a + 900b + 450{,}000c \end{aligned} \tag{2-55}$$

Equations (2-53), (2-54), and (2-55) may now be solved simultaneously. They lead to the following analytical expression for $K_p$:

$$K_p = 0.003805 + 1.500 \times 10^{-6}P + 5.63 \times 10^{-9}P^2 \tag{2-56}$$

For the general case we proceed as above to divide the experimental data into three equal (or nearly equal) groups. For each group we find the summations required by the expression

$$\sum y = na + b\sum x + c\sum x^2 \tag{2-57}$$

where the $y$'s and $x$'s are the known values of the dependent and independent variables, respectively. From the three equations so obtained it is possible to solve for the constants $a$, $b$, and $c$ and thereby to obtain an explicit relation for $y$ as a function of $x$.

***The method of least squares.*** With the method of least squares, we obtain three independent equations which the three constants of the quadratic equation must obey. The procedure follows from the assumption that the best expression is that for which the sum of the *squares* of the residuals is a minimum. If we define the residual for the general quadratic expression as

$$r = y - (a + bx + cx^2) \tag{2-58}$$

where $y$ and $x$ refer to experimentally determined values, then according to the method of least squares we should obtain an equation for which

$$\sum r^2 = \text{a minimum} \tag{2-59}$$

This condition will be satisfied when the partial derivative of $\Sigma r^2$ with respect to each of the constants, $a$, $b$, and $c$, respectively, is zero. Let us consider first the partial derivative with respect to $a$:

$$\sum r^2 = [y_1 - (a + bx_1 + cx_1^2)]^2 + [y_2 - (a + bx_2 + cx_2^2)]^2 + \cdots \tag{2-60}$$

$$\begin{aligned}\left(\frac{\partial}{\partial a}\sum r^2\right)_{b,c,x,y} &= -2[y_1 - a - bx_1 - cx_1^2] - 2[y_2 - a - bx_2 - cx_2^2]\cdots \\ &= 0 = -2[y_1 + y_2 + \cdots] - 2[-na] \\ &\qquad -2[-bx_1 - bx_2 - \cdots] - 2[-cx_1^2 - cx_2^2 - \cdots]\end{aligned} \tag{2-61}$$

Rearrangement gives

$$\sum y = na + b\sum x + c\sum x^2 \tag{2-62}$$

By a similar procedure we may obtain the following expression from the partial derivative of $\Sigma r^2$ with respect to the parameter $b$:

$$\sum yx = a\sum x + b\sum x^2 + c\sum x^3 \tag{2-63}$$

Similarly, the differentiation with respect to $c$ leads to an expression which can be reduced to

$$\sum yx^2 = a\sum x^2 + b\sum x^3 + c\sum x^4 \tag{2-64}$$

The three simultaneous equations (2-62), (2-63), and (2-64) may be used to solve for the constants $a$, $b$, and $c$.

In order to obtain the sums required for the solution of the three simultaneous equations, it is convenient to set up a table of the form of Table 2-7. To take a specific example, let us use the data in Table 2-6 for the synthesis of ammonia. The calculations leading to the required sums are tabulated in Table 2-8.

*Table 2-7*

*Outline of calculations for least-square quadratic equation*

| $y$ | $x$ | $x^2$ | $x^3$ | $x^4$ | $yx$ | $yx^2$ |
|---|---|---|---|---|---|---|
| . | . | . | . | . | . | . |
| . | . | . | . | | . | . |
| . | . | . | . | . | . | . |
| . | . | | . | . | . | . |
| . | . | . | . | . | . | . |
| . | . | . | . | . | . | . |
| . | . | . | . | . | . | . |
| . | . | . | . | . | . | . |
| . | . | . | . | . | . | . |
| . | . | . | . | . | . | . |
| . | . | . | . | . | . | . |
| . | . | . | . | . | . | . |
| $\Sigma y$ | $\Sigma x$ | $\Sigma x^2$ | $\Sigma x^3$ | $\Sigma x^4$ | $\Sigma yx$ | $\Sigma yx^2$ |

From the sums listed at the bottoms of the columns of Table 2-8, we can set up the following three specific simultaneous equations corresponding to the respective general equations (2-62), (2-63), and (2-64):

$$0.02706 = 6a + 1090b + 4.635 \times 10^5 c \tag{2-65}$$

$$6.1499 = 1090a + 4.635 \times 10^5 b + 2.44153 \times 10^8 c \tag{2-66}$$

$$2845.555 = 4.635 \times 10^5 a + 2.44153 \times 10^8 b + 1.3780707 \times 10^{11} c \tag{2-67}$$

Solution of these equations leads to the following least-square expression for the equilibrium constant as a function of the pressure:

$$K_p = 0.003743 + 3.392 \times 10^{-6} P + 2.083 \times 10^{-9} P^2 \tag{2-68}$$

Thus we have two methods of obtaining an analytical expression for representing data in a concise form. In practice, the method of averages is much more rapid, but it is not so sound from a theoretical point of view. Where data of high precision are available, the method of least squares should be used.

**Table 2-8**

*Calculations for the least-square quadratic equation*

| $K_p$ | $P$ | $P^2$ | $P^3$ | $P^4$ | $K_pP$ | $K_pP^2$ |
|---|---|---|---|---|---|---|
| 0.00381 | 10 | 100 | 1,000 | 10,000 | 0.0381 | 0.381 |
| 0.00386 | 30 | 900 | 27,000 | 810,000 | 0.1158 | 3.474 |
| 0.00388 | 50 | 2,500 | 125,000 | 6,250,000 | 0.1940 | 9.700 |
| 0.00402 | 100 | 10,000 | 1,000,000 | 100,000,000 | 0.4020 | 40.200 |
| 0.00498 | 300 | 90,000 | 27,000,000 | 8,100,000,000 | 1.4940 | 448.200 |
| 0.00651 | 600 | 360,000 | 216,000,000 | 129,600,000,000 | 3.9060 | 2,343.600 |
| 0.02706 | 1090 | 463,500 | 244,153,000 | 137,807,070,000 | 6.1499 | 2,845.555 |

## Exercises

**1.** Find the conversion factor for changing liter-atmosphere to: (a) erg, (b) calorie.

**2.** Find the conversion factor for changing calorie to: (a) cubic foot-atmosphere, (b) volt-faraday.

**3.** The area, $a$, of a rectangle may be considered a function of the breadth, $b$, and the length, $l$:

$$a = bl$$

$b$ and $l$ are then considered to be the independent variables; $a$ is the dependent one. Other possible dependent variables are the perimeter, $p$,

$$p = 2b + 2l$$

and the diagonal, $d$,

$$d = \sqrt{b^2 + l^2}$$

(a) Find the values of the following partial derivatives in terms of $b$ and $l$, or find a numerical answer:

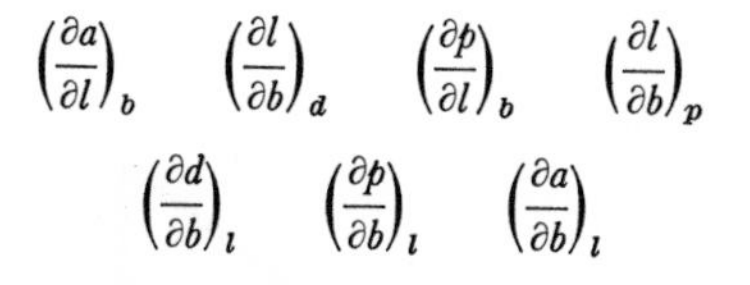

$$\left(\frac{\partial a}{\partial l}\right)_b \quad \left(\frac{\partial l}{\partial b}\right)_a \quad \left(\frac{\partial p}{\partial l}\right)_b \quad \left(\frac{\partial l}{\partial b}\right)_p$$

$$\left(\frac{\partial d}{\partial b}\right)_l \quad \left(\frac{\partial p}{\partial b}\right)_l \quad \left(\frac{\partial a}{\partial b}\right)_l$$

(b) Find suitable transformation expressions in terms of the partial derivatives given in (a) for each of the following derivatives, and then evaluate the results in terms of $b$ and $l$. (Do not substitute the equation for $p$ or $d$ into that for $a$.)

$$\left(\frac{\partial a}{\partial b}\right)_d \quad \left(\frac{\partial b}{\partial p}\right)_l \quad \left(\frac{\partial a}{\partial b}\right)_p$$

(c) Find suitable transformation expressions in terms of the preceding partial derivatives for each of the following derivatives, and then evaluate the results in terms of $b$ and $l$:

$$\left(\frac{\partial p}{\partial b}\right)_d \quad \left(\frac{\partial a}{\partial p}\right)_l \quad \left(\frac{\partial b}{\partial p}\right)_d \quad \left(\frac{\partial a}{\partial p}\right)_d$$

**4.** In a right triangle, such as is illustrated in Figure 2-4, the following relations are valid:

$$D^2 = H^2 + B^2$$
$$P = H + B + D$$
$$A = \tfrac{1}{2}BH$$

(a) Given the special conditions

$$H = 1000 \text{ cm} \qquad \left(\frac{\partial H}{\partial B}\right)_A = -2$$
$$\left(\frac{\partial H}{\partial B}\right)_D = -0.5 \qquad \left(\frac{\partial B}{\partial H}\right)_P = -1.309$$

compute the values of the following partial derivatives, using transformation relations if necessary:

$$\left(\frac{\partial A}{\partial B}\right)_H \quad \left(\frac{\partial A}{\partial H}\right)_B \quad \left(\frac{\partial A}{\partial B}\right)_D \quad \left(\frac{\partial A}{\partial H}\right)_P$$

(b) Given the following different set of special conditions:

$$B = 4 \text{ cm} \qquad \left(\frac{\partial H}{\partial A}\right)_P = -0.310 \qquad \left(\frac{\partial H}{\partial B}\right)_A = -2.0 \qquad \left(\frac{\partial P}{\partial B}\right)_A = -2.341$$

(1) compute the values of the following partial derivatives, using transformation relations if necessary:

$$\left(\frac{\partial H}{\partial A}\right)_B \quad \left(\frac{\partial B}{\partial A}\right)_P \quad \left(\frac{\partial P}{\partial A}\right)_B$$

(2) compute $A$.

**5.** Considering $E$ as a function of any two of the variables $P$, $V$, and $T$, prove that

$$\left(\frac{\partial E}{\partial T}\right)_P \left(\frac{\partial T}{\partial P}\right)_V = -\left(\frac{\partial E}{\partial V}\right)_P \left(\frac{\partial V}{\partial P}\right)_T$$

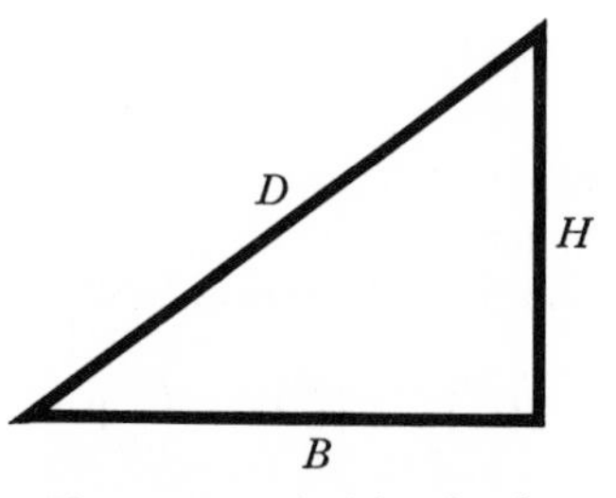


***Figure 2-4*** *A right triangle.*

**6.** Making use of the definition $H = E + PV$ and, when necessary, obtaining transformation relationships by considering $H$ (or $E$) as a function of any two of the variables $P$, $V$, and $T$, derive the following relationships:

(a) $$\left(\frac{\partial H}{\partial T}\right)_P = \left(\frac{\partial E}{\partial T}\right)_V + \left[P + \left(\frac{\partial E}{\partial V}\right)_T\right]\left(\frac{\partial V}{\partial T}\right)_P$$

(b) $$\left(\frac{\partial H}{\partial T}\right)_P = \left(\frac{\partial E}{\partial T}\right)_V + \left[V - \left(\frac{\partial H}{\partial P}\right)_T\right]\left(\frac{\partial P}{\partial T}\right)_V$$

(c) $$\left(\frac{\partial E}{\partial T}\right)_V = \left(\frac{\partial H}{\partial T}\right)_P - \left[\left(\frac{\partial H}{\partial T}\right)_P\left(\frac{\partial T}{\partial P}\right)_H + V\right]\left(\frac{\partial P}{\partial T}\right)_V$$

**7.** By a suitable experimental arrangement it is possible to vary the total pressure $P$ on a pure liquid independently of variations in the vapor pressure, $p$. (The temperature of both phases, however, must be identical if they are in equilibrium.) For such a system, the dependence of the vapor pressure on $P$ and $T$ is given by

$$\left(\frac{\partial p}{\partial P}\right)_T = \frac{V_l}{V_g}$$

$$\left(\frac{\partial p}{\partial T}\right)_P = \frac{\Delta H}{TV_g}$$

where $V_l$ and $V_g$ are the mole volumes of liquid and gas respectively, and $\Delta H$ is the molar heat of vaporization. Prove that

$$\left(\frac{\partial P}{\partial T}\right)_p = \frac{-\Delta H}{TV_l}$$

**8.** The length, $L$, of a wire is a function of the temperature, $T$, and the tension, $\tau$, on the wire. The linear expansivity, $\alpha$, is defined by

$$\alpha = \frac{1}{L}\left(\frac{\partial L}{\partial T}\right)_\tau$$

and is essentially constant over a small range of temperature. Likewise, the isothermal Young's modulus, $Y$, defined by

$$Y = \frac{L}{A}\left(\frac{\partial \tau}{\partial L}\right)_T$$

where $A$ is the cross-sectional area of the wire, is essentially constant over a small temperature range. Prove that

$$\left(\frac{\partial \tau}{\partial T}\right)_L = -\alpha A Y$$

**9.**[10] An ideal gas in state $A$ (Figure 2-5) is changed to state $C$. This transformation may be carried out by an infinite number of paths of which only two will be considered, one along a straight line from $A$ to $C$ and the other from $A$ to $B$ to $C$.

(a) Calculate and compare the changes in volume in going from $A$ to $C$ by each of the two paths, $AC$ and $ABC$, respectively.

[10] Adapted from H. Margenau and G. M. Murphy, *The Mathematics of Physics and Chemistry*, Van Nostrand, Princeton, N.J., 1943, pp. 8–11.

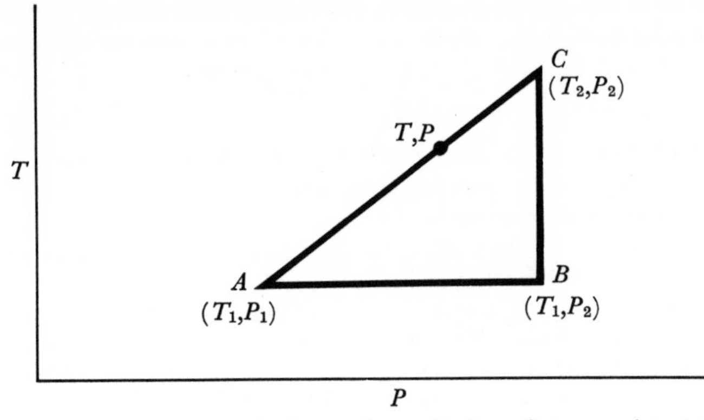


***Figure 2-5*** *Two paths for carrying an ideal gas from state A to state C.*

Proceed by integrating the differential equation

$$dV = \left(\frac{\partial V}{\partial T}\right)_P dT + \left(\frac{\partial V}{\partial P}\right)_T dP \tag{2-2}$$

or

$$dV = \frac{R}{P}\,dT - \frac{RT}{P^2}\,dP \tag{2-6}$$

Before the integration is carried out along the path $AC$, use the following relation to make the necessary substitutions:

$$\text{Slope of line } AC = \frac{T_2 - T_1}{P_2 - P_1} = \frac{T - T_1}{P - P_1} \tag{2-69}$$

Therefore

$$T = T_1 + \frac{T_2 - T_1}{P_2 - P_1}(P - P_1) \tag{2-70}$$

and

$$dT = \frac{T_2 - T_1}{P_2 - P_1}\,dP \tag{2-71}$$

Keep in mind that $T_1$, $T_2$, $P_1$, and $P_2$ are constants in this problem.

(b) Applying the reciprocity test to Eq. (2-6), show that $dV$ is an exact differential.

(c) Calculate and compare the works done in going from $A$ to $C$ by each of the two paths. Make use of the relation

$$dW = P\,dV = R\,dT - \frac{RT}{P}\,dP \tag{2-72}$$

and the substitution suggested by Eq. (2-70).

(d) Applying the reciprocity test to Eq. (2-72), show that $dW$ is an inexact differential.

**10.** For a wire, the change in length, $dL$, may be expressed by the following differential equation:

$$dL = \frac{L}{YA}\,d\tau + \alpha L\,dT$$

where $\tau$ is the tension, $T$ the temperature, and $A$ (cross-sectional area) $Y$ and $\alpha$ are essentially constant if the extension is not large.

(a) Is $dL$ an exact differential?

(b) Is the differential for the work of the stretching, $dW = -\tau\,dL$, an exact differential?

**11.** For an ideal gas, we shall show later that the entropy, $S$, is a function of the independent variables, volume, $V$, and temperature, $T$. The total differential $dS$ is given by the equation

$$dS = \frac{C_v}{T}\,dT + \frac{R}{V}\,dV$$

where $C_v$ and $R$ are constants.

(a) Find an expression for the change in volume of the gas as the temperature is changed at constant entropy, that is, for $(\partial V/\partial T)_S$. Your answer should contain finally only independent variables and constants.

(b) Is $dS$ exact?

**12.** The compressibility $\kappa$ and the coefficient of expansion, $\beta$, are defined by the partial derivatives below:

$$\kappa = -\frac{1}{V}\left(\frac{\partial V}{\partial P}\right)_T$$

$$\beta = \frac{1}{V}\left(\frac{\partial V}{\partial T}\right)_P$$

Show that

$$\left(\frac{\partial \beta}{\partial P}\right)_T + \left(\frac{\partial \kappa}{\partial T}\right)_P = 0$$

**13.** For an elastic body, the internal energy, $E$, is a function of three variables, the entropy, $S$, the volume, $V$, and the length, $L$. It is possible to show, with the aid of the laws of thermodynamics, that

$$dE = T\,dS - P\,dV + \tau\,dL$$

where $T$ is the absolute temperature, $P$ the pressure, and $\tau$ the tension on the elastic body. Prove the following relationships:

$$\left(\frac{\partial E}{\partial L}\right)_{S,V} = \tau$$

$$-\left(\frac{\partial \tau}{\partial V}\right)_{S,L} = \left(\frac{\partial P}{\partial L}\right)_{S,V}$$

**14.** The Gibbs free energy, $G$, is a thermodynamic property. If $(\partial G/\partial P)_T = V$ and $(\partial G/\partial T)_P = -S$, prove the following relation:

$$\left(\frac{\partial S}{\partial P}\right)_T = -\left(\frac{\partial V}{\partial T}\right)_P$$

**15.** The Helmholtz free energy, $A$, is a thermodynamic property. If $(\partial A/\partial V)_T = -P$ and $(\partial A/\partial T)_V = -S$, prove the following relation:

$$\left(\frac{\partial S}{\partial V}\right)_T = \left(\frac{\partial P}{\partial T}\right)_V$$

**16.** Examine the following functions for homogeneity and degree of homogeneity:

(a) $u = x^2y + xy^2 + 3xyz$

(b) $u = \dfrac{x^3 + x^2y + y^3}{x^2 + xy + y^2}$

(c) $u = \sqrt{x + y}$

(d) $u = e^{y/x}$

(e) $u = \dfrac{x^2 + 3xy + 2y^3}{y^2}$

**17.** Complete the calculations in Table 2-3 for the graphical differentiation of the data listed in Table 2-2. Draw a graph corresponding to that of Figure 2-2, but on a larger scale for more precise readings.

**18.** Complete the calculations in Table 2-5 for the graphical integration of the data listed in Table 2-4. Draw a graph of $\int C_p\,dT$ vs. temperature.

# 3 The First Law of Thermodynamics

Having reviewed the mathematical background, we must now develop the basic concepts and postulates of chemical thermodynamics upon which we shall build the theoretical framework. In discussing these fundamental postulates, which are essentially concise statements of much experience, we shall try to emphasize at all times their applications to chemical objectives, rather than to problems in engineering. Since every postulate is expressed in terms of certain accepted concepts, however, it will be necessary first to define a few of the basic concepts of thermodynamics.

## 3-1 DEFINITIONS

Critical studies of the logical foundations[1] of physical theory have emphasized the care which is necessary in the definition of fundamental concepts if contradictions between theory and observation are to be avoided. Our ultimate objective is clarity and precision in the description of the operations involved in measuring or recognizing the conception. Let us consider first a very simple example—a circle. At a primitive stage one might define a

[1] H. Poincaré, *Science and Hypothesis*, reprinted by Dover, New York, 1952; P. W. Bridgman, *The Logic of Modern Physics*, Macmillan, New York, 1927; *The Nature of Thermodynamics*, Harvard Univ. Press, Cambridge, Mass., 1941.

circle by the statement, "a circle is round." Such a definition would be adequate for children in the early grades of elementary school but could lead to long and fruitless arguments whether particular closed curves are circles. A much more satisfactory and refined definition is, "a group of points in a plane all of which are the same distance from an interior reference point called the center." This definition describes the operations which need to be carried out to generate a circle or to recognize one. The development of maturity in scientific insight consists in part in the recognition that an early "intuitive understanding" at the primitive level is often not sound and may on occasion lead to contradictory conclusions from two apparently consistent sets of postulates and observations.

The operational approach[2] to the definition of fundamental concepts in science has been emphasized by Mach, Poincaré, and Einstein and has been expressed in a very clear form by Bridgman.[1] In this approach a concept is defined in terms of a set of experimental or mental operations used to measure or recognize the quantity: "the concept is synonymous with the corresponding set of operations" (Bridgman). An operational definition may frequently fail to satisfy us in regard to feeling that we know now what the concept "really is." The question of scientific "reality" has been explored by many scientists and philosophers and is one which every student should examine. In the operational approach, however, we are not concerned whether our definition has also told us what the concept "really is"; what we need to know is how to measure it. The operational attitude has been succinctly stated by Poincaré in the course of a discussion of the concept of force: "When we say force is the cause of motion we talk metaphysics, and this definition if we were content with it, would be absolutely sterile. For a definition to be of any use, it must teach us to *measure* force; moreover that suffices; it is not at all necessary that it teach what force is in itself nor whether it is the cause or the effect of motion."

The power of the operational approach became strikingly evident in Einstein's theory of special relativity with its analysis of the meaning of presumably absolute intuitive concepts such as time or space. Newton defined absolute time as follows: "Absolute, True, and Mathematical Time, of itself, and from its own nature flows equably without regard to anything external." The difficulty with a definition of this type, based on properties or attributes, is that we have no assurance that anything of the given description actually exists in nature. Thus Newton's definition of time implies that it would be clear and meaningful to speak of two events in widely separated places (e.g., the flaring up of two novae) as occurring simultaneously;

[2] The operational concept had been used implicitly much earlier than the twentieth century. Thus Boyle defined a chemical element in terms of the experiments by which it might be recognized, in order to avoid the futile discussions of his predecessors, who identified elements with qualities or properties.

presumably each event occurs at the same point on the time scale which flows equably without regard to external events or of the activities of the individuals making the observations. In contrast in relativity theory, time is defined by a description of specific and exclusive manipulations with clocks, light signals, and measuring rods, and it turns out that events that are simultaneous for one observer will occur at different moments if viewed by another observer in a different state of motion. Which one is "correct"? In practice this question is meaningless. Both are correct. In fact there is no operational meaning to "absolute simultaneity," despite its intuitive reasonableness. All operations by which time is measured are relative ones. The term "absolute time" thus becomes meaningless.

Relativity theory, with its rigorous operational definitions of time and space led to many unexpected results, quite contrary to common experience, one being that the measured length of a body depends on the speed with which the body moves with respect to the observer. These new theorems from relativity theory removed apparent contradictions which had perplexed physicists in their measurements of the speed of light and also predicted a variety of new phenomena which have since been abundantly verified.

Thus physical scientists have become increasingly aware of the need of defining concepts in terms of operations instead of relying on intuitive feelings of a priori recognition. To avoid possible pitfalls in thermodynamic applications, it is desirable that all thermal and energy concepts likewise be approached with an operational attitude.

Before approaching these thermodynamic concepts we need to agree on the meaning of certain more primitive terms which will occur often in our analyses. We shall assume without analysis that the term *body* as an identifiable, definite thing has an obvious meaning. When we carry out experiments on, or make observations of a body in order to characterize it, we obtain information which we call the *properties* of the body. Similarly we shall speak of the properties of a *system*, which is any region of the universe, large or small, that is being considered in our analysis. Regions outside the boundaries of the system constitute the *surroundings*. A system is said to be in a certain *state* when all of its properties have specified values. In general only a few of the properties of a system in a given state can be expressed as independent variables and these are called *variables of state*. Relationships between dependent variables and the independent variables of state are specified by *equations of state*. If one or more of the properties of a system are found to be different at two different times then in this interval a *process* has taken place and a *change of state* has occurred. On occasion we shall also speak of a *closed* system by which we mean one which mass does not enter or leave. Obviously then an *open* system is one which mass may enter or leave. Finally an *insulated* or *adiabatic* system is one with the following characteristic: if the system, completely surrounded by an *insulating* wall, has attained complete thermal equilibrium then no change in state of the system can be produced from the surroundings except by movement of the wall.[3]

With these definitions of conventions we may proceed to an analysis of thermodynamic concepts.

## Temperature

The earliest concept of temperature was undoubtedly physiological, that is, based on the sensations of hot and cold. Of necessity such an approach is very crude, both in sensitivity and accuracy. As men became more familiar with the properties of various substances, however, they realized that certain of these properties were not the same at all times but depended upon the temperature, as measured by crude physiological responses. Ultimately it became evident that one of these properties—for example, the volume of a gas—might be used as a more precise measure of the temperature. In this way it became possible to do away with any dependence upon physiological sensations.

The definition of temperature in terms of the volume of a gas is an operational one. The concept is defined in terms of an experimental procedure by which it may be measured. As the precision of physical measurements has increased, it has also become evident that the details of the experimental procedure are more involved than was originally realized. Thus it was soon recognized that not all gases indicate the same temperature, even if they have all been set originally at the same reference temperature. Consequently, it becomes necessary to take a series of volume readings, $V$, at various pressures, $P$, and to extrapolate a suitable function of the pressure-volume product to zero pressure. Thus the ratio of two temperatures, $\theta$ and $\theta_0$, may be defined

$$\frac{\theta}{\theta_0} = \lim_{P \to 0} \frac{(PV)_\theta}{(PV)_{\theta_0}} \tag{3-1}$$

If, following the new international convention,[4] we take as our reference temperature, $\theta_0$, the temperature of the ice-point (0°C) and assign it the value 273.15° on the absolute scale, then the operations for establishing any $\theta$ are completely specified.

Difficulties arise if the thermometer is exposed to certain types of radiation. However, calculations indicate that under normal circumstances, these radiational fields raise the temperature by about $10^{-12}$°C,[5] a quantity

[3] If electrically charged bodies are present in the system, this definition of "adiabatic" is inadequate, but such situations will not be considered here.

[4] H. F. Stimson, *Am. J. Phys.*, **23**, 614 (1955).

[5] P. W. Bridgman, *The Nature of Thermodynamics*, Harvard Univ. Press, Cambridge, Mass., 1941, p. 16.

which is not detectable even with the most sensitive of present-day instruments. Similarly, we shall neglect relativistic corrections which arise at high velocities, for we shall not encounter such situations in ordinary thermodynamic problems.

So far we have considered the definition of the temperature concept in terms of a series of operations on gases. It is also possible to define the temperature concept in terms of certain heat quantities, as will be shown in Chapter 7, The Second Law of Thermodynamics. This too is an operational approach if the concept of heat is properly defined. For this purpose, therefore, as well as in preparation for the statement of the first law of thermodynamics, we shall analyze next the concept of heat.

## Heat

Let us recognize at the outset that the important thing, to paraphrase Poincaré, is to know how to measure heat, not to know what heat "really is." With this dictum in mind, probably the best way of defining the concept of heat is in terms of measurements with ice calorimeters. In these calorimeters, in which a solid and a liquid are in equilibrium, the absorption of heat is accompanied by a phase change, which in turn produces an alteration in the volume of the system. In this manner a quantity of heat is related to the measurement of a change in volume. In principle it would be necessary to use various substances in the ice calorimeters in order to cover a wide temperature range, and if one insists on a continuous range, it would be necessary to operate a given calorimeter under variable pressures.

By heat, then, we shall mean any effect other than work which produces a change in volume in an ice calorimeter.

The definition of heat in terms of volume changes in ice calorimeters has the special virtue of avoiding any dependence upon temperature measurements. Since the so-called "thermodynamic temperature scale" relates the temperature concept to measurements of heat quantities, it is necessary for this purpose to have a definition of heat which is independent of temperature measurements if we are to avoid the criticism of traveling in a logical circle.

For completeness it is also desirable to consider the operational meaning of heat as it is more commonly defined in terms of temperature changes. This method of defining heat depends upon the use of the common type of calorimeter—a large body of material, usually water, which on absorbing heat suffers a small change in temperature. We say that the heat absorbed is proportional to the *change* in temperature,

$$Q = C(T_2 - T_1) \tag{3-2}$$

where $Q$ is the heat absorbed, $C$ is the proportionality constant, $T_2$ is the final temperature, and $T_1$ is the initial temperature. Experience teaches us that if the quantity of material (for example, water) within the calorimeter is doubled, the change in temperature is halved (if the heat capacity of the calorimeter itself can be ignored). Thus the constant, $C$, is proportional to the mass of the substance within the calorimeter. Since $C$ is therefore a characteristic of the substance within the calorimeter, it is called the *heat capacity*. Also, since the magnitude of $C$ is proportional to the quantity of matter within the calorimeter, we may define a heat capacity per unit mass of substance. The unit of mass may be 1 g or 1 mole of material. In the former case we have defined the *specific heat*; in the latter case, the *molal heat capacity*.

As in the discussion of other concepts, our present description of the heat concept depends upon relatively crude experiments at first. Thus in the preceding paragraph we neglected the heat capacity of the calorimeter vessel. Similarly, we have assumed that the heat capacity, $C$, is independent of the temperature interval, whereas precise measurements indicate that $C$ varies with temperature. These refinements introduce no fundamental difficulties, however, since, as in the case of the temperature concept, we may make use of the process of extrapolation-to-a-limit. For heat capacity we can decrease the size of the temperature interval until the value of $C$ per unit mass approaches a constant.

Thus, generally speaking, if a process changes the state of a body, without work being done, we shall say that heat is being absorbed or evolved by the body.

Historically heat was treated as a "thing," the caloric fluid of Black, and in this form the concept proved very useful in interpreting early experiments in calorimetry. In time this form of the conception had to be discarded, for it was discovered that this caloric fluid was not conserved, but disappeared when mechanical work was done or could be created by mechanical work. Nevertheless, we still retain much of the early language of caloric theory such as when we speak of heat being "transferred" from one body to another or of "heat flow" from one system to another. Such terminology has persisted because of its utility; but we should recognize that it carries with it strong verbal implications which generate problems that are due to the language used rather than to the inherent nature of the concept. There is a strong verbal impulse that associates "transfer" or "flow" with a "thing," and hence mentally a student may still identify heat with a hypothetical fluid. Such a mental picture may be helpful under certain circumstances, but will lead to perplexities if the student is not aware that the picture arises from the language used in calorimetry but is not a necessary adjunct of the operational definition of heat.

Finally we must choose a sign convention for heat, $Q$. A body or system may absorb heat or may evolve it, and $Q$ may represent either one or the other situation. We shall adopt the convention that $Q$ represents the heat *absorbed* by a body. Thus a positive numerical value for $Q$ signifies that the body has received heat from its surroundings; a negative value means that the body has evolved heat to its environment.

## Work

For our purposes it will suffice to point out that work is defined as the product of a force by a displacement. Assuming, then, that force and displacement can be given suitable operational significance, the term "work" will also share this characteristic. The measurement of the displacement involves experimental determinations of a distance, which can be carried out, in principle, with a measuring rod. The concept of force is a little more complicated. It originated undoubtedly from the muscular sensation of resistance to external objects. A quantitative measure is readily obtained with an elastic body, such as a spring, whose deformation may be utilized as a measure of the force. This definition of force, however, is limited to static systems; for systems which are being accelerated, further refinements must be considered. Since these would take us too far from our main course, we shall merely make reference to Bridgman's critical analysis.[6] Nevertheless, for the definition of force in even the static situation, as well as in the definition of displacement, it should be emphasized that precision measurements require a number of precautions, particularly against changes in temperature. In dealing with these concepts, we generally assume implicitly that such sources of error have been recognized and accounted for.

A body or system may do work (on its outside environment) or may have work done upon it; we must agree, therefore, upon a sign convention for work, $W$. We shall follow the convention that $W$ represents the work done by the system on its surroundings. Thus a positive numerical value for $W$ signifies that the system has done work on the surroundings, a negative value that work has been done on the system by some agency in the surroundings.

Let us also examine the form that $DW$ may reduce to for some different types of work. The fundamental definition as the product of a force $F'$ and a displacement, $ds$ (Figure 3-1) may be written

$$DW = F'\,ds \tag{3-3}$$

Here $F'$ represents the magnitude of the force against which the body is doing work, and $F$ (Figure 3-1) represents the magnitude of the force within the body. For example, if the bottom side of Figure 3-1 represents a cylinder

[6] P. W. Bridgman, *The Logic of Modern Physics*, Macmillan, New York, 1927, pp. 102–108.

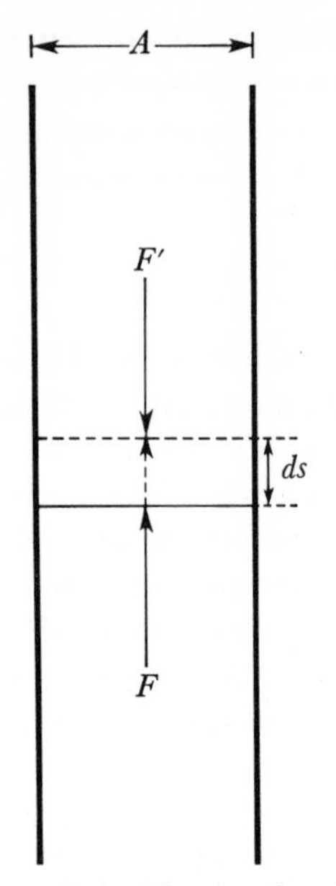


***Figure 3-1*** *Element of work.*

with a gas in it exerting a force $F$ on the walls of the container, then $F'$ represents the exterior force on the wall, for example, that due to a weight. The actual work done by the gas is measured by the displacement $ds$ undergone by the weight $F'$. In a reversible displacement, as we shall see shortly $F'$ and $F$ differ by an insignificantly small amount, and hence we may also write

$$DW = F\,ds \tag{3-4}$$

Furthermore, since pressure, $P$, is a force per unit area, $A$, of the surface of the wall, the expression for the element of work becomes

$$DW = PA\,ds \tag{3-5}$$

Finally, since $A\,ds$ corresponds to the element of volume, $dV$, swept out by the force in moving the distance, $ds$, Eq. (3-5) reduces to the familiar form for gas expansion

$$DW = P\,dV \tag{3-6}$$

Let us also consider the work done by a spring in increasing its length by an amount $dL$. If the spring is longer than its rest length it exerts a force, in this case called a tension, $\tau$, and the surroundings must do work *on* the spring if the length is to be further increased. Hence, keeping the sign convention for $W$ in mind, we write

$$DW = -\tau\, dL \tag{3-7}$$

Similarly, if we focus attention on the work of raising a body a certain height, $dh$, against the force of gravity, we must write

$$DW = -mg\, dh \tag{3-8}$$

where $m$ is the mass of the body and $g$ the gravitational constant. Again a negative sign appears in Eq. (3-8) because if the height above ground level is increased, that is, if $dh$ is positive, work must be done *on* the body, and hence $DW$, following our convention, must reduce to a negative quantity. Of course if the weight drops toward the ground, $dh$ will be negative and the body can do a positive amount of work, as would also follow from Eq. (3-8).

With these examples, equations for other types of work should follow naturally.

## 3-2 ENERGY: THE FIRST LAW OF THERMODYNAMICS

The first law is generally stated as a relation between certain quantities, $E$ (internal energy), $Q$ (heat), and $W$ (work), or their differentials, $dE$, $DQ$, and $DW$:

$$dE = DQ - DW \tag{3-9}$$

Even in an elementary approach the differentials are distinguished in notation by capital and lower-case $d$'s. This distinction is made in recognition of the fact that $DQ$ and $DW$ are inexact differentials; that is, the values of their line integrals depend upon the path as well as upon the initial and end points of a transformation.

The inexactness of these quantities is recognized quickly by consideration of one or two experimental examples. Thus in an electrical cell, the amount of heat evolved when useful work is done by the cell (for example, in the operation of a motor) differs substantially from that obtained when the electrodes are short-circuited, even though the initial and final chemical substances are the same in both cases. Similarly, the amount of work obtained from this system depends upon the rate at which the cell is discharged. If the counterpotential is near the potential of the cell, more work is obtained than when the electrodes are practically short-circuited. Again the nature of the chemical change is the same in both transformations.

Another example demonstrating the inexactness of $DQ$ and $DW$ is the isothermal expansion of a gas. When a confined gas is allowed to expand very slowly against an external pressure practically equal to that of the gas, the amount of work done and the quantity of heat absorbed, respectively, differ very greatly from the values obtained during the expansion of the gas into a vacuum, even though the initial pressure, temperature, and volume, and the final temperature, pressure, and volume are the same in both expansions. Obviously, then, the work and heat differentials are not exact.

Turning now to the internal energy quantity, $dE$, we might interpret Eq. (3-9) as follows: The change in internal energy, $dE$, within a bounded region of space is found as a matter of experiment to be equal to the quantity of heat absorbed, $DQ$, minus the amount of work done, $DW$, by the system. Upon careful consideration, however, such a statement appears too naïve, because it turns out that there are no independent operations that can be described for the measurement of the internal energy change, $dE$. The measurement of energy changes has meaning only in terms of Eq. (3-9), in other words, only in terms of measurements of work and heat. Internal energy changes have no independent operational significance. The significance of the first law cannot lie, therefore, in a statement of the equality of $dE$ and $(DQ - DW)$; such a statement would be mere tautology in view of the fact that $dE$ is measured in terms of $DQ$ and $DW$. Hence the essence of the first law must lie in the difference in the character of the differential $dE$ as contrasted with $DQ$ and $DW$. The energy differential, $dE$, is exact. In other words, despite the fact that the heat absorbed, $DQ$, and the work done, $DW$, in going from one state to another depend upon the particular path used in the transformation, the difference in these two quantities, $DQ - DW$, defined as $dE$, is independent of the method by which the change is accomplished. Furthermore, making use of another property of an exact differential, we can say that the integral of $dE$ around a closed path is zero. In other words, whenever the enclosed system is returned to its initial state, the difference between heat absorbed and work done, that is, the change in internal energy, is zero despite the fact that the heat and work quantities in themselves may differ very much from zero.

If we are dealing with large-scale changes for a given bounded region, we may state the first law in terms of the following equation in place of the differential form:

$$\Delta E = Q - W \tag{3-10}$$

By $\Delta E$ we mean $(E_2 - E_1)$, the difference between the energies of the final and initial states. Since $Q$ and $W$ have operational meaning, $\Delta E$ is also operationally significant.

Thus the first law may be considered to consist of two parts. First, it defines the concept of energy in terms of previous concepts, heat and work. Second, it summarizes a wide variety of experience in the statement that the internal energy function, so defined, is a thermodynamic property; that is, it depends only on the state of a system and not on the previous history of the system.

In contrast, work and heat are not thermodynamic properties. Consequently, it is inappropriate, in general, to speak of "work content" of a system since there is no unique, single value for the work one obtains from some transformation between specified initial and final states of the system. Rather the result depends on the path used in the process and may differ widely for two different paths. The work may be characteristic of the process but not of the system. For similar reasons it is inappropriate in general, to speak of "heat content," although this term is used to some extent in a different and specialized sense as we shall see in Chapter 4.

It should also be pointed out that the very definition of the energy concept precludes the possibility of determining absolute values; that is, we have defined only a method of measuring *changes* in internal energy. In this regard there is a significant difference between the character of the thermodynamic property energy and that of a property such as volume. We can specify an unambiguous value for the volume of a system in a particular state. On the other hand, it is appropriate to speak of "energy" only with reference to a transition from one configuration of a system to another, in other words only with reference to an energy change. There can be no single measurement of energy; the term acquires significance only with reference to a second corresponding measurement, the combination of the two leading to the observed energy change. To speak of "energy" in an absolute sense is only a form of expression of the observation that certain aspects of a transition depend uniquely on characteristics of the initial and final states only.

## 3-3 SOME CONDITIONS UNDER WHICH *W* OR *Q* DEPENDS ONLY ON INITIAL AND FINAL STATES

There are a number of situations in which $DW$ or $DQ$ reduces to an exact differential, for example, $dE$. We shall consider two specific examples. First, however, we should examine the concept of "reversible process."

### Reversibility

The "reversible process" was first conceived by Carnot in his analysis of the performance of heat engines. A reversible process in thermodynamics is the analog of linear frictionless motion in mechanics. Each is an idealized visualization of the actual behavior of real systems. Each is the limit which may be approached in real processes.

In a reversible process this limit may be approached from either of two directions. For example let us consider the process illustrated in Figure 3-1.

Work may be done by the body when the external force $F'$ is less than $F$ by a finite amount $\delta F$. The smaller one makes $\delta F$, that is, the closer $F'$ approaches $F$ (and hence the larger is $F'$), the more work is done for displacement through a fixed distance $ds$, since fundamentally

$$DW = F' \, ds \tag{3-11}$$

The reversible or *maximum* work performed by the body would be obtained in the limit as $F'$ approaches $F$. Thus the reversible work is given by

$$DW = F \, ds \tag{3-12}$$

Likewise, one may approach the limit from the opposite direction, that is, $F'$ may be made larger than $F$ by a finite amount $\delta F$. In this case work is done *on* the body (at the bottom part of Figure 3-1); the displacement $ds$ will be diametrically opposite to that of the first (or forward) process, and the work done will still be given by Eq. (3-11). Now we decrease $F'$ and let it approach $F$, that is we make $\delta F$ smaller and smaller. Then the work done by the external force decreases. In the limit as $F'$ approaches $F$, we reach the reversible or *minimum work* done on the body to produce the displacement $ds$ downward. Again the reversible work is given by Eq. (3-12).

Similarly, in processes where an exchange of heat occurs, a reversible change implies that the reservoir giving up the heat is at a temperature $T'$ which is only infinitesimally greater than $T$, the temperature of the body receiving the heat. Thus if $dT$ is reversed, that is, if $T'$ is made infinitesimally smaller than $T$, then the direction of heat flow is also reversed and heat goes from the body to the reservoir.

A reversible process is often described as a succession of states each of which is in a state of equilibrium, or as a "quasi-static process." Strictly speaking it would take infinite time to bring about a finite reversible change since in any finite time only an infinitesimal change can occur. All actual changes occur at finite speeds. The reversible path is the limit of the real path as the dynamic process is made slower and slower. The great virtue of the concept of reversibility is that it introduces the idea of continuity into our analysis of actual processes and hence permits the use of the calculus.

For a reversible process it is possible to draw a graph (or to derive a mathematical expression) to represent the change, since each state in the process is in a condition of equilibrium and the variables of state, such as pressure and temperature, are completely fixed. On the other hand, in a real process the system is not in equilibrium and hence we cannot assign unique values of the temperature and pressure to it. For example, in the expansion process of Figure 3-1, if the change occurs at a finite rate, the pressure immediately behind the piston will be somewhat less than that in the remainder of the medium (a gas, for example) because there is always a lag in the transmission of stresses. Hence no unique value can be assigned as the pressure within the medium. Thus if we use a graphical representation of the pressure and volume changes during the expansion of a substance, such as Figure 3-2, we are dealing, in a strict sense, only with a truly reversible process. In the irreversible, real change, no graphical representation can be made, since no unique values can be assigned to all the variables.

Returning to our consideration of the work of expansion, we see that only for the reversible process will $P$ in Eq. (3-6) have a definite value. Thus, strictly speaking, Eq. (3-6) and its integral,

$$W = \int_{V_1}^{V_2} P\,dV \tag{3-13}$$

have meaning only for reversible work of expansion.

## Constant-Volume Process: No Nonmechanical Work

Having derived an expression for the mechanical work of expansion, we can see quite readily from Eq. (3-13) that in a constant volume process ($dV = 0$), the work integral will be zero; that is, no net mechanical work is obtained. In Eq. (3-9), however, $W$ represents all types of work, nonmechanical (electrical, for example) as well as mechanical. Nevertheless, in most chemical experiments the only significant work done is due to expansion or contraction, since the small contributions due to changes in surface area are generally negligible, and only in special cases are reactions used to

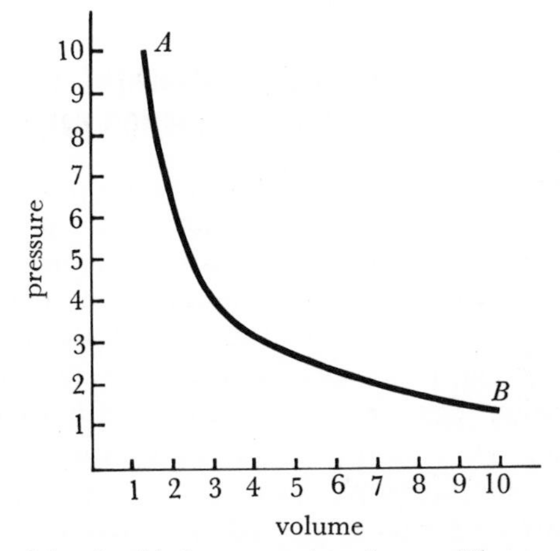


***Figure 3-2*** *Graphical representation of a reversible process.*

obtain electrical work. Consequently, in most situations of interest, if the reaction is carried out at constant volume, no work of any kind is obtained. It is evident, then, from Eqs. (3-9) and (3-10), that

$$dE_V = DQ_V = dQ_V \tag{3-14}$$

and

$$\Delta E_V = Q_V \tag{3-15}$$

that is, at constant volume $dQ_V$ is exact, and the heat quantity accompanying the process depends only upon the initial and final states.

### Adiabatic Process

It is also evident from Eq. (3-9) that if $DQ$ is zero, that is, if no heat is absorbed or evolved in a reaction, then

$$dE = -DW = -dW \tag{3-16}$$

In other words, in an adiabatic process the differential $dW$ is exact and the work done in the process depends only upon the initial and final states.

It should be pointed out that these two examples of situations where $dW$ or $dQ$ is exact are not isolated cases. Other processes will be mentioned later (for example, the isothermal expansion of an ideal gas) in which the work and heat differentials possess the property of exactness. It should be emphasized that in all these cases, by putting certain restrictions on the nature of the process which is to be treated, we are specifying, from the mathematical point of view, the path by which the change may take place. It is no surprise, then, that the heat and work quantities depend only upon the end points of these special processes.

## 3-4 ALTERNATIVE STATEMENT OF THE FIRST LAW OF THERMODYNAMICS

For all the laws of thermodynamics there are a number of alternative possible statements. The formulation presented in Section 3-2 follows essentially the historical approach which usually seems more concrete and real. We shall also describe a more sophisticated approach that does not presume a definition of heat and that thus avoids the notion of heat flow.

If we have a system surrounded by adiabatic walls, so that it is perfectly insulated thermally, then the work associated with a change from state $A$ to state $B$ of the system is independent of the path. This may be taken as our statement of the first law. If necessary, one may rationalize its experiential validity by pointing out that if it were not true one could construct a perpetual motion machine, producing net work out of nothing, by using the path with larger $W$ for the work-producing step and that with smaller $W$ to return the system to its initial state. Therefore, since adiabatic work depends only on the initial and final states of the system, we can define a function, $E$, of the state of the system, such that

$$W_{\text{adiabatic}} = -(E_B - E_A) \tag{3-17}$$

$E$ is then named the internal energy of the system.

So far we have not even mentioned the concept of heat. Let us now remove the adiabatic walls from the system. Many new *nonadiabatic* paths then become available for bringing the system from state $A$ to state $B$. The function of state, $E$, being a thermodynamic property still undergoes the change

$$\Delta E = E_B - E_A \tag{3-18}$$

On the other hand, it is known from long experience that $W$ in this non-adiabatic transformation depends on the path as well as the end points and hence that

$$W \neq \Delta E \tag{3-19}$$

We shall therefore *define* the heat absorbed, $Q$, as the quantity

$$Q = \Delta E + W \tag{3-20}$$

This definition of $Q$ is more abstruse than that described in Section 3-1, but it is also logically neater and more satisfying.

In any event, either statement of the first law of thermodynamics leads us to the same fundamental equation (3-10).

## Exercises

**1.** If the temperature of 1 cc of air at 1 atm pressure and 0°C is raised to 100°C, the volume becomes 1.3671 cc. Calculate the value of absolute zero for a thermometer using air. Compare your result with that in Table 2-1 of Chapter 2.

**2.** Let Figure 3-1 represent a plane surface (such as a soap film between wires) which is being expanded in the direction indicated. Show that the work of reversible expansion is given by the expression

$$W = -\int \gamma \, d\mathscr{A}$$

where $\gamma$ is the force per unit length, and $\mathscr{A}$ is the surface area.

**3.** Let $\tau$ represent the tension of a wire of length $L$, $A$ its cross-sectional area, and $Y$ the isothermal Young's modulus (see Exercise 8, Chapter 2). For a wire, $L$, $A$, and $Y$ are practically constant as the tension is increased. Show that the work for an isothermal increase in tension of a wire is given by

$$W = -\frac{1}{2AY}(\tau^2_{\text{final}} - \tau^2_{\text{initial}})$$

**4.** From the first law of thermodynamics, show that $DQ$ is exact for a process at constant pressure in which only mechanical work is done.

# 4 | Enthalpy and Heat Capacity

In the preceding chapter we defined a new function, the internal energy, and found that it is known from long experience (the first law of thermodynamics) to be a thermodynamic property; that is, $dE$ is exact. Making use of this proposition, we were able to show that in a process in which only $P\,dV$ work is done and for which the volume is constant, the heat absorbed is also independent of the path. For example, in a given chemical reaction, carried out in a closed vessel of fixed volume, the heat absorbed (or evolved) depends only upon the nature and condition of the initial and of the final reactants; it does not depend upon the mechanism by which the reaction occurs. Therefore if a catalyst speeds up the reaction, by changing the mechanism, it does not affect the heat quantity accompanying the reaction.

Most chemical reactions are carried out at constant (atmospheric) pressure. It is of interest to know whether the heat absorbed in a constant-pressure reaction depends upon the path, that is, upon the method by which the reaction is carried out, or whether, on the contrary, it too is a function of the initial and final states only. If the latter were true, it would be possible to tabulate heat quantities for given chemical reactions and to use known values to calculate heats for new reactions which can be expressed as sums of known reactions.

Actually, of course, this question was answered on empirical grounds long before thermodynamics was established on a sound basis. In courses in elementary chemistry one becomes familiar with Hess's law of constant heat summation, enunciated in 1840. Hess pointed out that the heat absorbed (or evolved) in a given chemical reaction is the same whether the process occurs in one step or in several steps. Thus, to cite a familiar example, the heat of formation[1] of $CO_2$ from its elements is the same if the process is the single step

$$\text{C (graphite)} + \text{O}_2\ \text{(gas)} = \text{CO}_2\ \text{(gas)} \qquad Q_{298^\circ\text{K}} = -94.0518\ \text{kcal mole}^{-1}$$

or the series of steps

$$\text{C (graphite)} + \tfrac{1}{2}\text{O}_2\ \text{(gas)} = \text{CO (gas)} \qquad Q_{298^\circ\text{K}} = -26.4157\ \text{kcal mole}^{-1}$$

$$\text{CO (gas)} + \tfrac{1}{2}\text{O}_2\ \text{(gas)} = \text{CO}_2\ \text{(gas)} \qquad Q_{298^\circ\text{K}} = -67.6361\ \text{kcal mole}^{-1}$$

$$\text{C (graphite)} + \text{O}_2\ \text{(gas)} = \text{CO}_2\ \text{(gas)} \qquad Q_{298^\circ\text{K}} = -94.0518\ \text{kcal mole}^{-1}$$

Of course we could introduce Hess's generalization into thermodynamics as another empirical law, similar to the first law. A good theoretical framework, however, depends upon a minimum of empirical postulates. The power of thermodynamics lies in the fact that it leads to so many predictions, if one makes only two or three basic assumptions. Hess's law need not be among these postulates, since it can be derived directly from the first law of thermodynamics, perhaps most conveniently with the use of a new thermodynamic function.

## 4-1 ENTHALPY

### Definition

This new thermodynamic quantity which we wish to introduce is known as the *enthalpy*, and sometimes also as *heat content*. It is defined in terms of thermodynamic variables which have been described already:

$$H = E + PV \tag{4-1}$$

From the definition it is evident that $H$, the enthalpy, is a thermodynamic property, since it is defined by an explicit function. All the quantities on the right-hand side of Eq. (4-1), $E$, $P$, and $V$, are properties of the state of a system, and consequently so is $H$.

Of course, it is also evident from the definition, Eq. (4-1), that absolute values of $H$ are unknown, since absolute values of $E$ cannot be obtained from classical thermodynamics alone. From an operational point of view,

[1] "Selected Values of Chemical Thermodynamic Properties," *Nat. Bur. Standards (U.S.), Circ. No. 500*, 1952.

therefore, it is more significant to consider changes in enthalpy, $\Delta H$. Obviously, such changes can be defined readily by the expression

$$\Delta H = \Delta E + \Delta(PV) \tag{4-2}$$

## Relation between $Q$ and $\Delta H$

Having defined this new thermodynamic property, the enthalpy, we may proceed to investigate the conditions under which it may become equal to the heat accompanying a process. Differentiating (4-1), we obtain

$$dH = dE + P\,dV + V\,dP \tag{4-3}$$

From the first law of thermodynamics we may introduce

$$dE = DQ - DW \tag{4-4}$$

and obtain

$$dH = DQ - DW + P\,dV + V\,dP \tag{4-5}$$

Equation (4-5) is of general validity. Let us consider a set of restrictions, however, which are realized in many chemical reactions: (1) constant pressure and (2) no work other than mechanical (against the atmosphere). Under these conditions it is evident that Eq. (4-5) may be simplified considerably since

$$DW = P\,dV \tag{4-6}$$

and

$$dP = 0 \tag{4-7}$$

Hence

$$dH_P = DQ_P = dQ_P \tag{4-8}$$

and

$$\Delta H_P = Q_P \tag{4-9}$$

where the subscript emphasizes the constancy of the pressure during the process. It should be emphasized, in addition, that Eq. (4-8) is valid only if no nonmechanical work is being done. Under these conditions $dQ$ is evidently an exact differential. In other words, for chemical reactions carried out at constant pressure (at atmospheric pressure, for example) in the usual laboratory or large-scale vessels, the heat absorbed depends only on the nature and conditions of the initial reactants and of the final products. Evidently, then, it does not matter if a given substance is formed in one step or in many steps. So long as the starting and final materials are the same and so long as the processes are carried out at constant pressure and with no nonmechanical work, the net $\Delta H$'s will be the same. Thus Hess's law is a consequence of the first law of thermodynamics.

## Relation between $Q_V$ and $Q_P$

We have just proved that $\Delta H$ equals $Q_P$ for a reaction at constant pressure. Although most calorimetric work is carried out at a constant pressure, some reactions must be observed in a closed vessel, that is, at constant volume. In such a closed system the heat quantity that is measured is $Q_V$. Yet for further chemical calculations it is frequently necessary to know $Q_P$. It is highly desirable, therefore, to derive some expression which relates these two heat quantities.

We shall make use of the following relation, which was proved in the preceding chapter,

$$\Delta E_V = Q_V \tag{4-10}$$

and Eq. (4-9),

$$\Delta H_P = Q_P \tag{4-9}$$

together with Eq. (4-2) restricted to a constant-pressure process:

$$\Delta H_P = \Delta E_P + \Delta(PV) \tag{4-11}$$

It has been found that $\Delta E_P$ is generally not significantly different from $\Delta E_V$. In fact, for ideal gases, as we shall see in a subsequent chapter, $E$ is independent of the volume or pressure, at a fixed temperature. Hence, as a rule,

$$\Delta E_P \cong \Delta E_V = Q_V \tag{4-12}$$

Substituting Eqs. (4-9) and (4-12) into (4-11), we obtain

$$Q_P = Q_V + \Delta(PV) \tag{4-13}$$

It should be emphasized that $Q_P$ and $Q_V$ refer to different changes of state.

In reactions involving only liquids and solids, the $\Delta(PV)$ term is usually negligible in comparison with $Q$, and hence the difference between $Q_P$ and $Q_V$ is slight. However, in reactions involving gases, $\Delta(PV)$ may be significant, since the changes in volume may be large. Generally this term may be estimated with sufficient accuracy by the use of the equation of state for ideal gases,

$$PV = nRT \tag{4-14}$$

where $n$ represents the number of moles of a particular gas. If the chemical reaction is represented by the expression

$$aA\,(g) + bB\,(g) + \cdots = lL\,(g) + mM\,(g) + \cdots \tag{4-15}$$

where $a$, $b$, $l$, and $m$ indicate the number of moles of each gas, then, since an isothermal change is being considered,

$$Q_P = Q_V + \Delta(PV) = Q_V + (n_LRT + n_MRT + \cdots - n_ART - n_BRT - \cdots)$$

or

$$Q_P = Q_V + (\Delta n)RT \tag{4-16}$$

It should be stressed that $\Delta n$ refers to the increase in number of moles *of gases only*. In common reactions, $\Delta nRT$ contributes a few kilocalories to the difference $Q_P - Q_V$ (see Exercise 3 at end of chapter).

## 4-2 HEAT CAPACITY

We have introduced the *enthalpy* function particularly because of its usefulness as a measure of the heat accompanying chemical reactions at constant pressure. We shall find it convenient also to have a function to relate heat quantities to temperature changes, at constant pressure or at constant volume. For this purpose we shall consider a new quantity, the *heat capacity*.

### Definition

***Fundamental statement.*** It was pointed out in Chapter 3 that the heat absorbed by a body (not at a transition temperature) is proportional to the change in temperature:

$$Q = C(T_2 - T_1) \tag{4-17}$$

The proportionality constant, $C$, is called the *heat capacity* and is in itself proportional to the mass of the substance undergoing the temperature change. Hence the heat capacity per gram may be called the *specific heat*, and that for 1 mole of material the *molal heat capacity*.

It has also been pointed out previously that the value of $C$,

$$C = \frac{Q}{T_2 - T_1} = \frac{Q}{\Delta T} \tag{4-18}$$

may itself depend on the temperature. For a rigorous definition of heat capacity, therefore, we must consider an infinitesimally small temperature interval. Consequently, we define the heat capacity by the expression

$$C = \frac{DQ}{dT} \tag{4-19}$$

where the capital $D$ in $DQ$ emphasizes the inexactness of the heat quantity. Since $DQ$ is inexact, $C$ has no unique limit but depends on the path or conditions under which heat is supplied. It is evident, of course, that we may lay certain restrictions upon Eq. (4-19), for example, constancy of pressure or constancy of volume. For these situations we may modify Eq. (4-19) to the following expressions:

$$C_p = \left(\frac{DQ}{\partial T}\right)_P \tag{4-20}$$

and

$$C_v = \left(\frac{DQ}{\partial T}\right)_V \tag{4-21}$$

***Derived relations.*** Equations (4-19) to (4-21) are fundamental definitions. From these and our previous thermodynamic principles, new relations may be derived which are very useful in further work.

If we have a substance which is only absorbing heat at a constant pressure, it is evident that the restrictions laid upon Eq. (4-8) are being fulfilled, and hence that

$$DQ_P = dH_P \tag{4-8}$$

Simple substitution into Eq. (4-20) leads to the important expression

$$C_p = \left(\frac{\partial H}{\partial T}\right)_P \tag{4-22}$$

Since $dH$ is exact, $C_p$ has a unique limit, a definite value for a particular substance in a specified state.

Similarly, if we have a substance which is merely absorbing heat at constant volume, it is evident that the restrictions placed upon Eq. (3-14) are being fulfilled and hence that

$$DQ_V = dE_V \tag{4-23}$$

Simple substitution into Eq. (4-21) leads to an additional basic relationship,

$$C_v = \left(\frac{\partial E}{\partial T}\right)_V \tag{4-24}$$

## Some Relations between $C_p$ and $C_v$

From the considerations of the preceding section there is no immediately apparent connection between the two heat capacities, $C_p$ and $C_v$. Once again, however, we may illustrate the power of thermodynamic methods by developing several such relationships without any assumptions beyond the first law of thermodynamics and the definitions which have been made already.

1. Starting with the derived relation for $C_p$,

$$C_p = \left(\frac{\partial H}{\partial T}\right)_P \tag{4-22}$$

we may introduce the definition of $H$:

$$C_p = \left[\frac{\partial(E + PV)}{\partial T}\right]_P = \left(\frac{\partial E}{\partial T}\right)_P + P\left(\frac{\partial V}{\partial T}\right)_P \tag{4-25}$$

The partial derivative $(\partial E/\partial T)_P$ is not $C_v$, but if it could be expanded into some relation with $(\partial E/\partial T)_V$, we should have succeeded in introducing $C_v$ into Eq. (4-25). The necessary relation may be derived readily by considering the internal energy, $E$, as a function of $T$ and $V$ and setting up the total differential:

$$dE = \left(\frac{\partial E}{\partial T}\right)_V dT + \left(\frac{\partial E}{\partial V}\right)_T dV \tag{4-26}$$

By the methods described in Chapter 2, we may obtain the following:

$$\left(\frac{\partial E}{\partial T}\right)_P = \left(\frac{\partial E}{\partial T}\right)_V + \left(\frac{\partial E}{\partial V}\right)_T \left(\frac{\partial V}{\partial T}\right)_P \tag{4-27}$$

Substituting Eq. (4-27) into (4-25) and factoring out the partial derivative $(\partial V/\partial T)_P$, we obtain the desired expression:

$$\begin{aligned} C_p &= \left(\frac{\partial E}{\partial T}\right)_V + \left[P + \left(\frac{\partial E}{\partial V}\right)_T\right] \left(\frac{\partial V}{\partial T}\right)_P \\ &= C_v + \left[P + \left(\frac{\partial E}{\partial V}\right)_T\right] \left(\frac{\partial V}{\partial T}\right)_P \end{aligned} \tag{4-28}$$

This expression will be of considerable value when we consider special cases for which values or equations for the partial derivatives $(\partial E/\partial V)_T$ and $(\partial V/\partial T)_P$ are available.

2. A second relationship may readily be derived by transformation of the second term in Eq. (4-28) so that the partial derivative $(\partial E/\partial V)_T$ is replaced by one containing $H$. Making use of the fundamental relationship between $E$ and $H$, we obtain

$$\left(\frac{\partial E}{\partial V}\right)_T = \left[\frac{\partial(H - PV)}{\partial V}\right]_T = \left(\frac{\partial H}{\partial V}\right)_T - P - V\left(\frac{\partial P}{\partial V}\right)_T \tag{4-29}$$

This expression may be placed in the bracketed factor in Eq. (4-28) to give

$$C_p = C_v + \left[P + \left(\frac{\partial H}{\partial V}\right)_T - P - V\left(\frac{\partial P}{\partial V}\right)_T\right] \left(\frac{\partial V}{\partial T}\right)_P \tag{4-30}$$

which may be reduced to

$$C_p = C_v + \left[\left(\frac{\partial H}{\partial P}\right)_T \left(\frac{\partial P}{\partial V}\right)_T - V\left(\frac{\partial P}{\partial V}\right)_T\right] \left(\frac{\partial V}{\partial T}\right)_P \tag{4-31}$$

$$= C_v + \left[\left(\frac{\partial H}{\partial P}\right)_T - V\right] \left(\frac{\partial P}{\partial V}\right)_T \left(\frac{\partial V}{\partial T}\right)_P \tag{4-32}$$

Reference to Eq. (2-8) will show that

$$\left(\frac{\partial P}{\partial V}\right)_T \left(\frac{\partial V}{\partial T}\right)_P = -\left(\frac{\partial P}{\partial T}\right)_V \qquad (4\text{-}33)$$

The insertion of this expression into Eq. (4-32) leads to the relation

$$C_p = C_v + \left[V - \left(\frac{\partial H}{\partial P}\right)_T\right]\left(\frac{\partial P}{\partial T}\right)_V \qquad (4\text{-}34)$$

another very useful equation.

3. A third relation between $C_p$ and $C_v$ may be obtained by several operations on the second term within the bracket in Eq. (4-34). If we consider $H$ as a function of $T$ and $P$, then

$$dH = \left(\frac{\partial H}{\partial T}\right)_P dT + \left(\frac{\partial H}{\partial P}\right)_T dP \qquad (4\text{-}35)$$

If $H$ is held constant, $dH = 0$, and

$$0 = \left(\frac{\partial H}{\partial T}\right)_P \left(\frac{\partial T}{\partial P}\right)_H + \left(\frac{\partial H}{\partial P}\right)_T \qquad (4\text{-}36)$$

Using Eq. (4-36) to substitute for $(\partial H/\partial P)_T$ in Eq. (4-34), we obtain

$$C_p = C_v + \left[V + \left(\frac{\partial H}{\partial T}\right)_P \left(\frac{\partial T}{\partial P}\right)_H\right]\left(\frac{\partial P}{\partial T}\right)_V \qquad (4\text{-}37)$$

Several other general relations between $C_p$ and $C_v$ are obtainable by procedures similar to those just outlined.

## Heat Capacities of Gases

From classical thermodynamics alone it is impossible to predict numerical values for heat capacities, and hence these quantities must be determined calorimetrically. With the aid of statistical mechanics, it is possible to determine heat capacities from spectroscopic data, instead of from direct calorimetric measurements. Even with spectroscopic information, however, it is convenient to correlate data over a range of temperature in terms of empirical equations.[2] The following expressions have been used most generally:

$$C_p = a + bT + cT^2 + dT^3 \qquad (4\text{-}38)$$

[2] A method has been described [B. L. Crawford, Jr., and R. G. Parr, *J. Chem. Phys.*, **16**, 233 (1948)] by means of which one may proceed directly from spectroscopic data to an empirical equation of the form of (4-38).

and

$$C_p = a + bT + \frac{c'}{T^2} \tag{4-39}$$

The results of several critical surveys by H. M. Spencer and his collaborators are summarized in Table 4-1 and are illustrated for comparative purposes in Figure 4-1.

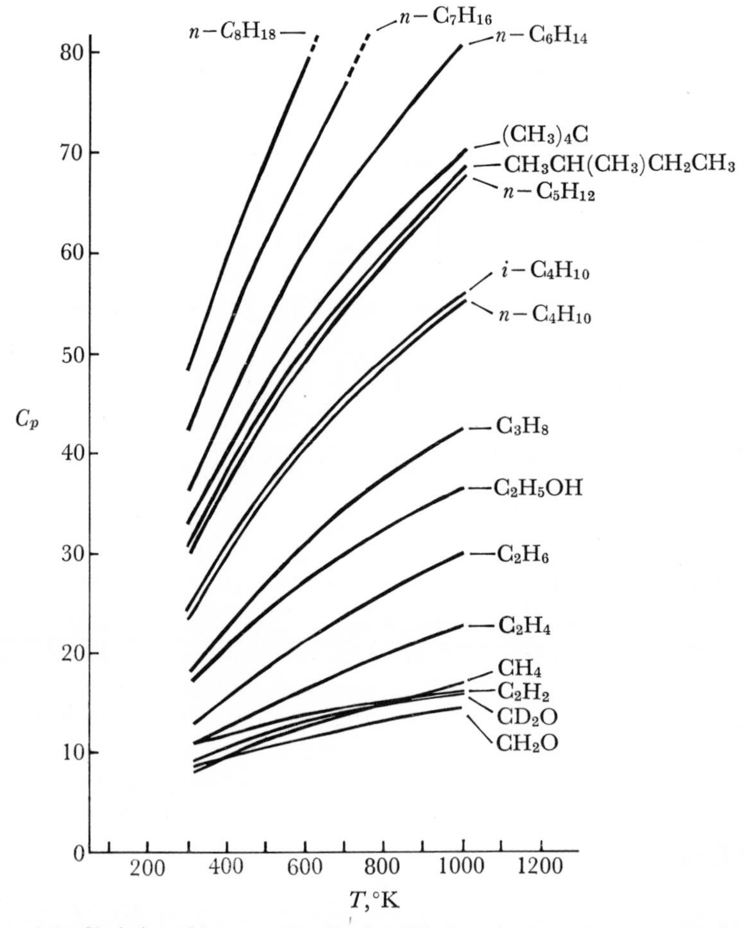


***Figure 4-1*** *Variation of heat capacity, $C_p$, in cal mole$^{-1}$ deg$^{-1}$, with temperatures for some organic compounds.*

***Table 4-1***

*Heat capacities at constant pressure*[a,b]

| Substance | Temperature range, °K | $a$ | $b \times 10^3$ | $c \times 10^7$ | $c' \times 10^{-5}$ | $d \times 10^9$ |
|---|---|---|---|---|---|---|
| $H_2(g)$ | 300–1500 | 6.9469 | −0.1999 | 4.808 | | |
| $O_2(g)$ | 300–1500 | 6.148 | 3.102 | −9.23 | | |
| $N_2(g)$ | 300–1500 | 6.524 | 1.250 | −0.01 | | |
| $Cl_2(g)$ | 300–1500 | 7.5755 | 2.4244 | −9.650 | | |
| $Br_2(g)$ | 300–1500 | 8.4228 | 0.9739 | −3.555 | | |
| $H_2O(g)$ | 300–1500 | 7.256 | 2.298 | 2.83 | | |
| $CO_2(g)$ | 300–1500 | 6.214 | 10.396 | −35.45 | | |
| $CO(g)$ | 300–1500 | 6.420 | 1.665 | −1.96 | | |
| $CNCl(g)$ | 250–1000 | 11.304 | 2.441 | | −1.159 | |
| $HCl(g)$ | 300–1500 | 6.7319 | 0.4325 | 3.697 | | |
| $SO_2(g)$ | 300–1800 | 11.895 | 1.089 | | −2.642 | |
| $SO_3(g)$ | 300–1200 | 6.077 | 23.537 | −96.87 | | |
| $SO_3(g)$ | 300–1200 | 3.603 | 36.310 | −288.28 | | 8.649 |
| $CH_4(g)$ | 300–1500 | 3.381 | 18.044 | −43.00 | | |
| $C_2H_6(g)$ | 300–1500 | 2.247 | 38.201 | −110.49 | | |
| $C_3H_8(g)$ | 300–1500 | 2.410 | 57.195 | −175.33 | | |
| $n$-$C_4H_{10}(g)$ | 300–1500 | 4.453 | 72.270 | −222.14 | | |
| $n$-$C_5H_{12}(g)$ | 300–1500 | 5.910 | 88.449 | −273.88 | | |
| Benzene($g$) | 300–1500 | −0.409 | 77.621 | −264.29 | | |
| Pyridine($g$) | 290–1000 | −3.016 | 88.083 | −386.65 | | |
| Carbon (graphite) | 300–1500 | −1.265 | 14.008 | −103.31 | | 2.751 |

[a] H. M. Spencer and J. L. Justice, *J. Am. Chem. Soc.*, **56,** 2311 (1934); H. M. Spencer and G. N. Flannagan, *ibid.*, **64,** 2511 (1942); H. M. Spencer, *ibid.*, **67,** 1859 (1945); H. M. Spencer, *Ind. Eng. Chem.*, **40,** 2152 (1948). Data on numerous other substances are given in these original papers. See also K. K. Kelley, *U.S. Bur. Mines Bull.* **476,** (1949); **584,** (1960).

[b] Constants are defined by Eqs. (4-38) and (4-39) and apply when the unit is cal mole$^{-1}$ deg$^{-1}$.

## Heat Capacities of Solids

Early in the nineteenth century, Dulong and Petit observed that the molal heat capacity of a solid element is generally near 6 cal deg$^{-1}$. Subsequent investigations, however, showed that $C_v$ (or $C_p$) varies strongly with the

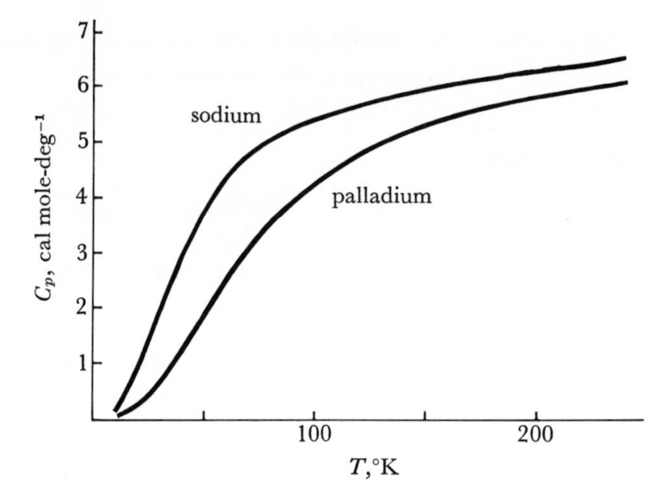


***Figure 4-2*** *Molal heat capacities of some solid elements.* [*Taken from data of G. L. Pickard and F. E. Simon, Proc. Phys. Soc.*, **61,** 1 (1948).]

temperature, in the fashion indicated by Figure 4-2, though the upper limiting value of about 6 cal mole$^{-1}$ deg$^{-1}$ is approached by the heavier elements at room temperature.

Once again it must be pointed out that it is impossible to predict values of heat capacities for solids by purely thermodynamic reasoning. The problem of the solid state has received much consideration, however, from an extrathermodynamic view, and several very important expressions for the heat capacity have been derived. For our purposes it will be sufficient to consider only the Debye equation, in particular its limiting form at very low temperatures:

$$C_v = \frac{12\pi^4}{5} R \frac{T^3}{\theta^3} = 464.5 \frac{T^3}{\theta^3} \text{ cal mole}^{-1} \text{ deg}^{-1} \tag{4-40}$$

$\theta$ is called the *characteristic temperature* and may be calculated from an experimental determination of the heat capacity at a low temperature. This equation has been very useful in the extrapolation of measured heat capacities[3] down to the neighborhood of 0°K, particularly in connection with calculations of entropies from the third law of thermodynamics. Strictly speaking, the Debye equation was derived only for an isotropic elementary

[3] Deviations from the $T^3$ law and their significance have been discussed by K. Clusius and L. Schachinger, *Z. Naturforsch.*, **2a**, 90 (1947), and by G. L. Pickard and F. E. Simon, *Proc. Phys. Soc.*, **61**, 1 (1948).

substance. Nevertheless it has been found to be applicable to most compounds also, particularly in the region close to absolute zero.

## Heat Capacities of Liquids

No adequate theoretical treatment has been developed which might serve as a guide in interpreting and correlating data on the heat capacities of liquids. It has been observed, nevertheless, that the molal heat capacity of a pure liquid is generally near that of the solid, so that if measurements are not available one may assume that $C_v$ is 6 cal deg$^{-1}$ (gram-atom)$^{-1}$. The heat capacities of solutions, however, cannot be predicted reliably from the corresponding properties of the components. Empirical methods of treating solutions will be considered in later chapters.

## Integration of Heat Capacity Equations

Later, in connection with calculations of enthalpies and entropies of substances, it will become necessary to integrate the values of the heat capacity over a given temperature range.

***Analytical method.*** If the heat capacity can be expressed as an analytic function of the temperature, the integration can be carried out in a simple, straightforward manner. For example, if $C_p$ can be expressed as a power series,

$$C_p = a + bT + cT^2 + \cdots \tag{4-41}$$

where $a$, $b$, and $c$ are constants, it is evident from Eq. (4-22) that

$$\int dH = \int C_p\, dT = \int (a + bT + cT^2)\, dT \tag{4-42}$$

if we neglect terms higher than second degree in Eq. (4-41), and that

$$H - H_0 = aT + \frac{b}{2} T^2 + \frac{c}{3} T^3 \tag{4-43}$$

where $H_0$ is the constant of integration.

***Graphical method.*** If the dependence of $C_p$ on temperature is too complicated to be expressed by a simple function, as for example in solids at low temperatures, then a graphical method of integration can be used. A typical example was worked out partially in Chapter 2 (Figure 2-3). As was pointed out there, if we take a small enough temperature interval, $\Delta T$, the product of $\ddot{C}_p$, the average value of the heat capacity in that region, by $\Delta T$, gives the area under the $C_p$ curve in that temperature interval.

Consequently, the integral may be approximated to any desired degree by summation of the areas:

$$\sum \dddot{C}_p \, \Delta T = \int C_p \, dT \tag{4-44}$$

The graphical method is applied very extensively in integrations of heat-capacity data for use in the prediction of the feasibility of chemical reactions on the basis of the third law of thermodynamics.

## Exercises

**1.** Molal heat capacities of solid *n*-heptane are listed in Table 2-4 of Chapter 2.

(a) Calculate $H_{182.5°K} - H_{0°K}$ by graphical integration.

(b) If the heat of fusion at 182.5°K is 3354 cal mole$^{-1}$, calculate $\Delta H$ for the transformation

$$n\text{-heptane (solid, 0°K)} = n\text{-heptane (liquid, 182.5°K)}$$

**2.** (a) Find the Debye equation for $C_v$ for *n*-heptane. Use the given value of $C_p$ at 15.14°K (see Exercise 1) as a sufficiently close approximation to $C_v$.

(b) Find $H_{15.14°K} - H_{0°K}$ by integrating the Debye equation for *n*-heptane. Using this analytical value in place of the graphical value for the same temperature range, and the graphical results above 15.14°K, determine $H_{182.5°K} - H_{0°K}$. Compare the answer with the result obtained entirely by graphical methods in Exercise 1.

**3.** Calculate the differences between $Q_P$ and $Q_V$ in each of the following reactions:

(a) $H_2 + \frac{1}{2}O_2 = H_2O$, at 25°C.

(b) Ethyl acetate + water = ethyl alcohol + acetic acid, at 25°C.

(c) Haber synthesis of ammonia, at 400°C.

**4.** Prove the following relations, using only definitions and mathematical principles:

$$\text{(a)} \quad \left(\frac{\partial E}{\partial V}\right)_P = C_p\left(\frac{\partial T}{\partial V}\right)_P - P \qquad \text{(b)} \quad \left(\frac{\partial E}{\partial P}\right)_V = C_p\left(\frac{\partial T}{\partial P}\right)_V$$

**5.** Using the equations in Exercise 4, find $(\partial E/\partial V)_P$ and $(\partial E/\partial P)_V$ for the special case of 1 mole of an ideal gas, for which $PV = RT$.

**6.** Referring back to Eq. (4-28) suggest a substance for which $C_p = C_v$ (under conditions other than 0°K), that is, one for which the second term on the right-hand side of the equation becomes zero under certain conditions.

# 5 Heat of Reaction

In Chapter 4 we were introduced to a new function, the enthalpy, and found among its properties a correspondence with the heat of reaction at constant pressure (when the only work is due to a volume change against that pressure). Most chemical reactions are carried out in some vessel exposed to the atmosphere, and under conditions such that no work other than that against the atmosphere is produced. For this reason, and because $\Delta H$ is independent of the path of a reaction and gives the heat absorbed in the reaction, the enthalpy change is a useful quantity.

Enthalpy changes also give pertinent information in several other problems in chemical thermodynamics. For a long time it was thought that the sign of $\Delta H$, that is, whether heat is absorbed or evolved, is a criterion of the spontaneity of a reaction. When this misconception was cleared up, it still was evident that this criterion is useful within certain limitations. If the $\Delta H$ values are large, their signs may still be used as the basis of a first guess with respect to the feasibility of a reaction.

In more rigorous applications, such as in the use of the third law of thermodynamics for evaluating the feasibility of a chemical transformation enthalpy changes must be known in addition to other quantities. $\Delta H$ values are also required to establish the magnitude of the temperature dependence of equilibrium constants. For all these reasons it is desirable to have tables of $\Delta H$ available, so that the heats of various transformations may be calculated readily. In many of these calculations we shall make use of the generalization of Hess, now firmly established on the basis of the first law of thermodynamics, and we shall use known values of $\Delta H$ to calculate heats for new reactions which can be expressed as sums of known reactions.

## 5-1 DEFINITIONS AND CONVENTIONS

It is evident that the heat of a reaction should depend upon the states of the substances involved. Thus in the formation of water,

$$H_2(g) + \frac{1}{2}O_2(g) = H_2O \tag{5-1}$$

if the $H_2O$ is in the liquid state, $\Delta H$ will differ from that observed if the $H_2O$ is a vapor. Similarly, the heat of the reaction will depend upon the pressure of any gases involved. Furthermore, for reactions involving solids (for example, sulfur), the $\Delta H$ depends upon which crystalline form (for example, rhombic or monoclinic) participates in the reaction. For these reasons, if we are to tabulate values of $\Delta H$, it is necessary to agree that the heats should refer to reactions with the compounds in certain standard states.

### Some Standard States

The states which by convention have been agreed upon as reference states in tabulating heats of reaction are summarized in Table 5-1. Other standard states may be adopted in special problems. When no state is specified, it may be assumed to be that listed in Table 5-1.

***Table 5-1***

*Standards and conventions for heats of reaction*

| | |
|---|---|
| Standard state of solid | The most stable form at 1 atm pressure and the specified temperature (unless otherwise specified)[a] |
| Standard state of liquid | The most stable form at 1 atm pressure and the specified temperature |
| Standard state of gas | Zero pressure[b] and the specified temperature |
| Standard state of carbon | Graphite |
| Standard temperature | 25°C |
| Sign of $\Delta H$ | + If heat is absorbed |

(*Footnotes on next page*)

## Heat of Formation

The tables of heats of reaction are generally listed in terms of the heats of formation of various compounds from their elements in their standard states at the specified temperature. Thus if the standard heat of formation, $\Delta Hf°$, of $CO_2$, at 25° is given as $-94.0518$ kcal mole$^{-1}$, the following equation is implied:

$$\underset{\substack{\text{(graphite at}\\ 298.15°\text{K, 1 atm)}}}{\text{C}} + \underset{\substack{\text{(gas at 298.15°K,}\\ \text{zero pressure)}}}{\text{O}_2} = \underset{\substack{\text{(gas at 298.15°K,}\\ \text{zero pressure)}}}{\text{CO}_2} \qquad (5\text{-}2)$$

$$\Delta Hf° = -94.0518 \text{ kcal mole}^{-1}$$

From this definition it is evident that the heat of formation of an element in its standard state is zero, *by convention.* In other words, elements in their standard states are taken as reference states in the tabulation of heats of reaction, just as sea level is the reference point in measuring geographic heights.

A few standard heats of formation have been assembled in Table 5-2. Data on other substances may be obtained from the following critical compilations:

*International Critical Tables*, McGraw-Hill, New York, 1933.

Landolt-Börnstein, *Physikalisch-chemische Tabellen*, 5th ed., Springer, Berlin, 1936; 6th ed., 1963.

W. M. Latimer, *Oxidation Potentials*. Prentice-Hall, 2nd ed., Englewood Cliffs, N.J., 1952.

"Selected Values of Chemical Thermodynamic Properties,"[1] *Nat. Bur. Standards (U.S.), Circ. 500*, 1952.

American Petroleum Institute Research Project 44, *Selected Values of Physical and Thermodynamic Properties of Hydrocarbons and Related Compounds*,[1] Carnegie Press, Pittsburgh, 1953.

Manufacturing Chemists' Association, *Selected Values of Properties of Chemical Compounds*,[1] Carnegie Inst. Technol., Pittsburgh, 1955.

D. R. Stull and G. C. Sinke, *Thermodynamic Properties of the Elements*, Am. Chem. Soc., Washington, D.C., 1956.

[1] These tables are being continually revised and expanded.

---

[a] Thus for some problems it may be convenient to assign a standard state to both rhombic sulfur and monoclinic sulfur, for example.

[b] It is shown in Chap. 19 that internal consistency in the definition of standard states requires that zero pressure be the standard state for the enthalpy of a gas. Unfortunately, however, most reference sources use the convention of 1 atm pressure. In most cases, the difference in enthalpy between these two pressures is very small.

**Table 5-2**

*Heats of formation[a] at 25°C*

| Substance | $\Delta Hf°$, kcal mole$^{-1}$ | Substance | $\Delta Hf°$, kcal mole$^{-1}$ |
|---|---|---|---|
| H(*g*) | 52.089 | Methane(*g*) | −17.889 |
| O(*g*) | 59.159 | Ethane(*g*) | −20.236 |
| Cl(*g*) | 29.012 | Propane(*g*) | −24.820 |
| Br(*g*) | 26.71 | *n*-Butane(*g*) | −30.15 |
| $Br_2$(*g*) | 7.34 | Ethylene(*g*) | 12.496 |
| I(*g*) | 25.482 | Propylene(*g*) | 4.879 |
| $I_2$(*g*) | 14.876 | 1-Butene(*g*) | −0.03 |
| $H_2O$(*g*) | −57.7979 | Acetylene(*g*) | 54.194 |
| $H_2O$(*l*) | −68.3174 | Benzene (*g*) | 19.820 |
| HF(*g*) | −64.2 | Toluene(*g*) | 11.950 |
| $(HF)_6$(*g*) | −426.0 | *o*-Xylene(*g*) | 4.540 |
| HCl(*g*) | −22.063 | *m*-Xylene(*g*) | 4.120 |
| HBr(*g*) | −8.66 | *p*-Xylene(*g*) | 4.290 |
| HI(*g*) | 6.20 | Methanol(*l*) | −57.02 |
| ICl(*g*) | 4.20 | Ethanol(*l*) | −66.356 |
| NO(*g*) | 21.600 | Glycine(*s*) | −126.33 |
| CO(*g*) | −26.4157 | Acetic acid(*l*) | −116.4 |
| $CO_2$(*g*) | −94.0518 | Taurine(*s*) | −187.8 |

[a] Selected from "Selected Values of Chemical Thermodynamic Properties," *Nat. Bur. Standards (U.S.) Circ. No. 500*, 1952, and *Selected Values of Physical and Thermodynamic Properties of Hydrocarbons*, American Petroleum Institute Project 44, 1953.

## 5-2 ADDITIVITY OF HEATS OF REACTION

It has been emphasized repeatedly that since the enthalpy is a thermodynamic property, the value of $\Delta H$ depends only upon the nature and state of the initial reactants and final products, and not upon the reactions which have been used to carry out the transformation. Thus one may use known $\Delta H$'s to calculate the heat of a reaction for which no data are available. Several examples of additivity will be given.

### Calculation of Heat of Formation from Heat of Reaction

As an example we may calculate the heat of formation of $Ca(OH)_2$ (solid) from data for other reactions such as the following:

$$CaO(s) + H_2O(l) = Ca(OH)_2(s) \qquad \Delta H_{18^\circ C} = -15{,}260 \text{ cal} \qquad (5\text{-}3)$$

$$H_2(g) + \tfrac{1}{2}O_2(g) = H_2O(l) \qquad \Delta H_{18^\circ C} = -68{,}370 \text{ cal} \qquad (5\text{-}4)$$

$$Ca(s) + \tfrac{1}{2}O_2(g) = CaO(s) \qquad \Delta H_{18^\circ C} = -151{,}800 \text{ cal} \qquad (5\text{-}5)$$

It is evident that the addition of the preceding three chemical equations leads to the following desired equation; hence the addition of the corresponding $\Delta H$'s gives the desired heat of formation:

$$Ca(s) + O_2(g) + H_2(g) = Ca(OH)_2(s) \qquad \Delta H_{18^\circ C} = -235{,}430 \text{ cal} \tag{5-6}$$

## Calculation of Heat of Formation from Heat of Combustion

This type of calculation is very common, since with most organic compounds the experimental data must be obtained for the combustion process, yet the heat of formation is the more useful quantity for further thermodynamic calculations. A typical example of such a calculation is outlined by the following equations:

$$C_2H_5OH(l) + 3O_2(g) = 2CO_2(g) + 3H_2O(l) \qquad \Delta H_{298^\circ} = -326{,}700 \text{ cal} \tag{5-7}$$

$$3H_2O(l) = 3H_2(g) + \tfrac{3}{2}O_2(g) \qquad \Delta H_{298^\circ} = 204{,}952 \text{ cal} \tag{5-8}$$

$$2CO_2(g) = 2C\text{ (graphite)} + 2O_2(g) \qquad \Delta H_{298^\circ} = 188{,}104 \text{ cal} \tag{5-9}$$

---

$$C_2H_5OH(l) = 3H_2(g) + \tfrac{1}{2}O_2(g) + 2C\text{ (graphite)} \qquad \Delta H = 66{,}356 \text{ cal} \tag{5-10}$$

Reversing Eq. (5-10), we obtain the heat of formation of ethyl alcohol:

$$3H_2(g) + \tfrac{1}{2}O_2(g) + 2C\text{(graphite)} = C_2H_5OH(l) \qquad \Delta Hf^\circ = -66{,}356 \text{ cal} \tag{5-11}$$

## Calculation of Heat of Transition from Heat of Formation

Calculations of this type are particularly important in consideration of changes of reference state from one allotropic form to another. As an example the case of carbon will be illustrated:

$$C\text{(graphite)} + O_2(g) = CO_2(g) \qquad \Delta H_{298^\circ} = -94{,}051.8 \text{ cal mole}^{-1} \tag{5-12}$$

$$C\text{(diamond)} + O_2(g) = CO_2(g) \qquad \Delta H_{298^\circ} = -94{,}505.0 \text{ cal mole}^{-1} \tag{5-13}$$

Subtracting the first reaction from the second, we obtain

$$C\text{(diamond)} = C\text{(graphite)} \qquad \Delta H_{298^\circ} = -453.2 \text{ cal mole}^{-1} \tag{5-14}$$

## 5-3 BOND ENERGIES

The calculation of the heat of formation of a given compound depends upon the determination of the heat of at least one reaction of this substance. Frequently, however, it is desirable to estimate the heat of a chemical reaction involving a hitherto unsynthesized compound, and hence a substance for which no enthalpy data are available. For the solution of problems of this type a system of bond energies has been established, so that if the atomic structure of the compound is known, it is possible to *approximate* the heat of formation by summation of the appropriate bond energies.

### Definition of Bond Energies

It is essential at the very outset to make a distinction between "bond energy" and the "bond dissociation energy" of a given linkage. The latter is a definite quantity referring to the energy required to break a given bond of some specific compound. On the other hand, bond energy is an intermediate value of the dissociation energies of a given bond in a series of different dissociating species.

The distinction between these two terms may be more evident if described in terms of a simple example, the O–H bond. The heat of dissociation of the O–H bond depends upon the nature of the molecular species from which the H atom is being separated. For example, in the water molecule,

$$H_2O(g) = H(g) + OH(g) \qquad \Delta H_{298^\circ} = 119.95 \text{ kcal mole}^{-1} \quad (5\text{-}15)$$

On the other hand, to break the O–H bond in the hydroxyl radical requires a different heat quantity,

$$OH(g) = O(g) + H(g) \qquad \Delta H_{298^\circ} = 101.19 \text{ kcal mole}^{-1} \quad (5\text{-}16)$$

The bond energy $\epsilon_{O-H}$ is defined as the average of these two values; in other words,

$$\epsilon_{O-H} = \frac{119.95 + 101.19}{2} = 110.57 \text{ kcal mole}^{-1} \quad (5\text{-}17)$$

Thus $\epsilon_{O-H}$ is half the value of the enthalpy change of the following reaction:

$$H_2O(g) = O(g) + 2H(g) \quad \epsilon_{O-H} = \frac{\Delta H}{2} = 110.57 \text{ kcal} \quad (5\text{-}18)$$

In the case of diatomic elements, such as $H_2$, the bond energy and bond dissociation energy are identical, for each refers to the following reaction:

$$H_2(g) = 2H(g) \qquad \epsilon_{H-H} = \Delta H_{298^\circ} = 104.178 \text{ kcal} \quad (5\text{-}19)$$

It should be noted that in general the bond energy refers to an intermediate average value of the dissociation energy of a given type of linkage in a molecule, at the start with the compound in the gaseous state and at the end with the dissociated atoms in the gaseous state. Thus the bond energy sum for a given molecule is equal to the heat of atomization of the substance, in the ideal gas state, to the atomic elements.

## Calculation of Bond Energies

The principle of the method has been illustrated with water and the O–H bond. However, this is a relatively simple case. Since bond energies are particularly of value in problems involving organic compounds, it is desirable to consider an example from this branch of chemistry, where the fundamental data are obtained from heats of combustion. We shall calculate the C–H bond energy from data on the heat of combustion of methane.

To find $\epsilon_{C-H}$ we need to know the heat of the following reaction:

$$CH_4(g) = C(g) + 4H(g) \qquad \epsilon_{C-H} = \frac{\Delta H}{4} \tag{5-20}$$

The $\Delta H$ for the preceding reaction can be obtained from the summation of those for the following reactions at 298°K:

$$CH_4(g) + 2O_2(g) = CO_2(g) + 2H_2O(l) \qquad \Delta H = -212.80 \text{ kcal} \tag{5-21}$$

$$CO_2(g) = C(\text{graphite}) + O_2(g) \qquad \Delta H = 94.05 \text{ kcal} \tag{5-22}$$

$$2H_2O(l) = 2H_2(g) + O_2(g) \qquad \Delta H = 136.64 \text{ kcal} \tag{5-23}$$

$$2H_2(g) = 4H(g) \qquad \Delta H = 208.36 \text{ kcal} \tag{5-24}$$

$$C(\text{graphite}) = C(g) \qquad \Delta H = 171.698 \text{ kcal} \qquad (5\text{-}25)^2$$

---

$$CH_4(g) = C(g) + 4H(g) \qquad \Delta H = 398.0 \text{ kcal} \tag{5-26}$$

It follows that at 298°K

$$\epsilon_{C-H} = \frac{398.0}{4} = 99.5 \text{ kcal mole}^{-1} \tag{5-27}$$

It is pertinent to point out that this value of the C–H bond energy does not correspond to the dissociation energy of the carbon-hydrogen link in methane,[3] 102 kcal mole$^{-1}$. However, it should also be emphasized that

[2] In the present calculation, the value chosen is that from "Selected Values of Chemical Thermodynamic Properties," *Natl. Bur. Standards (U.S.), Circ. No. 500*, 1952. More recent work favors 170.89 kcal mole$^{-1}$ for the heat of sublimation of carbon at 298°K; see T. L. Cottrell, *The Strengths of Chemical Bonds*, 2nd ed. Butterworths, London, 1958, pp. 155–160.

[3] G. B. Kistiakowsky and E. R. Van Artsdalen, *J. Chem. Phys.*, **12**, 469 (1944).

the latter energy refers to the equation

$$CH_4(g) = CH_3(g) + H(g) \tag{5-28}$$

and not to one-quarter of the $\Delta H$ associated with Eq. (5-26).

In the calculation of $\epsilon_{C-H}$ outlined above, enthalpy values at 298°K have been used, and hence the bond energy also refers to this temperature. For some purposes, it is the practice to calculate bond energies at 0°K, rather than 298°K. For $\epsilon_{C-H}$ one would obtain 98.2 kcal mole$^{-1}$ at 0°K, a value slightly lower than that at 298°K. In general the differences between the bond energies at the two temperatures are small. A list of bond energies at 298°K is given in Table 5-3.

In connection with estimates of the reliability of bond energies in the table, it should be emphasized that in some cases the value obtained depends upon that calculated previously for some other bond.[2] For example, to obtain $\epsilon_{C-C}$, one combines the heat of combustion of ethane with the proper multiples of the $\Delta H$'s in Eqs. (5-22) to (5-25) to obtain the enthalpy change for the reaction

$$C_2H_6(g) = 2C(g) + 6H(g) \tag{5-29}$$

On the basis of our definition of bond energy it is apparent that

$$\epsilon_{C-C} = \Delta H_{\text{Eq.(5-29)}} - 6\epsilon_{C-H} \tag{5-30}$$

Thus, the value of 82.6 kcal mole$^{-1}$ listed in Table 5-3 is based on an $\epsilon_{C-H}$ of 98.7 kcal mole$^{-1}$. Other estimates of $\epsilon_{C-H}$ would lead to different values for $\epsilon_{C-C}$.

## Estimation of the Heat of Reaction from Bond Energies

It has been pointed out that the primary value of bond energies lies in the calculation of the heat of a reaction involving a compound for which no enthalpy data are available. For example, the heat of formation of $Se_2Cl_2(g)$ may be calculated from bond energies by the following steps. Since the bond energy refers to the *dissociation* of Cl—Se—Se—Cl gas into gaseous atoms, the enthalpy change for the *formation* of this gaseous molecule should be given by

$$2Se(g) + 2Cl(g) = Se_2Cl_2(g) \qquad \Delta H = -[\epsilon_{Se-Se} + 2\epsilon_{Se-Cl}] \tag{5-31}$$

$$= -166 \text{ kcal mole}^{-1}$$

To estimate the heat of formation, however, it is necessary to add two reactions to Eq. (5-31), since by definition the heat of formation refers to the elements in their standard states. Therefore, we introduce the following enthalpy changes for converting the elements to their standard states at

*Table 5-3*

*Bond energies[a] at 298°K*

| Bond | kcal mole$^{-1}$ | Bond | kcal mole$^{-1}$ | Bond | kcal mole$^{-1}$ |
|---|---|---|---|---|---|
| H—H | 104.18 | Te=Te | 53* | O—Cl | 52 |
| Li—Li | 25* | I—I | 36.06 | F—Cl | 60.5* |
| C—C | 82.6 | Cs—Cs | 10.4* | Na—Cl | 98* |
| C=C | 145.8 | Li—H | 58* | Si—Cl | 91 |
| C≡C | 199.6 | C—H | 98.7 | P—Cl | 78 |
| N—N | 39 | N—H | 93.4 | S—Cl | 61 |
| N≡N | 225.8 | O—H | 110.6 | K—Cl | 101* |
| O—O | 35 | F—H | 135 | Cu—Cl | 88* |
| O=O | 119.1 | Na—H | 47* | As—Cl | 70 |
| F—F | 37 | Si—H | 76 | Se—Cl | 58 |
| Na—Na | 17* | P—H | 77 | Br—Cl | 52* |
| Si—Si | 53 | S—H | 83 | Rb—Cl | 102* |
| P—P | 48 | Cl—H | 103.1 | Ag—Cl | 72* |
| S—S | 54 | K—H | 43* | Sn—Cl | 76 |
| Cl—Cl | 57.87 | Cu—H | 66* | Sb—Cl | 74 |
| K—K | 11.8* | As—H | 59 | I—Cl | 50* |
| Ge—Ge | 45 | Se—H | 66 | Cs—Cl | 101* |
| As—As | 35 | Br—H | 87.4 | C—N | 72.8 |
| As≡As | 91* | Rb—H | 39* | C≡N | 212.6 |
| Se—Se | 50 | Ag—H | 58* | C—O | 85.5 |
| Se=Se | 65* | Te—H | 57 | C=O | 178 |
| Br—Br | 46.08 | I—H | 71.4 | C—S | 65 |
| Rb—Rb | 10.8* | Cs—H | 42* | C=S | 128 |
| Sn—Sn | 39 | Li—Cl | 115* | P≡N | 138* |
| Sb—Sb | 29 | C—Cl | 81 | S=O | 119 |
| Sb≡Sb | 69* | N—Cl | 46 | | |

[a] T. L. Cottrell, *The Strengths of Chemical Bonds*, 2nd ed., Butterworths, London, 1958, pp. 270–289. When values at 298°K have not been available, those at 0°K have been listed instead, and these are marked with an asterisk.

298°K:

$$Cl_2(g) = 2Cl(g) \qquad \Delta H = 57.87 \text{ kcal mole}^{-1} \tag{5-32}$$

$$2Se(\text{hexagonal}) = 2Se(g) \qquad \Delta H = 2 \times 48.4 \text{ kcal mole}^{-1} \tag{5-33}$$

The addition of Eqs. (5-31) through (5-33) leads to the expression

$$2Se(\text{hexagonal}) + Cl_2(g) = Se_2Cl_2(g) \qquad \Delta H = -11 \text{ kcal mole}^{-1} \tag{5-34}$$

If we wish to know the heat of formation of liquid $Se_2Cl_2$, we can estimate the heat of condensation (perhaps from Trouton's rule, or by comparison with related sulfur compounds) and add it to the value of $\Delta H$ obtained in Eq. (5-34).

By these methods it is possible to obtain fairly reliable estimates of heats of formation of many compounds. Difficulties are sometimes encountered, particularly in applications to organic compounds, where discrepancies arise which may be attributed to special factors such as steric effects and resonance. It is possible to set up secondary rules to take account of such special situations.[4]

## 5-4 HEAT OF REACTION AS A FUNCTION OF TEMPERATURE

In the preceding sections, methods of determining heats of reaction at a fixed temperature (generally 298.15°K) were discussed. In particular it was pointed out that it is possible to tabulate heats of formation and bond energies and to use these for calculating heats of reaction. These tables, of course, are available for only a few standard temperatures. Frequently it is necessary to know the heat of a reaction at a temperature different from those available in a reference table. It is pertinent, therefore, to consider at this point the procedures which may be used to determine the heat of reaction (at constant pressure) at one temperature from data at another temperature.

### Analytical Method

Since we are interested in the variation of enthalpy with temperature, we might recall first that

$$\left(\frac{\partial H}{\partial T}\right)_P = C_p \qquad (5\text{-}35)^5$$

It is evident that such an equation can be integrated, at constant pressure:

$$\int dH = \int C_p \, dT \qquad (5\text{-}36)$$

$$H = \int C_p \, dT + H_0 \qquad (5\text{-}37)$$

where $H_0$ represents an integration constant. If we are considering a chemical transformation, represented in general terms by

$$A + B + \cdots = M + N + \cdots \qquad (5\text{-}38)$$

[4] T. L. Cottrell, *op. cit*; C. T. Mortimer, *Reaction Heats and Bond Strengths*, Addison-Wesley, Reading, Mass., 1963.

[5] The corresponding equation for $\Delta H$ is often called the Person-Kirchhoff equation.

it is evident that we can write a series of equations of the form

$$H_A = \int C_{pA}\, dT + H_{0A} \tag{5-39}$$

$$H_B = \int C_{pB}\, dT + H_{0B} \tag{5-40}$$

$$H_M = \int C_{pM}\, dT + H_{0M} \tag{5-41}$$

$$H_N = \int C_{pN}\, dT + H_{0N} \tag{5-42}$$

For the chemical reaction (5-38) the enthalpy change, $\Delta H$, is given by

$$\begin{aligned} \Delta H &= H_M + H_N + \cdots - H_A - H_B - \cdots \\ &= (H_{0M} + H_{0N} + \cdots - H_{0A} - H_{0B} - \cdots) + \int C_{pM}\, dT \\ &\quad + \int C_{pN}\, dT + \cdots - \int C_{pA}\, dT - \int C_{pB}\, dT - \cdots \end{aligned} \tag{5-43}$$

If we define the quantities inside the parentheses as $\Delta H_0$, and if we group the integrals together, we obtain

$$\Delta H = \Delta H_0 + \int (C_{pM} + C_{pN} + \cdots - C_{pA} - C_{pB} - \cdots)\, dT \tag{5-44}$$

or

$$\Delta H = \Delta H_0 + \int \Delta C_p\, dT \tag{5-45}$$

Thus in order to obtain $\Delta H$ as a function of the temperature, it is necessary to know the dependence of the heat capacities of the reactants and products on the temperature, as well as one value of $\Delta H$ so that $\Delta H_0$ can be evaluated.

As an example, let us consider the heat of formation of $CO_2(g)$,

$$\text{C(graphite)} + O_2(g) = CO_2(g) \qquad \Delta H_{298.15} = -94{,}051.8 \text{ cal mole}^{-1} \tag{5-46}$$

The heat capacities of the substances involved may be expressed by the following equations:

$$C_{p(\text{C})} = -1.265 + 14.008 \times 10^{-3}\, T - 103.31 \times 10^{-7}\, T^2 \tag{5-47}$$

$$C_{p(\text{O}_2)} = 6.148 + 3.102 \times 10^{-3}\, T - 9.23 \times 10^{-7}\, T^2 \tag{5-48}$$

$$C_{p(\text{CO}_2)} = 6.214 + 10.396 \times 10^{-3}\, T - 35.45 \times 10^{-7}\, T^2 \tag{5-49}$$

Hence the difference in heat capacities of products and reactants is given by the equation

$$\Delta C_p = 1.331 - 6.714 \times 10^{-3}\, T + 77.09 \times 10^{-7}\, T^2 \qquad (5\text{-}50)$$

and consequently

$$\Delta H = \Delta H_0 + \int (1.331 - 6.714 \times 10^{-3}\, T + 77.09 \times 10^{-7}\, T^2)\, dT$$

$$= \Delta H_0 + 1.331\, T - 3.357 \times 10^{-3}\, T^2 + 25.70 \times 10^{-7}\, T^3 \qquad (5\text{-}51)$$

Since $\Delta H$ is known at 298.15°K, it is possible to substitute into the preceding equation and to calculate $\Delta H_0$:

$$\Delta H_0 = -94{,}218.3 \qquad (5\text{-}52)$$

Thus we may now write a completely explicit equation for the heat of formation of $CO_2$ as a function of the temperature:

$$\Delta H = -94{,}218.3 + 1.331\, T - 3.357 \times 10^{-3}\, T^2 + 25.70 \times 10^{-7}\, T^3 \qquad (5\text{-}53)$$

## Arithmetic Method

A second procedure, fundamentally no different from the analytic method, involves the addition of suitable equations to give the desired equation. For example, if we consider the freezing of water, the heat of the reaction is known at 0°C ($T_1$), but might be required at $-10$°C ($T_2$). We may obtain the desired $\Delta H$ by the addition of the following equations:

$$H_2O(l, 0°C) = H_2O(s, 0°C) \qquad \Delta H = 1436 \text{ cal mole}^{-1} \qquad (5\text{-}54)$$

$$H_2O(s, 0°C) = H_2O(s, -10°C) \qquad \Delta H = \int_{0°}^{-10°} C_{p(s)}\, dT$$

$$= C_{p(s)}\,(T_2 - T_1)$$

$$= -87 \text{ cal mole}^{-1} \qquad (5\text{-}55)$$

$$H_2O(l, -10°C) = H_2O(l, 0°C) \qquad \Delta H = \int_{-10°}^{0°} C_{p(l)}\, dT$$

$$= C_{p(l)}\,(T_1 - T_2)$$

$$= 180 \text{ cal mole}^{-1} \qquad (5\text{-}56)$$

---

$$H_2O(l, -10°C) = H_2O(s, -10°C) \qquad \Delta H = -1436 - 87 + 180$$

$$= -1343 \text{ cal mole}^{-1} \qquad (5\text{-}57)$$

## Graphical Method

It is obvious from the discussion of enthalpy change in the preceding chapter that if analytic equations for the heat capacities of reactants and products are unavailable, one may still carry out the integration required by Eq. (5-45) by graphical methods. In essence one replaces Eq. (5-45) by the expression

$$\Delta H = \Delta H_0 + \sum (\Delta C_p)(\Delta T) \tag{5-58}$$

In practice, however, this method is seldom necessary.

## Exercises

**1.** Find the heat of formation of ethyl alcohol in the *International Critical Tables* and the National Bureau of Standards tables. Compare the respective values.

**2.** According to K. Schwabe and W. Wagner, [*Chem. Ber.*, **91,** 686 (1958)] the heats of combustion in a constant-volume calorimeter for fumaric and maleic acids are $-319.60$ and $-325.15$ kcal mole$^{-1}$, respectively, at approximately 25°C.

(a) Find the heats of formation of these isomers.

(b) What is the difference in energy between these isomers?

**3.** Standard heats of formation of some sulfur compounds [W. N. Hubbard, D. R. Douslin, J. P. McCullough, D. W. Scott, S. S. Todd, J. F. Messerly, I. A. Hossenlopp, A. George, and G. Waddington, *J. Am. Chem. Soc.*, **80,** 3547 (1958)] are listed below, together with that for S($g$) from tables of the National Bureau of Standards:

| Substance | $\Delta Hf^{\circ}_{298.15}$, kcal mole$^{-1}$ |
|---|---|
| $C_2H_5—S—C_2H_5(g)$ | $-35.19$ |
| $C_2H_5—S—S—C_2H_5(g)$ | $-48.26$ |
| $S(g)$ | 53.25 |

From these data alone, compute $\epsilon_{S-S}$.

**4.** For $NF_3(g)$ at 25°C, $\Delta Hf^{\circ}$ is $-29.7$ kcal mole$^{-1}$ [G. T. Armstrong, S. Marantz, and C. F. Coyle, *J. Am. Chem. Soc.*, **81**, 3798 (1959)]. Making use of Table 5-3 for any necessary bond energies, find $\epsilon_{N-F}$.

**5.** From mass spectrometric experiments [S. N. Foner and R. L. Hudson, *J. Chem. Phys.*, **28**, 719 (1958)] it is possible to compute a value of 26 kcal for $\Delta H^{\circ}_{298}$ for the reaction

$$N_2H_4(g) = N_2H_2(g) + H_2(g)$$

Knowing in addition that $\Delta Hf^{\circ}_{298}$ of hydrazine gas, $N_2H_4$, is 22.7 kcal mole$^{-1}$, and assuming that the structure of $N_2H_2$ is HN=NH, find $\epsilon_{N=N}$.

**6.** Estimate $\Delta Hf^{\circ}$ of the gaseous N—H radical by using appropriate values from the table of bond energies.

**7.** Find the bond energy of the I—Cl bond at 25°C from the data listed in Table 5-2. Compare with the bond energy given in Table 5-3.

**8.** Taking the heat of combustion of ethane as $-372.8$ kcal mole$^{-1}$, find the C—C bond energy.

**9.** Find data for the standard heats of formation of $Cl(g)$, $S(g)$, $S_8(g)$, and $S_2Cl_2(g)$ from appropriate sources.

(a) Calculate the energy of the S—S bond. Assume that $S_8$ consists of eight such linkages.

(b) Calculate the energy of the S—Cl bond.

(c) Estimate the heat of formation of $SCl_2(g)$.

**10.** Derive an equation for the dependence of $\Delta H$ on temperature for the reaction

$$CO(g) + \tfrac{1}{2}O_2(g) = CO_2(g).$$

Appropriate data can be found in the tables of Chapters 4 and 5.

**11.** Heats of formation of solid alloy phases may be found from heats of solution of these phases in a suitable liquid metal. The pure metals and alloys listed below each originally at 31°C have each been dropped into liquid tin at 250°C and the heat of this process measured. The results [P. D. Anderson, *J. Am. Chem. Soc.*, **80,** 3171 (1958)] computed for 1 mole of material are listed below:

| Phase | $\Delta H$(cal mole$^{-1}$) |
|---|---|
| Ag | 4880 |
| Cd | 4540 |
| $\zeta(Ag_{0.5}Cd_{0.5})$ | 6560 |
| $\gamma(Ag_{0.412}Cd_{0.588})$ | 6680 |

(a) Find $\Delta Hf°$ of the $\zeta$ phase at 31°C.

(b) Find $\Delta Hf°$ of the $\gamma$ phase at 31°C.

**12.** The "proton affinity," $\mathscr{P}$, of a substance such as $NH_3$ may be defined as the change in energy for the reaction

$$NH_4^+(g) = NH_3(g) + H^+(g)$$

$\mathscr{P}_{NH_3}$ at 0°K may be computed from other thermal data through consideration of the Born–Haber cycle below (all substances except $NH_4Cl$ being gases):

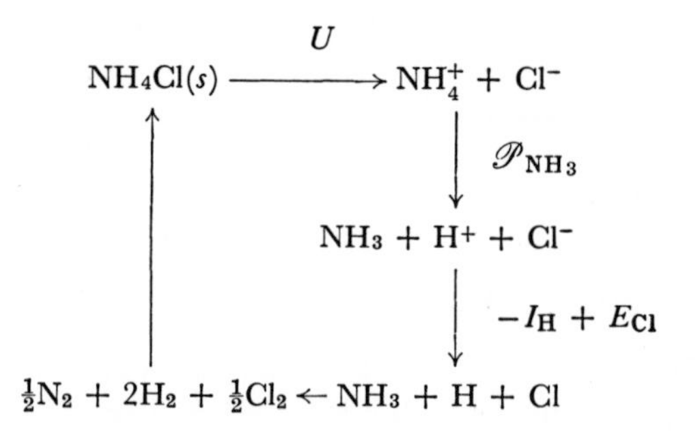


where $U$ represents the lattice energy of crystalline $NH_4Cl$, $I_H$ the ionization energy of a hydrogen atom, and $E_{Cl}$ the electron affinity of a chlorine atom. The values of these quantities are (in kcal mole$^{-1}$) 153, 312, and 92.5, respectively. Taking the heat of formation of $NH_4Cl(s)$ as $-75.1$ kcal mole$^{-1}$ and that of $NH_3(g)$ as $-10.9$, and finding any other energies you need from tables in Chapter 5, calculate $\mathscr{P}_{NH_3}$.

**13.** The adiabatic flame temperature is that temperature which would be attained if a compound were burned completely under adiabatic conditions so that all the heat evolved goes into heating the product gases. Find the adiabatic flame temperature for the burning of ethane in an air mixture containing originally twice as much air as is necessary for complete combustion to $CO_2$ and $H_2O(g)$. Assume that air is composed of 20% $O_2$ and 80% $N_2$ by volume. In using heat capacity equations neglect all terms containing $T^2$ or higher powers of $T$. Assume also that the combustion occurs at constant pressure.

# 6 Application of the First Law to Gases

It becomes of interest, as a prelude to the development of the second law of thermodynamics, to consider the information which is obtainable on the behavior of gases by application of the single thermodynamic postulate and the associated definitions which have been developed so far. Since the behavior of many gases may be approximated by the simple equation of state attributed to the *ideal gas*, it is convenient to begin our discussion with a consideration of this ideal substance.

## 6-1 IDEAL GASES

### Definition

An ideal gas is one which (1) obeys the equation of state

$$PV = nRT \tag{6-1}$$

where $n$ is the number of moles and $R$ is a universal constant; and (2) for which the internal energy, $E$, is a function of the temperature only, that is,

$$\left(\frac{\partial E}{\partial V}\right)_T = \left(\frac{\partial E}{\partial P}\right)_T = 0 \tag{6-2}$$[1]

It is pertinent to point out that Eq. (6-1) is a combination of Boyle's and Charles' laws, as can be seen readily by the following procedure.[2] Boyle's law may be expressed by the relation

$$V = \frac{nk_T}{P} \qquad (T \text{ constant}) \tag{6-4}$$

or

$$\left(\frac{\partial V}{\partial P}\right)_T = -\frac{nk_T}{P^2} \tag{6-5}$$

where $k_T$ is a constant at a fixed temperature. Similarly, Charles' law may be expressed by either of the following two expressions:

$$V = nk_P T \qquad (P \text{ constant}) \tag{6-6}$$

or

$$\left(\frac{\partial V}{\partial T}\right)_P = nk_P \tag{6-7}$$

If we consider the total differential of the volume, $V = f(T,P)$, we obtain

$$dV = \left(\frac{\partial V}{\partial T}\right)_P dT + \left(\frac{\partial V}{\partial P}\right)_T dP \tag{6-8}$$

Equations (6-5) and (6-7) may be used to substitute for the partial derivatives in (6-8), so that we may obtain

$$dV = nk_P\, dT - \frac{nk_T}{P^2}\, dP \tag{6-9}$$

The constants $k_P$ and $k_T$ may be replaced by the introduction of Eqs. (6-4) and (6-6).

$$dV = \frac{V}{T}\, dT - \frac{V}{P}\, dP \tag{6-10}$$

[1] We shall consider these two requirements as sufficient for the definition of an ideal gas. Occasionally an additional specification is made that the heat capacity at constant volume must be a constant, or

$$C_v = \text{constant} \tag{6-3}$$

[2] The procedure described is introduced as an example of the use of an equation for the total differential. Equation (6-1) can also be derived from Boyle's and Charles' laws by simple algebraic manipulations.

Rearranging expression (6-10), we obtain

$$\frac{dV}{V} = \frac{dT}{T} - \frac{dP}{P} \tag{6-11}$$

which may be integrated to give

$$PV = k'T \tag{6-12}$$

where $k'$ is the constant of integration. If we identify $k'$ with $nR$, we have Eq. (6-1), the ideal gas law.

It follows from Eq. (6-2) that if an ideal gas undergoes any isothermal transformation, its energy remains fixed. This restriction in the definition of an ideal gas actually is not independent, since it can be shown to follow from Eq. (6-1). However, this proof depends upon the use of the second law of thermodynamics,[3] and since this principle has not yet been considered, Eq. (6-2) will be considered tentatively as independent.

## Enthalpy a Function of the Temperature Only

It is simple to prove that the enthalpy, as well as the internal energy, is constant in any isothermal change of an ideal gas. Since

$$H = E + PV \tag{6-13}$$

$$\left(\frac{\partial H}{\partial V}\right)_T = \left(\frac{\partial E}{\partial V}\right)_T + \left(\frac{\partial [PV]}{\partial V}\right)_T \tag{6-14}$$

But from Eqs. (6-1) and (6-2) it is evident that each term on the right-hand side of Eq. (6-14) is zero. Consequently,

$$\left(\frac{\partial H}{\partial V}\right)_T = 0 \tag{6-15}$$

By an analogous procedure it can also be shown readily that

$$\left(\frac{\partial H}{\partial P}\right)_T = 0 \tag{6-16}$$

## Relation between $C_p$ and $C_v$

In Chapter 4 the following expression [Eq. (4-28)] was shown to be a general relation between the heat capacity at constant pressure and that at

[3] An objection might be raised later that we assume the properties of an ideal gas in developing the second law. It should be mentioned, therefore, that the second law can also be formulated without any dependence on the ideal gas.

constant volume:

$$C_p = C_v + \left[P + \left(\frac{\partial E}{\partial V}\right)_T\right]\left(\frac{\partial V}{\partial T}\right)_P \tag{6-17}$$

For 1 mole of an ideal gas,

$$\left(\frac{\partial E}{\partial V}\right)_T = 0 \tag{6-2}$$

and

$$\left(\frac{\partial V}{\partial T}\right)_P = \frac{R}{P} \tag{6-18}$$

It is evident immediately that the substitution of Eqs. (6-2) and (6-18) into (6-17) leads to the familiar expression

$$C_p = C_v + R \tag{6-19}$$

## Calculation of Thermodynamic Changes in Expansion Processes

***Isothermal.*** An expansion at a fixed temperature may be carried out reversibly. The reversible process may be visualized as shown in Figure 6-1. The general expression for the work done by the gas in the expansion is

$$W = \int_{V_1}^{V_2} P\,dV \tag{6-20}$$

Using Eq. (6-1) to eliminate $P$ from (6-20), we obtain

$$W = \int_{V}^{V_2} \frac{nRT}{V}\,dV = nRT\ln\frac{V_2}{V_1} \tag{6-21}$$

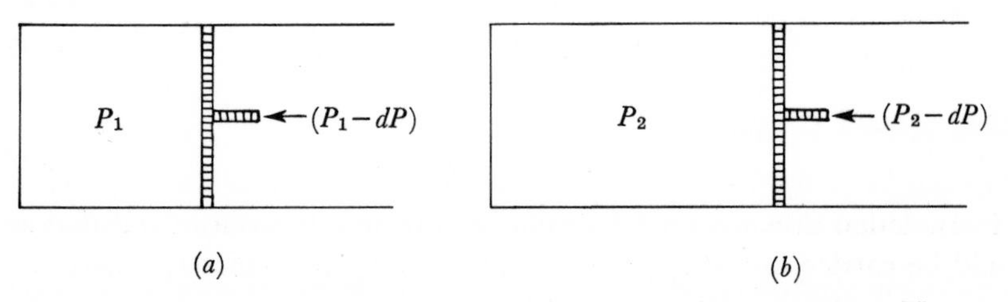


***Figure 6-1*** *Schematic representation of an isothermal reversible expansion. The external pressure is maintained only infinitesimally below the internal pressure.*

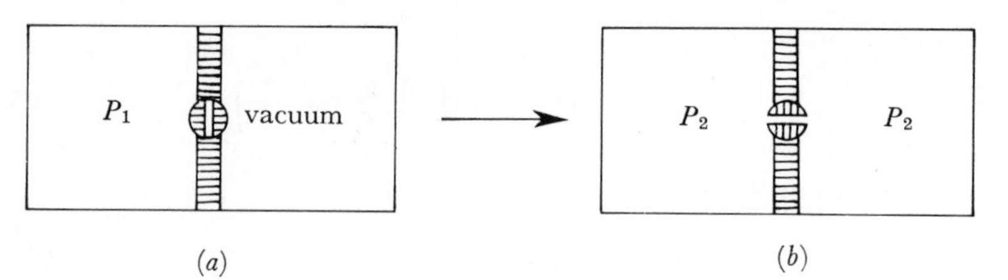


***Figure 6-2*** *Schematic representation of a free expansion. A small valve separating the two chambers in (a) is opened so that the gas may rush in from left to right. The initial volume of the gas may be called $V_1$, and the final volume $V_2$.*

In considerations of the change in energy of the enclosed gas, $\Delta E$, it is merely necessary to keep in mind that the process is isothermal and that $E$ depends only upon temperature. Hence

$$\Delta E = 0 \tag{6-22}$$

With this information and the use of the first law of thermodynamics, we can readily calculate the heat absorbed in the process:

$$Q = \Delta E + W = nRT \ln \frac{V_2}{V_1} \tag{6-23}$$

If we pass finally to the enthalpy change, $\Delta H$, it is evident that this quantity, like $\Delta E$, must be zero, since

$$\Delta H = \Delta E + \Delta(PV) = 0 + \Delta(nRT) = 0 \tag{6-24}$$

We may also readily visualize a completely free isothermal expansion (Figure 6-2) in which no work is done by the gas on the surroundings. Under the conditions described, the process may be carried out isothermally.[4] Hence for the gas

$$W = 0 \tag{6-25}$$

$$\Delta E = 0 \tag{6-26}$$

$$Q = \Delta E + W = 0 \tag{6-27}$$

and

$$\Delta H = \Delta E + \Delta(PV) = 0 \tag{6-28}$$

In an actual case, some work would be obtained; but since the expansion would be carried out at finite speed, the pressure immediately adjacent to

[4] Although temperature differences may be set up temporarily, when equilibrium is reached the temperature is the same as the initial one.

the piston wall would be slightly less than that in the interior at any given moment and the net work would be less than in the reversible expansion, though greater than zero.

$$0 < W < nRT \ln \frac{V_2}{V_1} \tag{6-29}$$

On the other hand, if isothermal conditions are maintained, there is still no change in energy, since for an ideal gas

$$\Delta E = 0 \tag{6-30}$$

To determine $Q$, we again use the first law,

$$Q = \Delta E + W = W \tag{6-31}$$

$$0 < Q < nRT \ln \frac{V_2}{V_1} \tag{6-32}$$

The enthalpy change is found from the relation

$$\Delta H = \Delta E + \Delta(PV) = 0 \tag{6-33}$$

In summary, we may compare these three isothermal expansions of an ideal gas by tabulating the corresponding thermodynamic changes for the gas (Table 6-1). This table serves to emphasize the difference between an exact and an inexact thermodynamic function. Thus $E$ and $H$, whose differentials are exact, undergo the same change in each of the three different paths used for the transformation. They are thermodynamic properties. On the other hand, the work and heat quantities depend upon the particular path chosen, even though the initial and final values of the

***Table 6-1***

*Thermodynamic changes in isothermal expansions of an ideal gas*

| Reversible | Free | Actual |
|---|---|---|
| $T_1 = T_2$ | $T_1 = T_2$ | $T_1 = T_2$ |
| $W = nRT \ln \frac{V_2}{V_1}$ | $W = 0$ | $0 < W < nRT \ln \frac{V_2}{V_1}$ |
| $\Delta E = 0$ | $\Delta E = 0$ | $\Delta E = 0$ |
| $Q = nRT \ln \frac{V_2}{V_1}$ | $Q = 0$ | $0 < Q < nRT \ln \frac{V_2}{V_1}$; $Q = W$ |
| $\Delta H = 0$ | $\Delta H = 0$ | $\Delta H = 0$ |

temperature, pressure, and volume, respectively, are the same in all these cases. Thus the heat and work functions are not thermodynamic properties. It is desirable to speak not of the heat (or work) contained in a system, but rather of the energy (or enthalpy) of the system, since the system may evolve different quantities of heat in going by different paths from a given initial to a specified final state. The heat and work quantities are manifested only during a transformation and their magnitudes depend upon the manner in which the system goes from one state to another. Since the work obtained in going from state $A$ to state $B$ may not be equal to that required to return the system from state $B$ to state $A$, it is misleading to speak of the work contained in the system.

***Adiabatic.*** By definition, an adiabatic expansion is one accompanied by no transfer of heat. Evidently, then,

$$DQ = 0 \tag{6-34}$$

It follows immediately from the first law of thermodynamics that

$$dE = -DW = -dW \tag{6-35}$$

This equality may be used, in turn, to specify the work done in a more explicit fashion, because if $\Delta E$ is known, $W$ is obtained immediately. For an ideal gas, $\Delta E$ in the adiabatic expansion may be determined by a simple procedure.

Considering the energy as a function of temperature and volume, $E = f(T,V)$, we may write an equation for the total differential:

$$dE = \left(\frac{\partial E}{\partial T}\right)_V dT + \left(\frac{\partial E}{\partial V}\right)_T dV \tag{6-36}$$

Since we are dealing with an ideal gas, it is evident that

$$\left(\frac{\partial E}{\partial V}\right)_T = 0 \tag{6-37}$$

and hence that Eq. (6-36) may be reduced to

$$dE = \left(\frac{\partial E}{\partial T}\right)_V dT = C_v\, dT = -dW \tag{6-38}$$

Hence the work done, $W$, and the energy change, $\Delta E$, may be obtained by integration of Eq. (6-38):

$$W = -\int_{T_1}^{T_2} C_v\, dT = -\Delta E \tag{6-39}$$

If $C_v$ is independent of temperature for this ideal gas, then

$$W = -\Delta E = -C_v(T_2 - T_1) \tag{6-40}$$

It is also simple to determine the enthalpy change in this adiabatic expansion, particularly if $C_v$ is constant. The equation of state for 1 mole of an ideal gas affords a simple substitution for $\Delta(PV)$ in the equation

$$\Delta H = \Delta E + \Delta(PV) \tag{6-41}$$

to give

$$\Delta H = \Delta E + \Delta(RT)$$
$$= C_v(T_2 - T_1) + (RT_2 - RT_1)$$

or

$$\Delta H = (C_v + R)(T_2 - T_1) = C_p(T_2 - T_1) \tag{6-42}$$

So far we have not had to specify whether the adiabatic expansion under consideration is reversible. The equations (6-34), (6-40), and (6-42), for the calculation of the thermodynamic changes in this process, evidently apply, then, for the reversible expansion, free expansion, or actual expansion, so long as we are dealing with an ideal gas.

The numerical values of $W$, $\Delta E$, and $\Delta H$, however, will not be the same for each of the three types of adiabatic expansion, since, as we shall see shortly, $T_2$, the final temperature of the gas, will differ in each case, even though the initial temperature may be identical in all cases.

If we consider the free expansion first, it is apparent from Eq. (6-40) that since no work is done, there is no change in temperature; that is, $T_2 = T_1$. Thus $\Delta E$ and $\Delta H$ must also be zero for this process. Reference to Table 6-1 shows, then, that an adiabatic free expansion and an isothermal free expansion are two different names for the same process.

Turning to the reversible adiabatic expansion, we find that a definite expression can be derived to relate the initial and final temperatures to the respective volumes or pressures. Again we start with Eq. (6-35). Recognizing the restriction of reversibility, we obtain

$$-dE = dW = P\,dV \tag{6-43}$$

Since we are dealing with an ideal gas, Eq. (6-38) is valid. Substitution from Eq. (6-43) into (6-38) leads to

$$C_v\,dT = -P\,dV \tag{6-44}$$

We may now make use of the equation of state for an ideal gas. It is evident that whatever the value of $n$ in Eq. (6-1), $C_v$ in Eq. (6-44) will equal $n$ times the molal heat capacity. Hence if we consider 1 mole of the substance,

$$C_v\,dT = -\frac{RT}{V}\,dV \tag{6-45}$$

Rearranging, we obtain

$$\frac{C_v}{T}\,dT = -\frac{R}{V}\,dV \tag{6-46}$$

which may be integrated within definite limits to give, when $C_v$ is constant,

$$C_v \ln\left(\frac{T_2}{T_1}\right) = -R\ln\left(\frac{V_2}{V_1}\right) \tag{6-47}$$

This equation in turn may be converted to

$$\left(\frac{T_2}{T_1}\right)^{C_v} = \left(\frac{V_2}{V_1}\right)^{-R} = \left(\frac{V_1}{V_2}\right)^{R} \tag{6-48}$$

or

$$\frac{T_2}{T_1} = \left(\frac{V_1}{V_2}\right)^{R/C_v} \tag{6-49}$$

Hence

$$T_2 V_2^{R/C_v} = T_1 V_1^{R/C_v} \tag{6-50}$$

Equation (6-50) says in essence that the particular temperature-volume function shown is constant during a reversible adiabatic expansion. Hence we may write

$$T V^{R/C_v} = \text{constant} \tag{6-51}$$

or

$$T^{C_v/R}\,V = \text{constant}'$$

Any one of the Eqs. (6-47) to (6-51) may be used to calculate a final temperature from the initial temperature and the observed volumes.

If one measures pressures instead of volumes, it is possible to use the following equation instead:

$$P V^{C_p/C_v} = \text{constant}'' \qquad \text{(6-52)}^{5}$$

Equation (6-52) may be derived readily from (6-51) by substitution from the equation of state of the ideal gas.

In any event it is evident, most directly perhaps from Eq. (6-49), that the final temperature, $T_2$, in the reversible adiabatic expansion (for the ideal gas) must be less than $T_1$, since $V_1$ is less than $V_2$, and $R$ and $C_v$ are

[5] Actually this equation can be derived without assuming the validity of the first law of thermodynamics; it follows directly from Boyle's law and the definitions of $C_p$ and $C_v$. See D. Shanks, *Am. J. Phys.*, **24**, 352 (1956).

both positive numbers. Thus the adiabatic reversible expansion is accompanied by a temperature drop which can be calculated readily from the measured volumes or pressures at the beginning and the end of the process. Knowing $T_2$ and $T_1$, we can then proceed immediately to the evaluation of $W$, $\Delta E$, and $\Delta H$ by simple substitution into Eqs. (6-40) and (6-42).

Considering, finally, an adiabatic expansion in any actual case, we can see again that $W$, the work done by the gas, would be less than in the reversible case, since in this actual process the lag in transmission of stresses would keep the pressure in the immediate vicinity of the moving piston somewhat lower than it would be in a corresponding reversible process. Thus if our final volume $V_2$ is the same as that in the reversible process (and if the initial state is the same in both processes), $T_2$ will not be as low in the actual expansion, since according to Eq. (6-38) the temperature drop, $dT$, depends directly upon the work done by the expanding (ideal) gas. Similarly, it is apparent from Eqs. (6-40) and (6-42) that $\Delta E$ and $\Delta H$, respectively, must also be numerically smaller in the actual expansion than in the reversible one.

Thus in the adiabatic expansion, from a common set of initial conditions to the same final volume, the values of the energy and enthalpy changes, as well as of the work done, appear to depend on the path (see summary in Table 6-2). At first glance, such behavior may appear to be in contradiction to the assumption of exactness of $dE$ and $dH$. However, careful consideration shows quickly that the basis of the difference lies in the different end point for each of the three paths; despite the fact that the final volume may be made the same in each case, the final temperature depends upon whether the expansion is free, reversible, or actual (Table 6-2).

***Table 6-2***

*Thermodynamic changes in adiabatic expansions of an ideal gas*

| Reversible | Free | Actual |
|---|---|---|
| $V_1$ | $V_1$ | $V_1$ |
| $V_2$ | $V_2$ | $V_2$ |
| $W = -C_v(T_2 - T_1) > 0$ | $W' = C_v(T_2' - T_1) = 0$ | $W'' = -C_v(T_2'' - T_1) > 0$; |
| | | $W'' < W$ |
| $\therefore T_2 < T_1$ | $\therefore T_2' = T_1$ | $\therefore T_2'' < T_1$; |
| | | but $T_2'' > T_2$ |
| $\Delta E = C_v(T_2 - T_1) < 0$ | $\Delta E' = 0$ | $\Delta E'' = C_v(T_2'' - T_1) < 0$ |
| $\Delta H = C_p(T_2 - T_1) < 0$ | $\Delta H' = 0$ | $\Delta H'' = C_p(T_2 - T_1) < 0$ |

## 6-2 REAL GASES

### Equations of State

We wish to turn our attention now to substances for which the ideal gas laws do not give an adequate description. Numerous representations have been used to describe real gases.[6] For our purposes, however, it will be sufficient to consider only four of the more common ones.

***van der Waals equation.*** This equation was one of the first to be introduced to describe deviations from ideality. The argument behind it is discussed adequately in elementary textbooks.[6] It is generally stated in the form

$$\left(P + \frac{a}{\mathrm{v}^2}\right)(\mathrm{v} - b) = RT \tag{6-53}$$

where v is the volume per mole and $a$ and $b$ are constants (Table 6-3). Alternative methods of expression will be considered later.

***Virial function.*** A very useful form of expression of deviations from the ideal gas law is the following equation:

$$P\mathrm{v} = A + BP + CP^2 + DP^3 + EP^4 + \cdots \tag{6-54}$$

where $A, B, C, D$, and $E$ are constants at a given temperature and are known as *virial coefficients* (Table 6-4). The term $A$ must reduce, of course, to $RT$, since at very low pressures all gases approach ideal gas behavior.

***Berthelot equation.*** This equation is too unwieldy to be used generally as an equation of state. However, it is very convenient in calculations of deviations from ideality near pressures of 1 atm and hence has been used extensively in determinations of entropies from the third law of thermodynamics. This aspect of the equation will receive further attention in subsequent discussions.

The Berthelot equation may be expressed as

$$P\mathrm{v} = RT\left[1 + \frac{9}{128}\frac{P}{P_c}\frac{T_c}{T}\left(1 - 6\frac{T_c^2}{T^2}\right)\right] \tag{6-55}$$

where $P_c$ and $T_c$ are the critical pressure[6] and critical temperature,[6] respectively.

***Compressibility factor.*** It has been found that the behavior of real gases can be represented with fair precision by a single chart[6] of the compressibility factor, $Z$, which is defined as

$$Z = \frac{P\mathrm{v}}{RT} \tag{6-56}$$

[6] See, for example, W. J. Moore, *Physical Chemistry*, 3rd ed., Prentice-Hall, Englewood Cliffs, N.J., 1962, pp. 17–24.

**Table 6-3**

*van der Waals constants for some gases*[a]

| Substance | $a$, atm-liter$^2$/mole$^2$ | $b$, liter/mole |
|---|---|---|
| Acetylene | 4.39 | 0.0514 |
| Ammonia | 4.17 | 0.0371 |
| Argon | 1.35 | 0.0322 |
| Carbon dioxide | 3.59 | 0.0427 |
| Carbon monoxide | 1.49 | 0.0399 |
| Chlorine | 6.49 | 0.0562 |
| Ethyl ether | 17.4 | 0.1344 |
| Helium | 0.034 | 0.0237 |
| Hydrogen | 0.244 | 0.0266 |
| Hydrogen chloride | 3.67 | 0.0408 |
| Methane | 2.25 | 0.0428 |
| Nitric oxide | 1.34 | 0.0279 |
| Nitrogen | 1.39 | 0.0391 |
| Nitrogen dioxide | 5.28 | 0.0442 |
| Oxygen | 1.36 | 0.0318 |
| Sulfur dioxide | 6.71 | 0.0564 |
| Water | 5.46 | 0.0305 |

[a] Values for other substances may be calculated from data in Landolt-Börnstein, *Physikalisch-chemische Tabellen*, 5th ed., Vol. I, Springer, Berlin, 1923, pp. 253–263.

**Table 6-4**

*Virial coefficients for some gases*[a]

| Substance | $t$, °C | $A$ | $B \times 10^2$ | $C \times 10^5$ | $D \times 10^8$ | $E \times 10^{11}$ |
|---|---|---|---|---|---|---|
| Hydrogen | 0 | 22.414 | 1.3638 | 0.7851 | −1.206 | 0.7354 |
| | 500 | 63.447 | 1.7974 | 0.1003 | −0.1619 | 0.1050 |
| Nitrogen | 0 | 22.414 | −1.0512 | 8.626 | −6.910 | 1.704 |
| | 200 | 38.824 | 1.4763 | 2.775 | −2.379 | 0.7600 |
| Carbon monoxide | 0 | 22.414 | −1.4825 | 9.823 | −7.721 | 1.947 |
| | 200 | 38.824 | 1.3163 | 3.052 | −2.449 | 0.7266 |

[a] Taken from C. F. Prutton and S. H. Maron, *Principles of Physical Chemistry*, 3rd ed., Macmillan, New York, 1958, p. 35. The values given for the constants apply to 1 mole of the gas, to the pressure expressed in atmospheres, and to the volume in liters.

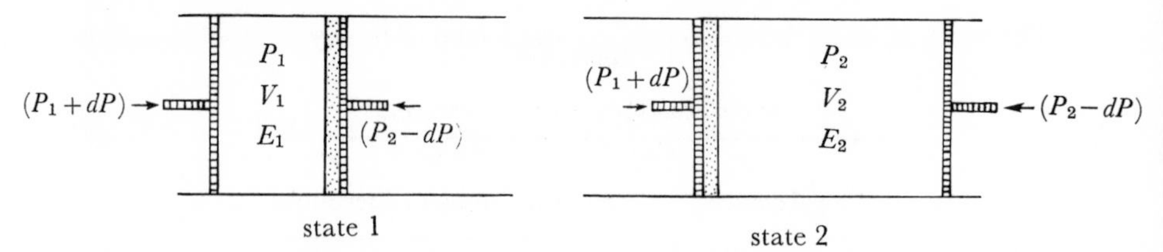


***Figure 6-3*** *Schematic representation of a Joule-Thomson porous-plug experiment. The entire apparatus is kept in a jacket and is well insulated from the surrounding environment.*

If $Z$ is plotted as a function of the reduced pressure, $P_r(= P/P_c)$, then at a given reduced temperature, $T_r(= T/T_c)$, all gases fit a single curve.[6] At another reduced temperature, $T_r$, a new curve is obtained for $Z$ vs. $P_r$, but it too fits all gases. It becomes possible, therefore, to condense into a single chart of compressibility factors a quantitative graphical representation of the behavior of real gases over a wide range of pressure and temperature.[7]

## Joule-Thomson Effect

One method of measurement of deviations from ideal behavior in a quantitative fashion is by determinations of the change in temperature in the Joule-Thomson porous-plug experiment (Figure 6-3). The enclosed gas initially of volume $V_1$, flows very slowly from the left-hand chamber through a porous plug into the right-hand chamber. The pressure on the left side is maintained constant at a value of $P_1$, while that on the right side is also constant but at a lower value, $P_2$. The apparatus is jacketed with a good insulator so that no heat is exchanged with the surroundings. In general for real gases, it is observed that the final temperature, $T_2$, differs from the initial one, $T_1$.

***Isenthalpic nature.*** Since the Joule-Thomson experiment is carried out adiabatically, we may write

$$Q = 0 \tag{6-57}$$

However, it does not follow that $\Delta H$ is also zero, since the process involves a change in pressure. Nevertheless, it can readily be shown that the process is an isenthalpic one, that is, that $\Delta H$ is zero.

[7] The compressibility factor can be represented to higher precision if it is expressed as a function of another parameter in addition to the reduced temperature and reduced pressure. See K. S. Pitzer, D. Z. Lippmann, R. F. Curl, Jr., C. M. Huggins, and D. E. Petersen, *J. Am. Chem. Soc.*, **77**, 3433 (1955).

The work done by the gas is that accomplished in the right-hand chamber,

$$W_2 = \int_0^{V_2} P_2 \, dV = P_2 V_2 \tag{6-58}$$

plus that done in the left-hand chamber,

$$W_1 = \int_{V_1}^{0} P_1 \, dV = -P_1 V_1 \tag{6-59}$$

Hence the net work

$$W = W_1 + W_2 = P_2 V_2 - P_1 V_1 \tag{6-60}$$

Similarly, the net gain in energy, $\Delta E$, is

$$\Delta E = E_2 - E_1 \tag{6-61}$$

Since $Q = 0$, it follows from the first law of thermodynamics that

$$E_2 - E_1 = -W = P_1 V_1 - P_2 V_2 \tag{6-62}$$

Therefore

$$E_2 + P_2 V_2 = E_1 + P_1 V_1 \tag{6-63}$$

$$H_2 = H_1 \tag{6-64}$$

$$\Delta H = 0 \tag{6-65}$$

Thus we have proved that the Joule-Thomson experiment is isenthalpic as well as adiabatic.

***Joule-Thomson coefficient.*** Knowing that the process is isenthalpic, we are in a position to formulate the Joule-Thomson effect in a quantitative manner.

*Definition.* Since it is the change in temperature which is observed as the gas flows from a higher to a lower pressure, the data are summarized in terms of a quantity, $\mu_{J.T.}$, which is defined by

$$\mu_{J.T.} = \left(\frac{\partial T}{\partial P}\right)_H \tag{6-66}$$

It is evident from this definition that the Joule-Thomson coefficient, $\mu_{J.T.}$, is positive when a cooling of the gas; that is, a temperature drop, is observed, because since $dP$ is always negative, $\mu_{J.T.}$ will be positive when $dT$ is negative. Conversely, $\mu_{J.T.}$ is a negative quantity when the gas warms on expansion, because $dT$ is then a positive quantity.

*Derived relations.* For purposes of evaluation, it is frequently necessary to have the Joule-Thomson coefficient expressed in terms of other partial derivatives.

Considering the enthalpy as a function of temperature and pressure, $H(T,P)$, we may write the total differential

$$dH = \left(\frac{\partial H}{\partial P}\right)_T dP + \left(\frac{\partial H}{\partial T}\right)_P dT \tag{6-67}$$

Placing a restriction of constant enthalpy on Eq. (6-67), we obtain

$$0 = \left(\frac{\partial H}{\partial P}\right)_T + \left(\frac{\partial H}{\partial T}\right)_P \left(\frac{\partial T}{\partial P}\right)_H \tag{6-68}$$

which can be rearranged to give

$$\left(\frac{\partial T}{\partial P}\right)_H = -\frac{(\partial H/\partial P)_T}{(\partial H/\partial T)_P} \tag{6-69}$$

or

$$\mu_{\text{J.T.}} = -\frac{1}{C_p}\left(\frac{\partial H}{\partial P}\right)_T \tag{6-70}$$

An additional relation of interest may be obtained by substitution of the fundamental definition of $H$ into Eq. (6-70):

$$\mu_{\text{J.T.}} = -\frac{1}{C_p}\left(\frac{\partial E}{\partial P}\right)_T - \frac{1}{C_p}\left(\frac{\partial [PV]}{\partial P}\right)_T \tag{6-71}$$

From either of these last two expressions it is evident that $\mu_{\text{J.T.}} = 0$ for an ideal gas, since each partial derivative is zero for such a substance.

*Inversion temperature.* For a gas which obeys the van der Waals equation, it can be shown readily that the sign of the Joule-Thomson coefficient depends upon the temperature and that at sufficiently high temperatures, $\mu_{\text{J.T.}}$ is negative for all gases, whereas at suitably low temperatures $\mu_{\text{J.T.}}$ is positive. Thus each gas has at least one temperature at which $\mu_{\text{J.T.}}$ changes sign, and hence is zero. The value of this inversion temperature,[8]

[8] Actually the inversion temperature depends upon the pressure at which the Joule-Thomson experiment is carried out. In the discussion given at this point, the assumption is made implicitly that higher terms in the expansion of the van der Waals equation may be neglected. If these higher terms are not omitted, the inversion temperature obeys the following condition, in which the solutions clearly depend upon the pressure:

$$\frac{2a}{RT_i} - \frac{3abP}{R^2T_i^2} - b = 0$$

It is apparent from this expression that there are *two* inversion temperatures for every pressure.

$T_i$, may be predicted if the constants in the van der Waals equation are known, for it can be shown that the Joule-Thomson coefficient is related to these constants. It will be proved later that

$$\left(\frac{\partial H}{\partial P}\right)_T = b - \frac{2a}{RT} \tag{6-72}$$ [9]

Hence it follows from Eq. (6-70) that

$$\mu_{J.T.} = \frac{1}{C_p}\left(\frac{2a}{RT} - b\right) \tag{6-73}$$

From Eq. (6-73) it is evident that for a given gas:

(1) At high temperatures, $2a/RT < b$; $\mu_{J.T.} < 0$; gas warms on expansion.

(2) At low temperatures, $2a/RT > b$; $\mu_{J.T.} > 0$; gas cools on expansion.

(3) At some intermediate temperature, $T_i$, $2a/RT_i = b$; $\mu_{J.T.} = 0$; no temperature change on expansion in the porous-plug apparatus.

Obviously the value of $T_i$ must be given by

$$T_i = \frac{2a}{Rb} \tag{6-74}$$

Hence, if the van der Waals constants are known, $T_i$ may be calculated. For all gases except hydrogen and helium, this inversion temperature is above common room temperatures.

## Calculation of Thermodynamic Quantities in Reversible Expansions

***Isothermal.*** The procedure used in calculations of the work and energy quantities in an isothermal reversible expansion of a real gas is similar to that used for the ideal gas. Into the expression for the work done,

$$W = \int_{V_1}^{V_2} P\,dV \tag{6-20}$$

we may substitute for $P$ (or for $dV$) from the equation of state of the gas and then carry out the required integration. For 1 mole of a van der Waals

[9] This equation is printed in type of smaller size to emphasize that it has not yet been proved.

gas, for example,

$$W = \int_{v_1}^{v_2} \left( \frac{RT}{v - b} - \frac{a}{v^2} \right) dv = RT \ln \frac{v_2 - b}{v_1 - b} + \frac{a}{v_2} - \frac{a}{v_1} \tag{6-75}$$

The change in energy in an isothermal expansion, however, cannot be expressed in a simple form without the introduction of the second law of thermodynamics. Nevertheless we shall anticipate this second basic postulate and use one of the deductions obtainable from it:

$$\left( \frac{\partial E}{\partial V} \right)_T = T \left( \frac{\partial P}{\partial T} \right)_V - P \tag{6-76}$$

For a van der Waals gas, Eq. (6-76) reduces to

$$\left( \frac{\partial E}{\partial V} \right)_T = \frac{a}{v^2} \tag{6-77}$$

$\Delta E$ may be obtained by integration of this equation:

$$\Delta E = \int_{v_1}^{v_2} \frac{a}{v^2} dv = -\frac{a}{v_2} + \frac{a}{v_1} \tag{6-78}$$

With the aid of the first law of thermodynamics we may now calculate readily the heat absorbed in the isothermal reversible expansion:

$$Q = \Delta E + W = RT \ln \frac{v_2 - b}{v_1 - b} \tag{6-79}$$

In turn, $\Delta H$ may be determined by integration of each of the terms in

$$dH = dE + d(PV) \tag{6-80}$$

The $PV$ product may be obtained from the equation

$$P = \frac{RT}{v - b} - \frac{a}{v^2} \tag{6-81}$$

by multiplying each term by v:

$$Pv = RT \frac{v}{v - b} - \frac{a}{v} \tag{6-82}$$

With a few algebraic manipulations one can show that

$$\Delta(Pv) = bRT \left[ \frac{1}{v_2 - b} - \frac{1}{v_1 - b} \right] - \frac{a}{v_2} + \frac{a}{v_1} \tag{6-83}$$

Adding Eq. (6-83) to (6-78), we obtain

$$\Delta H = bRT\left[\frac{1}{\mathrm{v}_2 - b} - \frac{1}{\mathrm{v}_1 - b}\right] - \frac{2a}{\mathrm{v}_2} + \frac{2a}{\mathrm{v}_1} \qquad (6\text{-}84)$$

***Adiabatic.*** The restriction of no heat exchange may be expressed by the equation

$$Q = 0 \qquad (6\text{-}85)$$

A calculation of the work and energy quantities, however, depends upon the solution of Eq. (6-36) for the change in energy. Furthermore, the specification of the equation of state for the gas does not automatically give an expression for the dependence of $C_v$ on temperature. When adequate equations, empirical or theoretical, for the variation of $E$ and of $C_v$ with $T$ and $V$ are available, however, they may be used in an equation equivalent to (6-38), that for the ideal gas, and the resultant expression may be integrable. If they are, the energy and work quantities may be calculated by a procedure similar to that used for the ideal gas.

## Exercises[10]

**1.** Derive an explicit equation for the reversible work of an isothermal expansion for each of the following cases:

(a) $P$ is a constant.

(b) $P$ is given by the equation of state of an ideal gas.

(c) $P$ is obtained from the van der Waals equation of state.

(d) $dV$ is obtained from the equation of state: $P\mathrm{v} = RT + BP + CP^2$.

(e) $dV$ is obtained from the Berthelot equation.

**2.** Rozen [*J. Phys. Chem.* (*USSR*), **19**, 469 (1945), and *Chem. Abstr.*, **40**, 1712 (1946)] characterizes gases by "deviation coefficients" such as $T(\partial P/\partial T)_V/P$, $P(\partial V/\partial T)_P/R$, and $P^2(\partial V/\partial P)_T/RT$. Find the values of these coefficients for (a) an ideal gas, (b) a gas which obeys van der Waals' equation, and (c) a gas which obeys the Dieterici equation of state

$$P = \frac{RT}{\mathrm{v}-b}e^{-a/RT\mathrm{v}}$$

**3.** Find expressions for $W$, $\Delta E$, $Q$, and $\Delta H$ in an isothermal reversible expansion of a gas that obeys the equation of state: $P\mathrm{v} = RT + BP$.

In calculating $\Delta E$, make use of the equation $(\partial E/\partial V)_T = T(\partial P/\partial T)_V - P$.

**4.** A gas obeys the equation of state

$$P\mathrm{v} = RT + BP$$

and has a heat capacity, $C_v$, which is independent of the temperature.

(a) Find an expression relating $T$ and $V$ in an adiabatic reversible expansion.

[10] When derivations or proofs of equations are called for, start from fundamental definitions and principles.

(b) Find an equation for $\Delta H$ in an adiabatic reversible expansion.

(c) Find an equation for $\Delta H$ in an adiabatic free expansion.

**5.** (a) Given the equation

$$C_p = C_v + \left[V - \left(\frac{\partial H}{\partial P}\right)_T\right]\left(\frac{\partial P}{\partial T}\right)_V$$

prove that for any substance

$$C_v = C_p\left[1 - \mu_{\text{J.T.}}\left(\frac{\partial P}{\partial T}\right)_V\right] - V\left(\frac{\partial P}{\partial T}\right)_V$$

(b) To what expression can this equation be reduced at the inversion temperature?

**6.** For 1 mole of a certain ideal gas, $C_v = \frac{3}{2}R$. Find the work done in an adiabatic reversible expansion of this gas by integration of Eq. (6-43), after appropriate substitution from Eq. (6-52).

**7.** An ideal gas absorbs 2250 cal of heat when it is expanded isothermally (at 25°C) and reversibly from 1.5 to 10 liters. How many moles of the gas are present?

**8.** Prove the following relation for an ideal gas:

$$\left(\frac{\partial E}{\partial V}\right)_P = \frac{C_v P}{R}$$

**9.** Keeping in mind that $dE$ is an exact differential prove that for an ideal gas

$$\left(\frac{\partial C_v}{\partial V}\right)_T = 0$$

$$\left(\frac{\partial C_p}{\partial P}\right)_T = 0$$

**10.** With the aid of a mathematical expansion it is possible to relate the constants of the virial equation to molecular properties, in particular to the van der Waals constants $a$ and $b$.

(a) Rearranging the van der Waals equation to the form

$$P\mathrm{v} = \frac{RT\mathrm{v}}{\mathrm{v} - b} - \frac{a}{\mathrm{v}}$$

and applying Maclaurin's theorem from the calculus, convert the van der Waals equation into the form

$$P\mathrm{v} = A + BP + CP^2$$

*Hint:* consider $P$ the independent variable, and $T$ fixed; then make use of the relation

$$\frac{d(PV)}{dP} = \frac{d(PV)}{dV}\frac{dV}{dP}$$

(b) Show that

$$B = b - \frac{a}{RT}$$

$$C = \frac{2RTab - a^2}{RT^3}$$

(c) The Boyle temperature is defined as that at which

$$\left(\frac{\partial(PV)}{\partial P}\right)_{P\to 0} = 0$$

Using only the first two terms in the virial form of the van der Waals equation show that

$$T_{\text{Boyle}} = \frac{a}{Rb}$$

**11.** Using $T$ and $V$ as coordinates, draw a graph showing the three adiabatic expansions of Table 6-2.

**12.** According to theoretical acoustics, the velocity of propagation of sound, $w$, through a gas is given by the equation

$$w^2 = \frac{\partial P}{\partial \rho}$$

where $\rho$ is the density of the gas.

(a) If the propagation of sound is assumed to occur adiabatically and if the transmitting gas acts as if it were ideal and as if it were undergoing reversible compressions and rarefactions, show that

$$w^2 = \frac{C_p}{C_v}\frac{RT}{M}$$

(*Hint:* take 1 mole of gas and start by finding a relation between $d\rho$ and $dV$.)

(b) Calculate $w$ for sound in air, taking $C_p/C_v$ as $\frac{7}{5}$.

(c) If the propagation of sound is assumed to occur isothermally, show that

$$w^2 = \frac{RT}{M}$$

**13.** Find an equation for the coefficient of thermal expansion

$$\beta = \frac{1}{V}\left(\frac{\partial V}{\partial T}\right)_P$$

for a gas which obeys the van der Waals equation.
(*Hint:* Equation (6-53) could be solved explicitly for $V$ and then differentiated. However, an equation explicit in $V$ would be cubic and very unwieldy. On the other hand, Eq. (6-81) is much less laborious to differentiate.)

# 7 The Second Law of Thermodynamics

## 7-1 THE NEED FOR A SECOND LAW

For the chemist the primary interest in thermodynamics lies in its ability to establish a criterion of the feasibility of a given chemical or physical transformation under specified conditions. As yet, however, we have given little attention to this objective, primarily because the first law of thermodynamics, and its consequences, do not supply a basis upon which to establish the desired criterion. As we shall see shortly, the functions developed so far do not in themselves form an adequate foundation for chemical applications.

The first law of thermodynamics summarizes many experimental observations in terms of a statement about the function $E$, the internal energy of a system. Extensive experience has shown with no exceptions that $E$ is a thermodynamic property; that is, its value depends only upon the state of the system. It follows, then, that any path used in going from an initial state $A$ to a final state $B$ will be accompanied by the same change in internal energy. It also follows that the change in internal energy in going from $B$ to $A$ must be equal, but opposite in sign, to that accompanying the forward change from $A$ to $B$:

$$\Delta E_{AB} \text{ (forward)} = -\Delta E_{BA} \text{ (reverse)}$$

But the first law makes no statement as to which reaction, the forward or the reverse, is the natural or spontaneous one. There are many spontaneous reactions for which $\Delta E$ is negative, that is, in which energy is evolved, for example the crystallization of water at $-10°C$:

$$H_2O(l, -10°) = H_2O(s, -10°) \qquad \Delta E = -1.3 \text{ kcal mole}^{-1}$$

There are also some reactions for which $\Delta E$ is positive and which nevertheless proceed spontaneously, such as the vaporization of water at low pressure:

$$H_2O(l, 25°) = H_2O(g, P = 10 \text{ mm}, 25°) \qquad \Delta E = 9.9 \text{ kcal mole}^{-1}$$

Clearly, then, $\Delta E$ cannot be used as a criterion of spontaneity.

Of the other thermodynamic quantities that have been introduced thus far, the enthalpy, $H$, is also a thermodynamic property. For a long time it was believed that $\Delta H$ could be used as a criterion of spontaneity, since most spontaneous reactions at constant pressure are accompanied by an evolution of heat. Thus both Thomsen and Berthelot believed that a reaction would proceed in a stated direction if $\Delta H < 0$. This rule is a useful approximation, within limits which will be discussed later. As more reactions were investigated, however, and as the precision of experimental technique increased, it became abundantly evident that there are many reactions which proceed spontaneously though accompanied by a positive $\Delta H$. One example of these is spontaneous uptake of hydrogen ions by sulfate ions (under standard conditions[1]) in aqueous solution:

$$H^+(aq, 25°) + SO_4^{=}(aq, 25°) = HSO_4^-(aq, 25°)$$
$$\Delta H = 5.2 \text{ kcal mole}^{-1}$$

Thus it is evident that both $\Delta E$ and $\Delta H$ fail as reliable criteria of the direction in which a reaction may proceed. Apparently the first law of thermodynamics does not contain within it the basis of any criterion of spontaneity. Some further principle is necessary that will summarize in a general form the observed tendency of systems of many different types to change in a given direction.

## 7-2 THE NATURE OF THE SECOND LAW

### Natural Tendencies toward Equilibrium

Before attempting to express in some general statement the tendency of systems to proceed toward a condition of equilibrium, we shall find it desirable to recognize the many different forms in which this tendency

[1] For the definition of standard states in solutions, see Chapters 19 and 20.

exhibits itself. One of the most obvious examples is the flow of heat from a warm body to a colder body. Also, a clock always tends to run down; in fact, any spring tends to relax. Turning to phenomena in gases, we observe that effusion will always occur into a vacuum. And if a barrier separating two pure gases is removed, spontaneous mixing occurs. Similarly, if aqueous solutions of NaCl and $AgNO_3$ are mixed, AgCl is formed spontaneously. In chemical reactions a multitude of examples may be cited in which the mixing of two substances results in the formation of other substances.

It would be desirable to express this tendency toward a condition of equilibrium in all these systems in some common statement, which in turn should be convertible into a mathematical form capable of serving as a criterion of spontaneity.

## Statement of the Second Law

There are a number of alternative possible statements that fulfill these requirements. The more elegant are the more abstruse. For an introductory discussion, an historical approach seems more concrete and real, although it may appear roundabout, for the founders of thermodynamics groped about in some confusion before their ideas were clearly formulated and the great generality of their concepts was realized.

As was pointed out in Chapter 1, the origin of thermodynamics lies in Carnot's analysis of the performance of steam engines. Although a steam engine may seem a very distant and unpromising source for generalized principles of chemical change, the fact is that in the idealized form conceived by Carnot it has provided the mental construct which was historically the central pillar in the logical development of the second law of thermodynamics. In this connection the basic contribution of Carnot, in addition to the idea of *reversibility*, is the series of isothermal and adiabatic changes which combined in the proper order constitute the *Carnot cycle*. We shall, therefore, consider shortly some properties of the Carnot cycle, so that we may use it, in conjunction with some suitable statement which expresses our basic assumption in the formulation of the second law of thermodynamics.

The statement which we shall choose as the fundamental expression of the second law of thermodynamics (that of Clausius) is in a form that resembles the statements of other fundamental principles of physical science. Our statement will be expressed in a form which has been called (Whittaker)[2] a "principle of impotence," that is, an assertion of the impossibility of carrying out a particular process. In physics such "principles of impotence" occur frequently. The impossibility of sending a signal with a speed greater

[2] E. Whittaker, *From Euclid to Eddington*, Dover, New York, 1958, pp. 58–60.

than that of light forms the basis of the theory of relativity. Similarly, wave mechanics may be considered a consequence of the impossibility of measuring simultaneously the position and velocity of an elementary particle. In an analogous fashion, we may state the first law of thermodynamics in terms of man's impotence to construct a machine capable of producing energy, a so-called "perpetual-motion machine of the first kind."

Therefore, for the *second law of thermodynamics* we shall use the following (Clausius') statement:

> *It is impossible to construct a machine which is able to convey heat by a cyclical process from one reservoir (at a lower temperature) to another at a higher temperature unless work is done on the machine by some outside agency.* (I)

This expression of the second law is a condensed statement of much experience. The term "cyclical process" implies one in which the system carrying out the transfer of heat has returned to its initial state. Such a transfer may occur even in a cyclical process if the net result is an expenditure of work—for example, in a refrigerator heat from the inner compartment is transferred to the surroundings at a higher temperature, but this process is accompanied by a net input of work. The second law states that an equivalent process *without* an input of work is impossible.

It should be emphasized that the second law is not an a priori principle,[3] that is, it is not a statement which might be deduced from earlier principles, for example, the first law. The second law is a statement summarizing the experience of many men over a long period of time. Except perhaps in submicroscopic phenomena, no exceptions to this law have ever been found.[4]

## Mathematical Counterpart of the Verbal Statement

The second law, in the form in which it has been expressed thus far, is not a statement that can be applied conveniently to chemical problems. The principal objective for most chemists is to use the second law of thermodynamics to establish a criterion by which we can determine whether a chemical reaction, or even a phase change, will proceed spontaneously. Such a criterion would be available if we could obtain a function which, as a consequence of the second law of thermodynamics, possessed the following two characteristics:

(1) It should be a thermodynamic property; that is, its value should

[3] The other principles of impotence described above also are subject to this same statement.

[4] These submicroscopic phenomena must be treated by special methods, which are outside the scope of classical thermodynamics.

depend only upon the state of the system and not upon the particular path by which the state has been reached.

(2) It should change in a characteristic manner (for example, always increase) when a reaction proceeds spontaneously.

A function which satisfies these requirements has been devised and is known by the name "entropy."

## 7-3 THE DEFINITION OF S, THE ENTROPY OF A SYSTEM

The entropy of a system is defined in terms of a differential equation for $dS$, the infinitesimal change in entropy. For any infinitesimal portion of a process which is carried out in a reversible manner,

$$dS = \frac{DQ_{\mathrm{rev}}}{T} \tag{7-1}$$

where $DQ$ is the heat absorbed in this infinitesimal reversible portion and $T$ is the absolute temperature at which the heat is absorbed.

One might ask at this early stage in the discussion, what led anyone even to suspect that this particular combination of thermodynamic quantities $DQ$ and $T$ might have the unique characteristics which it has been found to possess? As has been pointed out, the concept of entropy occurs first, but only implicitly, in Carnot's monograph. Nevertheless, his comparison of a water turbine and heat engine suggests the following analogy. In the turbine, the quantity of water entering at the top can be expressed as

$$\frac{\text{gravitational energy (mgh) taken in}}{\text{height of reservoir (h)}}$$

By analogy in a heat engine, a thermal quantity, defined by the expression

$$\frac{\text{thermal energy (heat) taken in}}{\text{temperature of reservoir } (T)}$$

might be viewed as entering from the higher temperature boiler, and, subsequently, as in the water turbine, being expelled unchanged in quantity (although carrying a lesser energy since $T$ is lower) into a reservoir at a lower temperature—the cooling system.

The first *explicit* formulation of Eq. (7-1), however, is due to Clausius, and his original discovery of this combination of $DQ$ and $T$ stemmed from an analysis of a different type of problem. In Chapter 6, we considered a number of different processes involving changes in state of a gas, e.g., isothermal, isobaric, isochoric (constant volume), isenthalpic (constant enthalpy). In each of these processes, some thermodynamic variable remained unchanged, e.g., $T$, $P$, $V$, and $H$, respectively. In an *adiabatic* reversible expansion, however, none of these thermodynamic properties, nor $E$, the internal energy, remains unchanged. True, $DQ$ is zero in an adiabatic expansion, but $Q$ is not a thermodynamic property, that is, it is not a function of the state of a system. We might ask, therefore, is an adiabatic expansion unique or is there some quantity, so far overlooked, which is a thermodynamic property, yet remains unchanged in an adiabatic expansion?

If we consider our simplest model system—an ideal gas undergoing a reversible expansion—we find, following Clausius, an interesting answer. Focussing on $DQ$ we may write from what we have learned in Chapter 6

$$DQ = dE + DW = C_v\,dT + P\,dV \tag{7-2}$$

$$= C_v\,dT + \frac{RT}{V}\,dV \tag{7-3}$$

As we know, $DQ$ is inexact, and this characteristic is confirmed by an examination of the right-hand side of Eq. (7-3), for it is not integrable unless we specify a path. Notice, however, what we obtain if we divide both sides of Eq. (7-3) by $T$:

$$\frac{DQ}{T} = C_v\frac{dT}{T} + R\frac{dV}{V} \tag{7-4}$$

Now the right-hand side *is* integrable. Clearly then there exists an explicit function for $\int DQ/T$, to wit,

$$\int \frac{DQ}{T} = C_v \ln T + R \ln V + \text{constant} \tag{7-5}$$

It follows then that $DQ/T$ is exact, even though $DQ$ alone is inexact. Consequently, this combination of quantities merits a new symbol, $dS$, and name, entropy. Furthermore, in answer to our original question about adiabatic processes, we find that for a reversible one with an ideal gas, since $DQ$ is zero,

$$dS = \frac{DQ_{\text{rev}}}{T} = 0 \tag{7-6}$$

that is, this process is isentropic. Thus, we see that $DQ_{\text{rev}}/T$ has interesting properties at least for an ideal gas and hence it might be considered a function worth further examination.

It should be emphasized that the entropy of Eq. (7-1) has been defined in an operational manner, that is, in terms of the operations by which it is measured. The definition specifies that the entropy change can be measured only when $DQ$ is known for a *reversible* change and when the temperature has been specified. No statement is made about entropy changes in irreversible processes. However, as a consequence of the second law of thermodynamics it can be shown that $dS$ is an exact differential,[5] or in other words that $S$ is a thermodynamic property and depends only upon the state of a system. Hence the change in entropy in any system going from a specified initial state to a given final state is independent of the path by which the change is carried out.

The proof that the change in entropy is independent of the path will be carried out in four steps.

(1) It will be proved that $dS$ is an exact differential for an ideal gas carried through a Carnot cycle. Actually we have already shown this, in principle, in the discussion of Clausius' approach to the entropy function, but we shall use also an additional procedure which is more convenient for the steps that follow.

(2) It will be proved that $dS$ is an exact differential for any substance carried through a Carnot cycle.

(3) It will be proved that $dS$ is an exact differential for any substance carried through any reversible cycle.

(4) It will be proved that the entropy is a function only of the state of a system.

## 7-4 THE PROOF THAT S IS A THERMODYNAMIC PROPERTY

### Ideal Gas in a Carnot Cycle

***Net work and heat quantities***. The Carnot cycle is the name for a series of four changes that a substance (in principle, any substance) may undergo. In the forward direction these are: isothermal expansion, adiabatic expansion, isothermal compression, and adiabatic compression, in that order. At the end of this series of changes, the substance must have been returned to its initial state.

Such a cycle is represented most frequently by a pressure-volume diagram, as in Figure 7-1. It is more convenient for the purposes of the following proof, however, to refer to a temperature-volume diagram, as in Figure 7-2. The latter diagram emphasizes more strongly the isothermal nature of the first and third steps in the cycle.

When an ideal gas is carried through a Carnot cycle, the quantities of work done and heat absorbed in each of the steps may be calculated readily from relations previously derived. For an isothermal reversible expansion of 1 mole of an ideal gas the change in energy is zero, and hence

$$W = Q = RT \ln \frac{V_{\text{final}}}{V_{\text{initial}}} \tag{7-7}$$

[5] Since $DQ$ is an inexact differential and $(1/T) \times DQ$ makes the resultant function an exact differential, the factor $1/T$ is an *integration factor*.

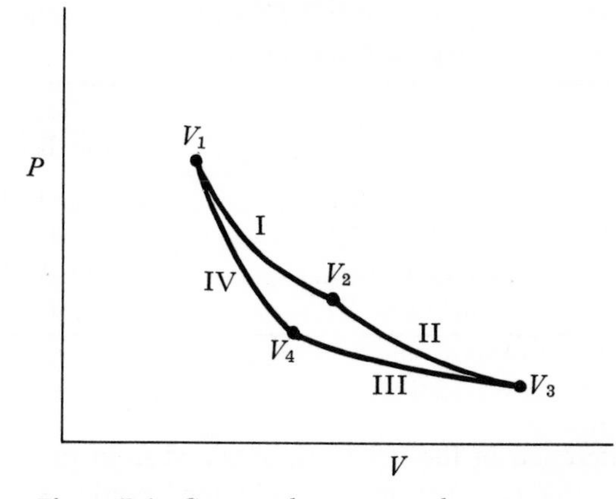


***Figure 7-1*** *Carnot cycle; pressure-volume diagram.*

In the adiabatic reversible expansion the quantity of heat absorbed is zero and hence, if $C_v$ is a constant,

$$W = -C_v\,(T_{\text{final}} - T_{\text{initial}}) = -\Delta E \tag{7-8}$$

Using these relations, we may tabulate $W$ and $Q$ (Table 7-1) for the steps specified in the reversible cycle in Figure 7-2.

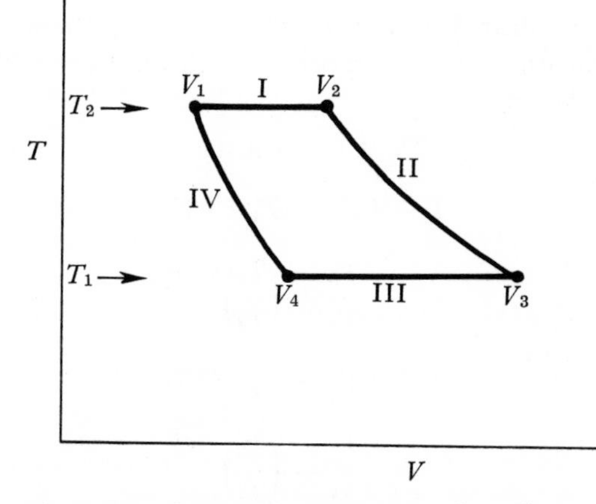


***Figure 7-2*** *Carnot cycle; temperature-volume diagram.*

***Table 7-1***

*Work and heat in Carnot cycle*

| Step | Work done | Heat absorbed |
|---|---|---|
| I | $RT_2 \ln (V_2/V_1)$ | $RT_2 \ln (V_2/V_1)$ |
| II | $C_v(T_2 - T_1)$ | 0 |
| III | $RT_1 \ln (V_4/V_3)$ | $RT_1 \ln (V_4/V_3)$ |
| IV | $C_v(T_1 - T_2)$ | 0 |

We shall be interested in the net work obtained from the ideal gas in this complete cycle; this quantity may be obtained readily by summation of the works done in the individual steps. Thus

$$W = RT_2 \ln \frac{V_2}{V_1} + C_v(T_2 - T_1) + RT_1 \ln \frac{V_4}{V_3} + C_v(T_1 - T_2) \tag{7-9}$$

The second and fourth terms in Eq. (7-9) are equal but opposite in sign, so that we may reduce the expression to

$$W = RT_2 \ln \frac{V_2}{V_1} + RT_1 \ln \frac{V_4}{V_3} \tag{7-10}$$

It can be shown readily that $V_3$ and $V_4$ are related in a very definite manner to $V_2$ and $V_1$, so that Eq. (7-10) may be simplified even further. A glance at Figure 7-2 shows that $V_2$ and $V_3$ are end points of an adiabatic reversible process, step II. Similarly, $V_4$ and $V_1$ are the initial and final volumes, respectively, of the adiabatic reversible compression, step IV. As has been demonstrated previously, the volume and temperature at any point in an adiabatic reversible process for an ideal gas with constant $C_v$ must obey the relation

$$T^{C_v/R} V = \text{constant} \tag{7-11}$$

In step II, then,

$$T_2^{C_v/R} V_2 = T_1^{C_v/R} V_3 \tag{7-12}$$

or

$$\frac{V_3}{V_2} = \left(\frac{T_2}{T_1}\right)^{C_v/R} \tag{7-13}$$

Similarly, for step IV

$$T_2^{C_v/R} V_1 = T_1^{C_v/R} V_4 \tag{7-14}$$

or

$$\frac{V_4}{V_1} = \left(\frac{T_2}{T_1}\right)^{C_v/R} \tag{7-15}$$

Equating (7-13) and (7-15), we obtain

$$\frac{V_3}{V_2} = \frac{V_4}{V_1} \tag{7-16}$$

from which it follows that

$$\frac{V_1}{V_2} = \frac{V_4}{V_3} \tag{7-17}$$

The result of Eq. (7-17) may be introduced into the expression (7-10) for the net work done by the gas in the cycle to give

$$W = RT_2 \ln \frac{V_2}{V_1} + RT_1 \ln \frac{V_1}{V_2} = RT_2 \ln \frac{V_2}{V_1} - RT_1 \ln \frac{V_2}{V_1} \tag{7-18}$$

Let us now consider the ratio of the net work, $W$, to the heat absorbed by the gas, $Q_2$, during the isothermal expansion at the temperature $T_2$:

$$\frac{W}{Q_2} = \frac{R(T_2 - T_1) \ln (V_2/V_1)}{RT_2 \ln (V_2/V_1)} \tag{7-19}$$

This ratio, frequently called the *efficiency* of the machine with a particular substance in the cycle, may be reduced, by cancellation of equivalent factors, to

$$\frac{W}{Q_2} = \frac{T_2 - T_1}{T_2} \tag{7-20}$$

(The term *efficiency* is used because $W/Q_2$ gives the ratio of the useful work obtained from the heat which must be supplied.)

***Entropy change.*** At the completion of the cycle the ideal gas has been returned to its initial state, so that the net change in energy is zero. Hence it follows from the first law of thermodynamics that

$$0 = Q_{\text{total}} - W_{\text{total}} \tag{7-21}$$

$W_{\text{total}}$ has been evaluated in terms of Eq. (7-18). Since steps II and IV in the cycle are adiabatic, $Q_{\text{total}}$ is given by the sum of heats $Q_2$ and $Q_1$, absorbed at the two temperatures $T_2$ and $T_1$, respectively. Therefore

$$W_{\text{total}} = W = Q_{\text{total}} = Q_2 + Q_1 \tag{7-22}$$

Substituting the result of (7-22) in the expression (7-20), we obtain

$$\frac{W}{Q_2} = \frac{Q_2 + Q_1}{Q_2} = \frac{T_2 - T_1}{T_2} \tag{7-23}$$

Rearrangement leads to

$$Q_2 + Q_1 = Q_2 - \frac{T_1}{T_2} Q_2$$

$$\frac{Q_1}{T_1} = -\frac{Q_2}{T_2}$$

$$\frac{Q_1}{T_1} + \frac{Q_2}{T_2} = 0 \tag{7-24}$$

or

$$\sum \frac{Q}{T} = 0 \tag{7-25}$$

If the ideal gas in the Carnot cycle is considered as being carried through a series of infinitesimally small steps, then the summation of Eq. (7-25) may be replaced by

$$\int \frac{DQ}{T} = 0 \tag{7-26}$$

Since this process has been carried out reversibly, we may make use of the definition of entropy in Eq. (7-1), and by indicating explicitly the cyclical nature of the process, we arrive at the following expression for an ideal gas being carried through the reversible Carnot cycle:

$$\oint dS = 0 \tag{7-27}$$

Thus for the conditions specified it has been proved that $dS$ is an exact differential and, consequently, that the entropy, $S$, is a thermodynamic property.

## Any Substance in a Carnot Cycle

At this stage we wish to eliminate any restrictions as to the nature of the substance being carried through the Carnot cycle and thus to show that $dS$ is exact for any material in this reversible process. It is desirable to prepare for this proof by consideration of a few numerical examples of work and heat quantities involved in a Carnot cycle with an ideal gas.

***Some numerical examples with ideal gas in Carnot cycle.*** Referring to Figure 7-2, let us consider a situation in which the temperature of the upper heat reservoir is twice that of the lower, for example, 200° and 100°K, respectively. If $V_2$ is also taken as exactly twice $V_1$, then it can be shown from Eq. (7-18) that

$$W = 138 \text{ cal}$$

It can also be shown readily (see Table 7-1) that the heat absorbed at the upper temperature is

$$Q_2 = 276 \text{ cal}$$

Since the energy change in a complete cycle is zero,

$$W = Q_2 + Q_1$$

Therefore

$$Q_1 = -138 \text{ cal}$$

that is, 138 cal of heat is *evolved* by the ideal gas during isothermal compression at the lower temperature, $T_1$. These results may be tabulated conveniently as follows:

$$\begin{aligned} Q_2 &= \phantom{-}276 \text{ cal} \\ W &= \phantom{-}138 \text{ cal} \\ Q_1 &= -138 \text{ cal} \end{aligned} \tag{a}$$

A Carnot cycle may be run in reverse also; that is, the series of stages may be in the following order: adiabatic expansion, isothermal expansion, adiabatic compression, isothermal compression. If Figure 7-2 is used to represent this reverse cycle, the order of the steps would be IV, III, II, I. By methods analogous to those used in the description of the forward cycle, it can be shown readily that

$$\begin{aligned} W \text{ (reverse)} &= -W \text{ (forward)} \\ Q_2 \text{ (reverse)} &= -Q_2 \text{ (forward)} \\ Q_1 \text{ (reverse)} &= -Q_1 \text{ (forward)} \end{aligned} \tag{b}$$

For the numerical conditions specified above, the reverse Carnot cycle would be accompanied by an absorption of 138 cal of heat at the temperature $T_1$, 138 cal of work would be done *on* the ideal gas, and 276 cal of heat would be evolved by the gas at the temperature $T_2$. These changes may be tabulated as follows for comparison with the forward cycle:

$$\begin{aligned} Q_2 &= -276 \text{ cal} \\ W &= -138 \text{ cal} \\ Q_1 &= \phantom{-}138 \text{ cal} \end{aligned} \tag{c}$$

It is of interest to note in passing that the Carnot cycle in reverse corresponds to an ideal refrigerating engine, since the result of the cycle is the removal of a quantity of heat from a reservoir at low temperature and the deposition of a quantity of heat into a reservoir at a higher temperature. It should be emphasized, however, that this result does not contradict the second law of thermodynamics, because net work *was done* on the gas during the process.

***Principle of the proof.*** We may turn our attention now to the proof that $dS$ is exact for any substance carried through the reversible Carnot cycle. Reference to the proof for this cycle with an ideal gas shows that the basic relation which must be established is that

$$\text{efficiency} \equiv \frac{W}{Q_2} = \frac{T_2 - T_1}{T_2} \tag{7-20}$$

Once the applicability of this relation has been demonstrated, it is a simple matter to show, as has been done above, that $\oint dS = 0$.

The proof that the efficiency for any substance in a Carnot cycle is given by Eq. (7-20) may be carried out in two steps.

(1) We shall assume first that this other substance (not an ideal gas) gives an efficiency greater than $(T_2 - T_1)/T_2$. Using this assumption, we shall arrive at a contradiction of the second law. Consequently we shall have proved that the efficiency for this other substance cannot be greater than $(T_2 - T_1)/T_2$.

(2) We shall assume that this other substance (not an ideal gas) gives an efficiency less than $(T_2 - T_1)/T_2$. Using this assumption, we shall arrive at a contradiction of the second law. Consequently, we shall have proved that the efficiency for this other substance cannot be less than $(T_2 - T_1)/T_2$.

Since the efficiency for this other substance (not an ideal gas) can be neither greater than nor less than $(T_2 - T_1)/T_2$, it must be equal to $(T_2 - T_1)/T_2$. Equations (7-20) and (7-27) apply, therefore, for any substance in a Carnot cycle.

***Proof that efficiency for a real substance in the Carnot cycle cannot exceed that for the ideal gas.*** The details of this proof may be understood more readily if a numerical special case is used first. Let us assume that a given Carnot cycle is being operated between reservoirs of which the upper is at a temperature, $T_2$, which is exactly twice that of the lower, $T_1$. If $T_2 = 2T_1$, then the efficiency for an ideal gas in this cycle is 0.5. If 100 cal of heat were absorbed at $T_2$, 50 cal would be converted into work at the completion of the cycle and 50 cal would be evolved to the reservoir at the lower temperature, $T_1$. If 120 cal were absorbed at $T_2$, 60 cal would be converted into work and 60 cal would be evolved at $T_1$. These changes may be tabulated conveniently as follows:

$$\begin{aligned} Q_2 &= 100 \text{ cal} & Q_2 &= 120 \text{ cal} \\ W &= 50 \text{ cal} & W &= 60 \text{ cal} \\ Q_1 &= -50 \text{ cal} & Q_1 &= -60 \text{ cal} \end{aligned} \tag{d}$$

If the Carnot cycle were run in reverse and 50 cal of heat were absorbed at $T_1$, 50 cal of work would be done on the ideal gas and 100 cal of heat would be evolved at $T_2$. The results for the reverse cycles corresponding to the forward cycles tabulated in (d) may be summarized as follows:

$$\begin{aligned} Q_2 &= -100 \text{ cal} & Q_2 &= -120 \text{ cal} \\ W &= -\ \ 50 \text{ cal} & W &= -\ \ 60 \text{ cal} \\ Q_1 &= \ \ \ \ 50 \text{ cal} & Q_1 &= \ \ \ \ 60 \text{ cal} \end{aligned} \tag{e}$$

Let us now take the other substance (not an ideal gas) assumed to give an efficiency greater than 0.5 (say 0.6), run it through a Carnot cycle in a forward direction, and use the work obtained from this forward cycle to carry an ideal gas through a reverse Carnot cycle. If 100 cal of heat is absorbed at $T_2$ in the forward cycle with the other substance, 60 cal of work will be obtained (since the efficiency is 0.6) and 40 cal of heat will be given up to the reservoir at the lower temperature. If the 60 cal of work is now used to operate the reverse Carnot cycle with the ideal gas, then, since the efficiency with the ideal gas is 0.5, 60 cal of heat will be absorbed at $T_1$ and 120 evolved at $T_2$. These changes together with their net results are presented in Table 7-2.

At the conclusion of the two cycles both substances have been returned to their initial conditions. Yet the net result for both substances is an evolution of 20 cal of heat at $T_2$ and an absorption of 20 cal at $T_1$. The net result for the reservoirs is a loss of 20 cal by the low-temperature source and a gain of 20 cal by the source at high temperature. Since the net work done during these changes is zero, we have transferred 20 cal of heat from a low-temperature reservoir to one at a higher temperature without doing any net work. Since the second law of thermodynamics proclaims the impossibility of such an accomplishment, our initial assumption that the efficiency for the Carnot cycle containing the other substance is 0.6 must be wrong.

***Table 7-2***

*Coupling of two Carnot cycles*

| | Other substance, efficiency = 0.6 (forward cycle), cal | Ideal gas efficiency = 0.5 (reverse cycle), cal | Net change for working substances, cal | Net change in reservoirs, cal |
|---|---|---|---|---|
| $Q$ at $T_2$ | 100 | −120 | −20 | 20 |
| $W$ for complete cycle | 60 | − 60 | 0 | 0 |
| $Q$ at $T_1$ | −40 | 60 | 20 | −20 |

Strictly speaking, of course, we have succeeded in proving so far only that the efficiency for the other substance cannot be 0.6 when that for an ideal gas is 0.5. It is apparent, however, that if the efficiency for the other substance were any value greater than 0.5, the net result in Table 7-2 would be similar.

The proof may be given also in a generalized form in which the values of $Q_2$ are not specified numerically. Again we operate the Carnot cycle in a forward direction using the other substance (not an ideal gas). $Q_2$ cal of heat is absorbed at the higher temperature, $T_2$, and $W$ cal of work is obtained from the complete cycle. Therefore $Q_1$ (or since $\Delta E$ is zero, $W - Q_2$) cal of heat is absorbed at $T_1$. (Actually, of course, heat is evolved at $T_1$, but this merely means that $Q_1$ is a negative number.) If an ideal gas were operated in a Carnot cycle in the forward direction, with the same two reservoirs at $T_2$ and $T_1$ and in a manner such that $W$ is the same as for the other substance, then, since the efficiency given by the latter is assumed greater than that given by the ideal gas, that is,

$$\frac{W}{Q_2} > \frac{W}{Q_2'} \tag{7-28}$$

we may write

$$Q_2' > Q_2 \tag{7-29}$$

where $Q_2'$ is the heat absorbed at $T_2$ by the ideal gas in a forward cycle. If the work, $W$, obtained from the forward cycle with the other substance is used to operate the ideal gas in a reverse cycle, then $Q_2'$ cal of heat is *evolved* at $T_2$.

Similarly, in the isothermal step at $T_1$ the other substance in the forward cycle evolves $Q_1$ cal; and if the ideal gas were operated in the forward direction to produce the same quantity of work $W$, the heat evolved, $Q_1'$, would be greater in absolute value than $Q_1$.[6] Since the $Q$'s are negative numbers, $Q_1'$ must be algebraically less than $Q_1$. Thus, remembering that $\Delta E = 0$ for a complete cycle, we can write

$$W = Q_2 + Q_1 = Q_2' + Q_1' \tag{7-30}$$

and since

$$Q_2' > Q_2 \tag{7-31}$$

$$Q_1' < Q_1 \tag{7-32}$$

[6] If this conclusion is not evident, it may be made clear by the following additional details. Since both substances are operating in closed cycles, $\Delta E = 0$. Therefore, $Q_1' = W - Q_2'$ and $Q_1 = W - Q_2$. But $W$ is the same for both substances. On the other hand, $Q_2' > Q_2$; hence $Q_1'$ must be larger in absolute value than $Q_1$. However, since $Q_1$ and $Q_1'$ are both negative numbers in a forward cycle, $Q_1'$ must be algebraically less than $Q_1$.

*Table 7-3*

*Coupling of two Carnot cycles*

| | Other substance, efficiency > $\frac{T_2 - T_1}{T_2}$ (forward cycle) | Ideal gas, efficiency = $\frac{T_2 - T_1}{T_2}$ (reverse cycle) | Net change for working substances | Net change in reservoir |
|---|---|---|---|---|
| $Q$ at $T_2$ | $Q_2$ | $-Q'_2$ | $Q_2 - Q'_2 < 0$ | $-(Q_2 - Q'_2) > 0$ |
| $W$ for complete cycle | $W$ | $-W$ | 0 | 0 |
| $Q$ at $T_1$ | $Q_1$ | $-Q'_1$ | $Q_1 - Q'_1 > 0$ | $-(Q_1 - Q'_1) < 0$ |

Keeping these relative values of the heats and works in mind, let us tabulate the results of operating the other substance in a forward direction and using the work obtained to run the ideal gas in a reverse Carnot cycle (Table 7-3).

Again we observe in this general case, as in the specific numerical example outlined above, that the net result of our double cycle is the transfer of heat in a cyclical process from the low-temperature source at $T_1$ to the high-temperature reservoir without the expenditure of any work. Since the possibility of such a transfer is contrary to accumulated experience as expressed in the second law, the assumption upon which the transfer was predicated must be incorrect. It follows, then, that no substance carried through a Carnot cycle can give an efficiency greater than $(T_2 - T_1)/T_2$.

***Proof that efficiency for a real substance in a Carnot cycle cannot be less than that for the ideal gas.*** The second step in our complete proof requires the establishment of the impossibility of the other substance giving an efficiency less than $(T_2 - T_1)/T_2$. Obviously, this step may be demonstrated in a manner analogous to that used in the proof of the first step. We assume that the other substance gives an efficiency less than that given by the ideal gas. Again we operate the more efficient substance (this time the ideal gas) in the forward direction and the less efficient substance (this time the other substance) in the reverse direction. Using a specific numerical example first, let us assume again that $T_2 = 2T_1$ (so that the efficiency for the ideal gas will remain 0.5) and that the other substance gives an efficiency of 0.40. The results of operating with the ideal gas in the forward direction and using the work obtained to carry the other substance through a reverse cycle are given in Table 7-4.

***Table 7-4***

*Coupling of two Carnot cycles*

| | Ideal gas, efficiency = 0.5 (forward cycle), cal | Other substance, efficiency = 0.4 (reverse cycle), cal | Net change for working substances, cal | Net change in reservoirs, cal |
|---|---|---|---|---|
| $Q$ at $T_2$ | 80 | −100 | −20 | +20 |
| $W$ for complete cycle | 40 | − 40 | 0 | 0 |
| $Q$ at $T_1$ | −40 | + 60 | +20 | −20 |

Clearly the second law has been violated.

We may state the proof of the second step in general terms as follows. We assume that the ideal gas gives a greater efficiency than the other substance, so that if both are operated upon in a forward direction with the same reservoirs at $T_2$ and $T_1$ and give the same net work, $W$, the following relation must be valid (where the prime again refers to the ideal gas):

$$\frac{W}{Q_2'} > \frac{W}{Q_2} \tag{7-33}$$

Therefore

$$Q_2 > Q_2' \tag{7-34}$$

In a complete cycle $\Delta E = 0$, and hence, from the first law of thermodynamics,

$$W = Q_2 + Q_1 = Q_2' + Q_1' \tag{7-30}$$

Since

$$Q_2 > Q_2' \tag{7-35}$$

$$Q_1 < Q_1' \tag{7-36}$$

Thus $Q_1$ is algebraically less than $Q_1'$. (Since these heats are negative numbers in the forward cycles, $Q_1$ must be greater in absolute magnitude than $Q_1'$.) The results of operating with the ideal gas in a forward cycle and using the work, $W$, obtained to carry the other substance through in reverse may be summarized as in Table 7-5.

***Table 7-5***

*Coupling of two Carnot cycles*

| | Ideal gas, efficiency $= \frac{T_2 - T_1}{T_2}$ (forward cycle) | Other substance, efficiency $< \frac{T_2 - T_1}{T_2}$ (reverse cycle) | Net change for working substances | Net change in reservoirs |
|---|---|---|---|---|
| $Q$ at $T_2$ | $Q_2'$ | $-Q_2$ | $Q_2' - Q_2 < 0$ | $-(Q_2' - Q_2) > 0$ |
| $W$ for complete cycle | $W$ | $-W$ | 0 | 0 |
| $Q$ at $T_1$ | $Q_1'$ | $-Q_1$ | $Q_1' - Q_1 > 0$ | $-(Q_1' - Q_1) < 0$ |

A glance at the last column in Table 7-5 will show that the second law of thermodynamics has been contradicted. Clearly our postulate that the other substance gives an efficiency less than that given by the ideal gas is incorrect.

***Conclusion.*** Since the efficiency of the machine containing this other substance (not an ideal gas) can be neither greater than nor less than $(T_2 - T_1)/T_2$, it follows that for any substance carried through a Carnot cycle,

$$\frac{W}{Q_2} = \frac{T_2 - T_1}{T_2} \tag{7-20}$$

Therefore

$$\oint dS = 0 \tag{7-27}$$

## Any Substance in Any Reversible Cycle

Having removed the restrictions on the nature of the substance, we must proceed to remove any specifications as to the nature of the reversible cycle through which the substance is being carried. Let us represent such a cycle by the example illustrated in Figure 7-3*a*, which may be approximated by Carnot cycles, as illustrated in Figure 7-3*b*, if we proceed along the heavy-lined path. It can be shown readily, by the following procedure, that

$$\oint dS = 0 \tag{7-27}$$

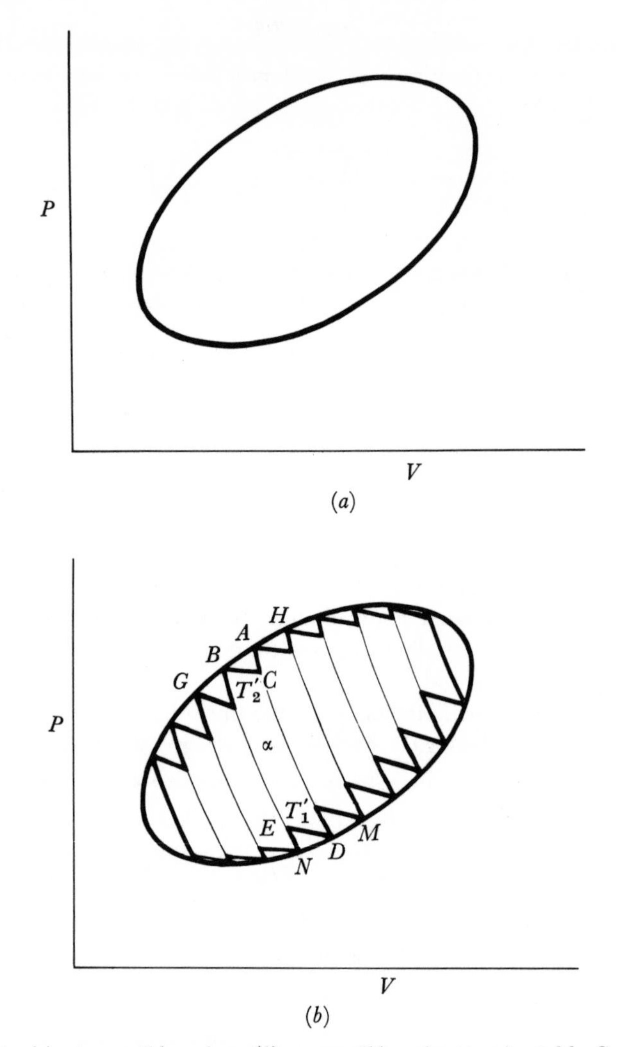


***Figure 7-3*** *(a) A reversible cycle; (b) a reversible cycle approximated by Carnot cycles.*

In order to obtain this integral we must evaluate

$$\left(\frac{DQ}{T}\right)_{G\to B} + \left(\frac{DQ}{T}\right)_{B\to A} + \cdots + \left(\frac{DQ}{T}\right)_{M\to D} + \left(\frac{DQ}{T}\right)_{D\to N} + \cdots$$

$$= \oint dS \qquad (7\text{-}37)$$

We can make this evaluation by examining the small Carnot cycles in more detail. For example for the cycle labeled $\alpha$, we may definitely state, since the adiabatic steps contribute nothing to $DQ/T$, that

$$\left(\frac{DQ_2'}{T_2'}\right)_{B\to C} + \left(\frac{DQ_1'}{T_1'}\right)_{D\to E} = \left(\sum \frac{DQ}{T}\right)_{\text{cycle } \alpha} = 0 \qquad (7\text{-}38)$$

where the primes are used to emphasize that the quantities refer to the approximating Carnot cycle, not to the actual path of Figure 7-3 *a*. In the $P$–$V$ diagram of Figure 7-3*b*, we also note that for the small area $BACB$,

$$\oint_{BACB} P\,dV = \text{area } BACB = \oint_{BACB} DW = \oint_{BACB} DQ \qquad (7\text{-}39)$$

the last equality following from the fact that for a cycle $\Delta E = 0$. Hence it follows that

$$\text{area } BACB = \oint DQ = (DQ)_{B\to A} + 0 + (DQ)_{C\to B} \qquad (7\text{-}40)$$

Noticing that

$$(DQ)_{C\to B} = -(DQ)_{B\to C} \qquad (7\text{-}41)$$

we conclude that

$$(DQ)_{B\to A} = (DQ_2')_{B\to C} + \text{area } BACB \qquad (7\text{-}42)$$

A better approximation to the actual cycle of Figure 7-3*a* would be a larger number of Carnot cycles in Figure 7-3*b*. In each such approximation, Eq. (7-42) would be valid, but as the number of cycles used for the approximation is increased, the area $BACB$ becomes smaller and smaller. Clearly in the limit of an infinite number of cycles, where the approximation to the actual cycle becomes perfect,

$$\text{area } BACB \to 0 \qquad (7\text{-}43)$$

$$(DQ)_{B\to A} = (DQ_2')_{B\to C} \qquad (7\text{-}44)$$

For every pair of sections, $BA$ and $DN$, of the actual path, we have corresponding (isothermal) pairs, $BC$ and $DE$ which are parts of an approximating Carnot cycle. Hence we may write

$$\oint_{\text{actual}} dS = \left(\frac{DQ}{T}\right)_{B\to A} + \cdots + \left(\frac{DQ}{T}\right)_{D\to N} + \cdots = \left(\frac{DQ_2'}{T_2'}\right)_{B\to C} + \cdots + \left(\frac{DQ_1'}{T_1'}\right)_{D\to E} + \cdots = 0 \qquad (7\text{-}45)$$

Thus we conclude that for any reversible cycle, $dS$ is an exact differential.

### Entropy S Depends Only upon the State of the System

In going from a state $a$ to a state $b$, as is shown in Figure 7-4, we may proceed by any one of an infinite number of paths. Two *reversible* paths, $acb$ and $adb$, are illustrated in Figure 7-4. Despite the great difference between the shapes of these two paths, the change in entropy must be the same for each, because in the complete cycle, $acbda$, the change in entropy is zero:

$$\int_{\substack{\text{path}\\ abc}} dS + \int_{\substack{\text{path}\\ bda}} dS = 0 \tag{7-46}$$

Hence

$$\int_{\substack{\text{path}\\ acb}} dS = -\int_{\substack{\text{path}\\ bda}} dS = \int_{\substack{\text{path}\\ adb}} dS \tag{7-47}$$

The right-hand equality sign in Eq. (7-47) is valid because the path is the same but with the limits interchanged. As a result of (7-47) it is obvious that all reversible paths from $a$ to $b$ are accompanied by the same change in entropy. Since $S_b - S_a$ is independent of the reversible path used to calculate it, the entropies, $S_b$ and $S_a$, must be functions only of the states of the systems $b$ and $a$, respectively.

## 7-5 ALTERNATIVE STATEMENT OF THE SECOND LAW OF THERMODYNAMICS

There are a number of possible formulations of the second law in addition to the fundamental verbal statement which we have adopted. In

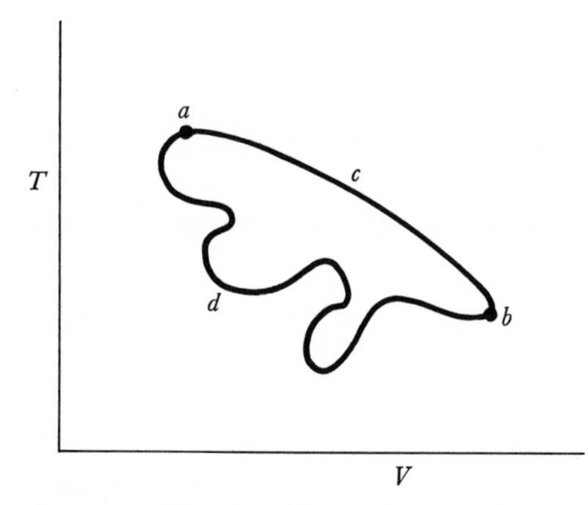


***Figure 7-4*** *Two reversible paths from one point to another.*

general, any one of these alternatives may be assumed as the basic expression of long experience and all of the others may be proved from it. We shall continue to use the original statement we adopted [(I), page 99] and shall prove any others from it.

A very useful enunciation of the second law is the following (Kelvin-Planck statement):

*It is impossible to construct a machine that, operating in a cycle, will take heat from a reservoir at constant temperature and convert it into work without accompanying changes in the reservoir or its surroundings.* (II)

In other words, it is impossible to carry out a cyclical process in which heat from a reservoir at a fixed temperature has been converted into work.

The proof of this statement is straightforward. Once again we assume that it *is* possible to carry out the process which the new statement denies. As a result of this assumption we shall contradict our original statement of the second law. Since this contradiction violates all of our observations, the assumption must be incorrect.

If we could carry out a cyclical process in which heat from a reservoir at a constant temperature, $T_1$, would be converted into work, it still follows from the first law of thermodynamics that the net change in energy, $\Delta E$, of the machine must be zero, since this system has returned to its initial state. Nevertheless, since a certain quantity of heat has been converted into work, $W$, we may use the work obtained to operate a reversible Carnot cycle in the reverse direction. The net result of this Carnot cycle in reverse (a refrigerating cycle) would be the transfer of a quantity of heat from a reservoir at the lower temperature, $T_1$, to one at a higher temperature, $T_2$, by a cyclical process. The net work done in the isothermal process and reverse Carnot cycle combined is zero. We have stipulated that the isothermal process is cyclical, and, of course, so is the Carnot cycle. Our net result, the transfer of heat from $T_1$ to $T_2$, therefore violates the original statement of the second law. Hence the new assumption that heat may be converted into work in an isothermal cyclical process is incorrect. Consequently statement (II) of the second law of thermodynamics stands proved.

## 7-6 ENTROPY CHANGES IN REVERSIBLE PROCESSES

Having established the exactness of the entropy differential, let us turn our attention to some considerations of the value of this entropy function in specific situations.

### Steps in the Carnot Cycle

The four steps of the Carnot cycle fall into one or the other of two categories: (1) isothermal changes and (2) adiabatic changes. For each category the calculation of the entropy change is obvious from the definition of $dS$ in Eq. (7-1).

For isothermal reversible changes it is clear that the entropy change for the system is given by

$$\Delta S_{sys} = \int dS = \int \frac{DQ}{T} = \frac{1}{T} \int DQ = \frac{Q}{T} \tag{7-48}$$

For the specific case of the expansion of 1 mole of an ideal gas, since $\Delta E = 0$,

$$Q = W = RT \ln \frac{V'}{V} \tag{7-49}$$

where $V'$ is the final volume and $V$ the initial volume. Hence

$$\Delta S_{gas} = \frac{Q}{T} = R \ln \frac{V'}{V} \tag{7-50}$$

It is pertinent to point out that in any isothermal stage of a Carnot cycle if $Q$ is the heat absorbed by the system, then $-Q$ must be the heat absorbed by the surroundings. Therefore

$$\Delta S_{surr} = -\frac{Q}{T} \tag{7-51}$$

Hence for the system plus surroundings or *universe*,

$$\Delta S_{total} = \Delta S_{sys} + \Delta S_{surr} = 0 \tag{7-52}$$

In the adiabatic steps of the Carnot cycle there is no heat exchange. It is thus immediately obvious that

$$\Delta S_{sys} = \Delta S_{surr} = \Delta S_{total} = 0 \tag{7-53}$$

## Phase Transitions

A change from one phase to another, for example, from ice to water, may be carried out reversibly and at a constant temperature. Clearly, under these conditions Eq. (7-48) is applicable. Equilibrium phase transitions are also generally carried out at a fixed pressure. Since no work is expended in these transitions, except against the atmosphere, $Q$ is given by the heat of transition, and hence

$$\Delta S_{subs} = \frac{\Delta H_{trans}}{T} \tag{7-54}$$

In these isothermal, reversible phase transitions, as in the isothermal steps of a Carnot cycle, for every infinitesimal quantity of heat absorbed by the substance an equal quantity of heat must have been released by the surroundings. Consequently,

$$\Delta S_{\text{surr}} = -\Delta S_{\text{subs}} \tag{7-55}$$

and hence again the entropy change for the combination as a whole must be zero.

As a specific example of a calculation of $\Delta S$ for a phase transition we may consider the data on the fusion of ice at 0°C:

$$H_2O(s, 0°C) = H_2O(l, 0°C) \qquad \Delta H = 1436 \text{ cal mole}^{-1}$$

$$\Delta S_{\text{water}}^{7} = \frac{1436}{273.15} = 5.257 \text{ cal mole}^{-1} \text{ deg}^{-1}$$

$$\Delta S_{\text{surr}} = -5.257 \text{ cal mole}^{-1} \text{ deg}^{-1}$$

$$\Delta S_{\text{total}} = 0$$

## Isobaric Temperature Rise

In many cases it is necessary to calculate the change in entropy accompanying the rise in temperature of a substance. Such a temperature increase can be carried out in a reversible manner so that one may substitute an expression for the heat absorbed in the process into the equation for the calculation of the entropy change. Since the process is carried out at constant pressure,

$$\Delta S_{\text{sys}} = \int \frac{DQ}{T} = \int \frac{dH}{T} = \int \frac{C_p\, dT}{T} = \int C_p\, d \ln T \tag{7-56}$$

Should $C_p$ be constant,

$$\Delta S = C_p \ln \frac{T_2}{T_1} \tag{7-57}$$

where $T_2$ is the final temperature and $T_1$ is the initial temperature.

Once again let us emphasize that the entropy change in the surroundings is equal but opposite in sign to that for the substance and consequently that $\Delta S$ for the combination or universe is zero.

## Isochoric Temperature Rise

The entropy changes for a temperature rise at a constant volume are analogous to those at constant pressure, except that $C_v$ replaces $C_p$. Thus

[7] Other notations for unit of entropy (if heat is in cal and temperature in deg) are (1) eu, and (2) gibbs mole$^{-1}$.

since $P\,dV = 0$,

$$\Delta S_{\text{sys}} = \int \frac{DQ}{T} = \int \frac{dE}{T} = \int \frac{C_v\,dT}{T} = \int C_v\,d\ln T \qquad (7\text{-}58)$$

Here, too, the entropy change for the universe is zero.

### General Statement

From the law of conservation of energy, it is evident that whenever a system absorbs a quantity of heat, $DQ$, the surroundings lose an equal quantity of heat. Thus,

$$DQ_{\text{sys}} = -DQ_{\text{surr}} \qquad (7\text{-}59)$$

It follows that in a reversible process

$$\frac{DQ_{\text{sys}}}{T} + \frac{DQ_{\text{surr}}}{T} = 0 \qquad (7\text{-}60)$$

Hence it is clear that

$$\int dS = 0 \qquad (7\text{-}61)$$

(1) for *the system plus surroundings* undergoing *any reversible process*, and (2) for the *system* undergoing a *reversible cyclic process.*

## 7-7 ENTROPY CHANGES IN IRREVERSIBLE PROCESSES

Thus far calculations of entropy changes have been described only for reversible paths. To determine the change of entropy in an irreversible process it is necessary to discover a reversible change between the same initial and final states. Since $S$ is a property of a system, $\Delta S$ is the same for the irreversible as for the reversible process. Thus the entropy change must be calculated from the characteristics of the reversible path.

### Isothermal Expansion of an Ideal Gas

It has been shown already that in the reversible isothermal expansion of an ideal gas

$$\Delta S_{\text{gas}} = R \ln \frac{V'}{V} \qquad (7\text{-}50)$$

From the fact that $S$ is a thermodynamic property, it follows that $\Delta S_{\text{gas}}$ is the same in an irreversible isothermal process from the same initial volume $V$ to the same final volume, $V'$. The change in entropy of the surroundings, however, differs in the two types of processes. First let us consider an extreme case, an isothermal expansion into a vacuum with no work being done. Since the process is isothermal, $\Delta E$ for the perfect gas must be zero, and consequently the heat absorbed by the gas, $Q$, is also zero:

$$Q = \Delta E + W = 0 \tag{7-62}$$

Thus the surroundings have given up no heat and, in fact, have undergone no change in state. Consequently

$$\Delta S_{\text{surr}} = 0 \tag{7-63}$$

$$\Delta S_{\text{total}} = R \ln \frac{V'}{V} + 0 > 0 \tag{7-64}$$

In other words, for the universe this irreversible expansion has been accompanied by an increase in entropy.

In any actual isothermal expansion the work done by the gas is not zero but is less than that obtained by reversible means.[8] Since $\Delta E$ is still zero for an ideal gas and since

$$W_{\text{irrev, gas}} < RT \ln \frac{V'}{V} \tag{7-65}$$

it follows that

$$Q_{\text{irrev, gas}} < RT \ln \frac{V'}{V} \tag{7-66}$$

Nevertheless *the entropy change for the gas is still given by Eq.* (7-50), *since it is equal to that for the reversible process between the same end points.*

Turning our attention to the surroundings, we can have the actual isothermal expansion occur with the gas in a vessel immersed in a large quantity of an ice–water mixture at equilibrium at constant pressure and temperature.[9] The heat lost by the surroundings must be numerically equal but opposite in sign to that gained by the gas:

$$Q_{\text{surr}} = -Q_{\text{irrev, gas}} \tag{7-67}$$

For the ice–water mixture at constant pressure and temperature, however,

[8] It will be shown in Chapter 8 (pp. 161–162) that in an isothermal process the reversible work is the maximum work.

[9] This specification of an ice–water mixture does not in any way limit the isothermal temperature to 0°C. By a suitable change in pressure, the equilibrium temperature may be varied over a wide range. If this range is inadequate, other systems consisting of two phases in equilibrium may be used in place of ice and water.

the change in entropy depends only upon the quantity of heat evolved:

$$\Delta S_{\text{surr}} = \frac{Q_{\text{surr}}}{T} \tag{7-68}$$

since the change in state of the ice–water mixture during this process is exactly the same as that which would occur if the same quantity of heat had been given up to the gas during a reversible isothermal expansion. In view of the conditions expressed by Eqs. (7-66)–(7-68), it follows that $Q_{\text{surr}}/T$ is smaller in absolute magnitude than is $R \ln (V'/V)$ [see Eq. (7-66)] and hence that the change in entropy for the gas plus surroundings must be positive.

$$\Delta S_{\text{total}} = \Delta S_{\text{gas}} + \Delta S_{\text{surr}} = R \ln \frac{V'}{V} + \frac{Q_{\text{surr}}}{T}$$

$$= R \ln \frac{V'}{V} - \frac{Q_{\text{irrev, gas}}}{T} > 0 \tag{7-69}$$

## Irreversible Adiabatic Expansion of an Ideal Gas

Strictly speaking, an irreversible process cannot be represented by a path on a diagram such as Figure 7-5, because in such a process not all

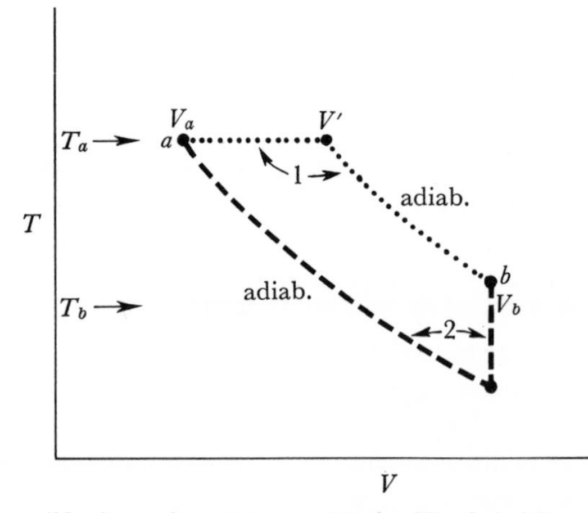


***Figure 7-5*** *Irreversible change from state a to state b. The dashed lines represent two possible reversible paths through the same end points.*[10]

[10] The student should recall the demonstration in Chapter 6 (Table 6-2) that the final temperature in an adiabatic reversible expansion from $V_a$ to $V_b$ is lower than that reached in an actual irreversible expansion.

parts of the substance have the same properties at any given instant of time. As has been pointed out previously, in an expansion, for example, there is a lag in the transmission of stresses, so that the pressure and temperature immediately adjacent to the piston may differ considerably from those in the body of the gas. Nevertheless, the initial state, $a$, and the final state, $b$, may be represented on the diagram.

To determine the entropy change in this irreversible adiabatic process, it is necessary to consider a reversible path from $a$ to $b$. An infinite number of reversible paths are possible, and two are illustrated by the dotted lines in Figure 7-5. The first consists of two steps: (1) an isothermal reversible expansion at the temperature $T_a$ until the volume $V'$ is reached; (2) an adiabatic reversible expansion from $V'$ to $V_b$. The entropy change for the gas is given by the sum of the entropy changes for the two steps:

$$\Delta S_{\text{gas}} = R \ln \frac{V'}{V_a} + 0 \tag{7-70}$$

Since $V' > V_a$, the entropy change for the gas is clearly positive for the reversible path and, therefore, also for the irreversible change.

The surroundings, on the other hand, undergo no change in state during the *irreversible* expansion, since the process is adiabatic. Hence for the surroundings

$$\Delta S_{\text{surr}} = 0 \tag{7-71}$$

Consequently for the system plus surroundings,

$$\Delta S_{\text{total}} = \Delta S_{\text{gas}} + \Delta S_{\text{surr}} = R \ln \frac{V'}{V} > 0 \tag{7-72}$$

Thus once again we have found that an irreversible process is accompanied by a net increase in entropy.

## Flow of Heat from a Higher to a Lower Temperature

For convenience in visualizing this process, imagine the flow of heat, by means of a conductor, from a very large reservoir at the higher temperature, $T_2$, to a very large reservoir at a lower temperature, $T_1$. By introducing large reservoirs into the mental picture, we may consider the heat sources to be at constant temperature, despite the gain or loss of a small quantity of heat, $Q$.

To calculate the change in entropy in this irreversible flow, it is necessary to consider a corresponding reversible process. There are an infinite number of ways in which this process may be carried out reversibly. One of them would be to allow an ideal gas to absorb reversibly the quantity of heat, $Q$, at the temperature $T_2$. The gas may then be expanded adiabatically and reversibly (therefore with no change in entropy) until it reaches the temperature $T_1$. At $T_1$ the gas is compressed reversibly and evolves the quantity of heat $Q$. During this reversible process the reservoir at $T_2$ loses heat and undergoes the entropy change

$$\Delta S_{\substack{\text{hot}\\\text{reservoir}}} = -\frac{Q}{T_2} \tag{7-73}$$

Since the same change in state occurs in the irreversible process, $\Delta S$ for the hot reservoir is still given by Eq. (7-73). During the reversible process the reservoir $T_1$ absorbs heat and undergoes the entropy change

$$\Delta S_{\substack{\text{cold}\\\text{reservoir}}} = \frac{Q}{T_1} \tag{7-74}$$

Since the same change in state occurs in the irreversible process, $\Delta S$ for the cold reservoir is still given by Eq. (7-74). *In the irreversible process the two reservoirs are the only substances that undergo any changes.* Since $T_2 > T_1$, the entropy change for the system as a whole is positive:

$$\Delta S_{\text{sys}} = \Delta S_{\substack{\text{hot}\\\text{reservoir}}} + \Delta S_{\substack{\text{cold}\\\text{reservoir}}} = -\frac{Q}{T_2} + \frac{Q}{T_1} > 0 \tag{7-75}$$

Again we see that an irreversible process is accompanied by an increase in entropy of the universe.

## Phase Transition

A convenient illustration of an irreversible phase transition is the crystallization of water at $-10°C$ and constant pressure:

$$H_2O(l, -10°C) = H_2O(s, -10°C) \tag{7-76}$$

Here, too, to calculate the entropy changes it is necessary to consider a series of reversible steps leading from the liquid water at $-10°C$ to solid ice at $-10°C$. One such series might be the following: (1) heat supercooled water at $-10°C$ very slowly (reversibly) to 0°C; (2) convert the water at 0°C very slowly (reversibly) to ice at 0°C; (3) cool the ice very slowly (reversibly) from 0° to $-10°C$. Since each of these steps is reversible, the entropy changes may be calculated readily by the methods discussed earlier. Since $S$ is a thermodynamic property, the sum of these entropy changes is equal to $\Delta S$ for the process indicated by (7-76). The necessary calculations are summarized in Table 7-6, where $T_2$ represents 0°C and $T_1$ represents $-10°C$.

*Table 7-6*

*Entropy change in spontaneous crystallization of water*

$H_2O\ (l, -10°C) = H_2O\ (l, 0°C)$

$$\Delta S_1 = \int \frac{DQ}{T} = \int \frac{C_p\, dT}{T} = C_p \ln \frac{T_2}{T_1} = 0.671 \text{ cal mole}^{-1} \text{ deg}^{-1}$$

$H_2O\ (l, 0°C) = H_2O\ (s, 0°C)$

$$\Delta S_2 = \int \frac{DQ}{T} = \frac{\Delta H}{T} = \frac{-1436}{273.15} = -\ 5.257 \text{ cal mole}^{-1} \text{ deg}^{-1}$$

$H_2O(s, 0°C) = H_2O(s, -10°C)$

$$\Delta S_3 = \int \frac{DQ}{T} = \int \frac{C_p dT}{T} = C_p \ln \frac{T_1}{T_2} = -0.324 \text{ cal mole}^{-1} \text{ deg}^{-1}$$

Adding:

$H_2O\ (l, -10°C) = H_2O(s, -10°C)$

$$\Delta S_{H_2O} = \Delta S_1 + \Delta S_2 + \Delta S_3 = -4.910 \text{ cal mole}^{-1} \text{ deg}^{-1}$$

It should be noted that there has been a decrease in the entropy of the water (that is, $\Delta S$ is negative) upon crystallization at $-10°C$ despite the fact that the process is irreversible. This example emphasizes the fact that the sign of the entropy change *for the system plus surroundings*, and not merely for any component, is related to irreversibility. To obtain $\Delta S$ for the combination, we must consider the entropy change in the surroundings, since the process described by Eq. (7-76) occurs irreversibly. If we consider the water as being in a large reservoir at a temperature of $-10°C$, then the crystallization will evolve a certain quantity of heat, $Q$, which will be absorbed by the reservoir without a significant rise in temperature. The change in state of the reservoir is the same as would occur if it were heated reversibly, and hence $\Delta S$ is given by

$$\Delta S_{\text{reservoir}} = \int \frac{DQ}{T} = -\frac{\Delta H}{T} = -\frac{(-1343)}{263.15} = 5.103 \text{ cal deg}^{-1} \qquad (7\text{-}77)$$

where $\Delta H$ represents the heat of crystallization of water at $-10°C$. Clearly, for the universe, the entropy has increased:

$$\Delta S_{\text{total}} = \Delta S_{H_2O} + \Delta S_{\text{reservoir}} = -4.910 + 5.103 = 0.193 \text{ cal deg}^{-1} \qquad (7\text{-}78)$$

## Chemical Reaction

As a final specific example we might examine a particular chemical reaction,

$$H_2(g) + \tfrac{1}{2}O_2(g) = H_2O(l) \qquad (7\text{-}79)$$

This formation of water from gaseous hydrogen and oxygen is a spontaneous reaction at room temperature, although its rate may be unobservably small in the absence of a catalyst. At 298°K, the heat of the irreversible reaction at constant pressure is $-68{,}317$ cal mole$^{-1}$. To calculate the entropy change we must carry out the same transformation reversibly, which could be done electrochemically with a suitable set of electrodes. Under reversible conditions the heat of reaction for Eq. (7-79) is $-11{,}627$ cal mole$^{-1}$. Hence for the irreversible or reversible change

$$\Delta S_{\text{chem}} = \frac{-11{,}627}{298.15} = -39.00 \text{ eu} \tag{7-80}$$

In regard to the surrounding reservoir in the actual spontaneous reaction, the heat absorbed is 68,317 cal and this heat produces the same change in state of the reservoir as the absorption of an equal amount of heat supplied reversibly. Making the surroundings large enough to keep the temperature essentially constant, we may compute its entropy change as

$$\Delta S_{\text{reservoir}} = \frac{68{,}317}{298.15} = 229.12 \text{ eu} \tag{7-81}$$

Clearly in the spontaneous formation of water, the system plus surroundings, chemicals plus environment, increases in entropy content:

$$\Delta S_{\text{total}} = -39.00 + 229.12 = 190.12 \text{ eu} \tag{7-82}$$

## General Statement

From the examples cited it is evident that in these specific cases irreversible processes are accompanied by an increase in total entropy. It remains to be shown that such an increase occurs generally for isolated systems. By an isolated system we shall mean a region large enough to include all the changes under consideration, so that no matter or heat is exchanged between this isolated region and the outside world. Thus the isolated region is adiabatically insulated during the course of any spontaneous processes occurring within its walls.

Take any irreversible process in which an isolated system goes from state $a$ to state $b$, as shown in Figure 7-6. Since the process is irreversible, we can indicate only the end points (and not the path) on the diagram. Nevertheless, let us complete the cycle by going back from $b$ to $a$ by a series of reversible steps indicated by the dotted lines in Figure 7-6. The adiabatic path $bc$ is followed to some temperature $T_c$ which may be higher or lower than $T_a$. In Figure 7-6, $T_c$ is indicated as being above $T_a$, but in some specific case it may be lower. The only requirement in fixing $T_c$ is that it be a temperature at which an isothermal reversible process can be carried

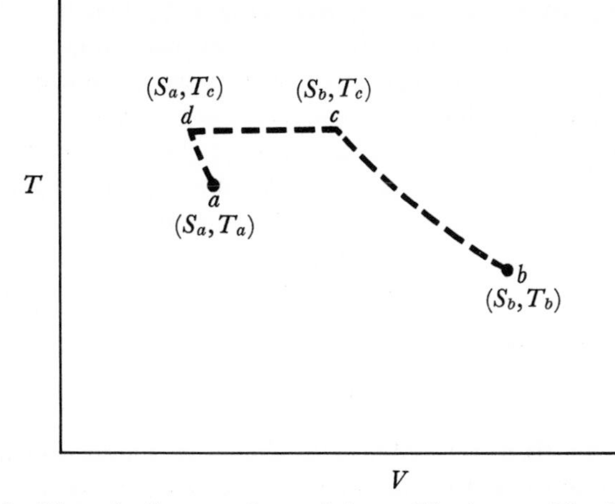


***Figure 7-6*** *Schematic diagram of general irreversible change. The dashed line represents one possible reversible path through the same end points.*

out from state $c$ to state $d$, where state $d$ is chosen in such a way that a reversible adiabatic change will return the system to its initial state, $a$. By means of these three reversible steps, the system has been returned from state $b$ to state $a$. The first and third steps in this reversible process being adiabatic, no changes in entropy are obtained. Consequently the entropy of state $c$ must be the same as that of state $b$, namely, $S_b$. Similarly, the entropy of state $d$ must be $S_a$. An entropy change does occur, however, along the path $cd$. Since this is an isothermal reversible process,

$$S_d - S_c = S_a - S_b = \frac{Q}{T_c} \tag{7-83}$$

This entropy change, $S_a - S_b$, must be a negative number; that is, $Q < 0$, since if $Q$ were a positive number ($Q > 0$), we should have violated the second law of thermodynamics as stated in the alternative form (II), as will be evident from the following considerations. Since in the complete cycle (irreversible adiabatic process from $a$ to $b$ followed by the three reversible steps),

$$\Delta E_{\text{cycle}} = 0 \tag{7-84}$$

it follows that

$$Q_{\text{cycle}} = W_{\text{cycle}} \tag{7-85}$$

Furthermore, in the four steps of the cycle (Figure 7-6) three are adiabatic (one irreversibly, two reversibly). Hence, $Q_{\text{cycle}}$ is identical with $Q$ of the isothermal step, that is $Q$ of Eq. (7-83). If $Q > 0$, then $W > 0$; that is work would have been *done* by the system. In other words if $Q$ were positive, we should have succeeded in carrying out a cyclical process in which heat at a constant temperature, $T_c$, has been converted into work. According to the alternative form (II) of the second law, such a process cannot be carried out. Hence $Q$ cannot be a positive number. Since $Q$ must be a negative number,[11] it follows from Eq. (7-83) that $S_a - S_b$ must also be negative; that is,

$$S_a - S_b < 0 \tag{7-86}$$

Obviously its reverse is positive; that is,

$$S_b - S_a > 0 \tag{7-87}$$

We have used the three reversible steps shown in Figure 7-6 merely to allow us to calculate the entropy change for the *actual* irreversible process. We may now dispense with the reversible steps and focus attention on the isolated, adiabatic spontaneous process alone. It occurred in an isolated region of space. The entropy change within this region has been shown to be positive:

$$\Delta S_{\substack{\text{isolated}\\ \text{region}}} = (S_b - S_a) > 0 \tag{7-88}$$

There are no changes outside this isolated region. Hence we have demonstrated that there must be an increase in entropy in an isolated system undergoing an irreversible transformation.[12]

## 7-8 ENTROPY AS AN INDEX OF EXHAUSTION

We have thus been able to prove that for a closed section of space including all the changes under observation,

$$\Delta S \geqq 0 \tag{7-89}$$

the equality sign applying to isolated systems at equilibrium, the inequality to all systems capable of undergoing spontaneous changes. Reversible changes, as has been emphasized, are only idealizations of certain actual changes. In many cases actual transformations can be carried out under conditions exceedingly close to the limiting ideal case; nevertheless, strictly

[11] It may be observed that if $Q$ is not greater than zero, then $Q$ may still equal zero. However, if $Q = 0$, then it is clear that all the reversible steps in Figure 7-6 must be adiabatic, and hence $\Delta S$ for going from $b$ to $a$ must be zero. But if $S_a = S_b$ then the initial step from $a$ to $b$ must also be reversible adiabatic and hence cannot be irreversible.

[12] An alternative proof based on a temperature-entropy diagram is easier to visualize. After having read Section 7-11 of this chapter, the reader is urged to examine Exercise 12, p. 140.

speaking all observable changes are really irreversible, that is, for all observable changes, $\Delta S$ is positive for the system plus surroundings, or universe.

This realization led Clausius to his famous aphorism, "Die Energie der Welt ist konstant; die Entropie der Welt strebt einem Maximum zu" (the energy of the universe is constant; the entropy tends toward a maximum). To a beginning student this form of statement is probably the source of more perplexity than enlightenment. The constancy of energy causes no difficulty of course. Since energy is conserved, it fits into the category of concepts to which we attribute permanence. In thought one usually pictures energy as a kind of material fluid, and hence even if it flows from one place to another, its conservation may be visualized readily. However, when one carries over an analogous mental picture to the concept of entropy one immediately is faced with the bewildering realization that entropy is being created out of nothing whenever there is an increase in entropy in a totally isolated system undergoing a spontaneous transformation.

The heart of the difficulty of "understanding" the concept of increase in entropy is a verbal one. It is very difficult to dissociate the unconscious verbal implications of a word which we have used all of our lives in other contexts without critical analysis. In speaking of "increase in entropy" we are using language appropriate for the description of material bodies. Automatically, therefore, we associate with entropy other characteristics of material bodies which are at variance with the nature of entropy and hence which are a source of confusion.

Ultimately one must realize that entropy is essentially a mathematical function. It is a concise function of the variables of experience; temperature, pressure, and composition. Natural processes tend to occur only in certain directions, that is, the variables pressure, temperature, and composition change only in certain ways, but very complicated ways, which are most concisely described by the change in a single function, the entropy function ($\Delta S > 0$).

Some of the historical reluctance to assimilate the entropy concept into general scientific thinking, and much of the introductory student's bewilderment, might have been avoided if Clausius had defined entropy (as would have been perfectly legitimate to do) as

$$dS' = -\frac{DQ_{\text{rev}}}{T} \tag{7-90}$$

with a negative sign instead of a positive one. With this definition all the thermodynamic consequences which we have derived would be just as valid except that some relations would change in sign. Thus in place of Eq. (7-89) we would find that for an isolated system,

$$\Delta S' \leqq 0 \tag{7-91}$$

the equality sign applying to isolated systems at equilibrium, the inequality to isolated systems capable of spontaneous changes. Now, however, we would recognize that for all isolated sections of space undergoing actual changes, the entropy *decreases.* Likewise paraphrasing Clausius, we would say, "die Entropie der Welt strebt einem *Minimum* zu." This statement would accord more obviously with our experience that observable spontaneous changes go in the direction that *decreases* the capacity for further spontaneous change, and that the universe (or at least the solar system) changes in time toward a state in which (ultimately) no further spontaneous change will be possible. We need merely reiterate a few examples such as those mentioned earlier in this chapter: solutes always diffuse from a more concentrated solution to a dilute one; clocks tend to run down; magnets become self-demagnetized. Although some of these individual changes can be reversed by some outside agency, this outside agent must itself undergo a transformation which decreases its capacity for further spontaneous change. It is impossible to restore every system back to its original condition. On earth our ultimate sources of energy for work are the sun, or nuclear power; in either case these ultimate nuclear reactions proceed unidirectionally and toward the loss of capacity for spontaneous change.

Thus we ought to view entropy as an index of condition or character rather than as a measure of content of some imaginary fluid. It is an index of the capacity for spontaneous change. By historical accident the index was actually defined so that it *increases* as the capacity of an isolated system for spontaneous change *decreases.* Hence we should preferably say that *entropy is an index of exhaustion*; the more a system has lost its capacity for spontaneous change, the more this capacity has been exhausted, the greater is the entropy.

In some respects, especially pedagogical ones, it might have been better to change the sign of the original definition of the index so that it would measure residual capacity rather than loss of capacity. However, with the development of statistical mechanics and the identification of entropy (in terms of kinetic-molecular theory) with the degree of disorder of a system, the original sign chosen by Clausius turns out to be the more convenient one. The universal tendency of all changes to reduce everything to a state of equilibrium may be correlated with the rearrangements of molecules from orderly to disorderly configurations. And since there are more disorderly arrangements than orderly ones it is appropriate that the entropy index increase with the approach of all things to a state of equilibrium.

Although we have stressed in this section differences in useful modes of visualization of entropy vs. energy, we should also emphasize that from a formal thermodynamic view each one is equally real, or unreal. To reiterate, experience has shown that although $DQ$ and $DW$ are inexact differentials, the difference $DQ - DW$ possesses the property of exactness and hence merits a new name and symbol, $dE$. Likewise, experience has shown that although $DQ$ is inexact, $DQ_{\text{rev}}/T$ is exact (and possesses other useful properties) and hence it too merits a new name and symbol, $dS$. Both $E$ and $S$ are mathematical functions which form exact differentials in the variables of state and hence are thermodynamic properties of state despite the fact that the quantities in terms of which they are defined are not thermodynamic properties. Both $E$ and $S$ summarize in a concise form the possible, highly complicated ways in which the variables of experience (e.g., temperature, pressure, and composition) may change in natural processes.

## 7-9 GENERAL EQUATIONS FOR THE ENTROPY OF GASES

### Entropy of the Ideal Gas

Using the mathematical statements of the two laws of thermodynamics, we can obtain an explicit equation for the entropy of an ideal gas. In carrying out its derivation, we shall assume that the transformations which the gas undergoes are of a reversible nature. Once we have obtained our final result, however, the equation will be applicable to irreversible processes also, since the entropy is a function only of the state of the system.

In a system where only expansion work is possible, the first law may be stated as

$$dE = DQ - P\,dV \tag{7-92}$$

Since we are considering a reversible transformation,

$$dS = \frac{DQ}{T} \tag{7-93}$$

But

$$DQ = P\,dV + dE \tag{7-94}$$

and thus

$$dS = \frac{dE}{T} + \frac{P\,dV}{T} \tag{7-95}$$

For an ideal gas the internal energy, $E$, is a function of the temperature only. Consequently

$$dE = \left(\frac{\partial E}{\partial T}\right)_V dT = C_v\,dT \tag{7-96}$$

Using (7-96) as a replacement for $dE$ and substituting for $P/T$ in (7-95) by means of the equation of state of an ideal gas, we obtain

$$dS = \frac{C_v\,dT}{T} + \frac{R\,dV}{V} \tag{7-97}$$

If $C_v$ is constant this latter expression may be integrated readily to give

$$S = C_v \ln T + R \ln V + S_0 \tag{7-98}$$

where $S_0$ is an integration constant characteristic of the gas. This integration constant cannot be evaluated explicitly by classical thermodynamic methods. It can be evaluated, however, with the aid of kinetic-molecular theory and statistical methods. For a monatomic gas, $S_0$ was formulated explicitly originally by Tetrode[13] and by Sackur.[14]

## Entropy of a Real Gas

The procedure used to derive a general equation for the entropy of a real gas is analogous to that for an ideal gas. In the preceding section the discussion up to Eq. (7-95) is general and hence not restricted to ideal gases. This equation, therefore, may be used as the starting point for the consideration of a real gas. For nonideal gases we may no longer make the substitution of Eq. (7-96) or of the ideal equation of state. However, a suitable substitution may be made for the total differential, $dE$, in (7-95) if we use the partial derivatives obtained on considering the internal energy, $E$, as a function of $V$ and $T$:

$$dE = \left(\frac{\partial E}{\partial T}\right)_V dT + \left(\frac{\partial E}{\partial V}\right)_T dV \tag{7-99}$$

Thus

$$dS = \frac{1}{T}\left(\frac{\partial E}{\partial T}\right)_V dT + \frac{1}{T}\left(\frac{\partial E}{\partial V}\right)_T dV + \frac{P}{T} dV \tag{7-100}$$

If we recognize that the entropy, $S$, may also be considered as a function of $V$ and $T$, we may obtain a second equation for the total differential, $dS$:

$$dS = \left(\frac{\partial S}{\partial T}\right)_V dT + \left(\frac{\partial S}{\partial V}\right)_T dV \tag{7-101}$$

A comparison of the coefficients of the $dT$ terms in Eqs. (7-100) and (7-101) leads to the following equality:

$$\left(\frac{\partial S}{\partial T}\right)_V = \frac{1}{T}\left(\frac{\partial E}{\partial T}\right)_V = \frac{1}{T} C_v \tag{7-102}$$

It can be shown also, most readily by the procedure to be outlined in

[13] H. Tetrode, *Ann. Physik.* [4], **38**, 434; **39**, 255 (1912).
[14] O. Sackur, *Ann. Physik.* [4], **40**, 67 (1913).

Chapter 8 (p. 147), that the following relation is true:

$$\left(\frac{\partial S}{\partial V}\right)_T = \left(\frac{\partial P}{\partial T}\right)_V \qquad (7\text{-}103)^{15}$$

Thus it follows that

$$dS = \frac{C_v}{T}\, dT + \left(\frac{\partial P}{\partial T}\right)_V dV \qquad (7\text{-}104)$$

Therefore

$$S = \int C_v\, d\ln T + \int \left(\frac{\partial P}{\partial T}\right)_V dV + \text{constant} \qquad (7\text{-}105)$$

To integrate this expression, it is necessary to know the equation of state of the gas and the dependence of $C_v$ on temperature.

If a gas obeys the van der Waals equation of state, it can be shown readily that

$$S = \int C_v\, d\ln T + R\ln(\text{v} - b) + \text{constant} \qquad (7\text{-}106)$$

## 7-10 TEMPERATURE SCALES

In addition to establishing the entropy function and its properties, the second law of thermodynamics permits us to set up a temperature scale without reference to the properties of an ideal gas, but rather to the properties of an ideal engine. Nevertheless, the two scales turn out to be identical. To show this identity we shall consider the gas scale first in some detail.

### Ideal Gas Scale

The ideal gas scale defines temperature in terms of measurements of the volume of an ideal gas at a fixed pressure; that is, the ratio of two temperatures is determined by the ratio of the volumes of the gas at a fixed pressure:

$$\frac{T_2}{T_1} = \frac{V_2}{V_1} \qquad (7\text{-}107)$$

To complete the definition, it is necessary to choose the size of the unit on the temperature scale. Conventionally this size is established by the equation

$$T_{\text{b.p.}} - T_{\text{f.p.}} = 100 \qquad (7\text{-}108)$$

[15] See exercise 3(b) for suggested route to a proof not involving the free-energy function.

where b.p. refers to the boiling point and f.p. to the freezing point of pure water at 1 atm pressure and in the presence of air.

## Thermodynamic Temperature Scale

Tentatively we shall allow thermodynamic temperature to be represented by the symbol $\theta$. The ratio of two temperatures, $\theta_2$ and $\theta_1$, is given by the ratio of the absolute values of the heats absorbed in a Carnot cycle working between two reservoirs at the temperatures $\theta_2$ and $\theta_1$, respectively; that is,

$$\frac{\theta_2}{\theta_1} = \frac{|Q_2|}{|Q_1|} \tag{7-109}$$

Here too we may choose any size for a unit difference on the scale, but conventionally the unit is established in terms of the freezing and boiling points of water:

$$\theta_{\text{b.p.}} - \theta_{\text{f.p.}} = 100 \tag{7-110}$$

The thermodynamic scale thus eliminates reference to the properties of a nonexistent ideal substance. On the other hand, it is defined in terms of the characteristics of a nonexistent perfect engine.

## Equivalence of the Thermodynamic and Ideal Gas Scales

We have shown previously that when an ideal gas is carried through a Carnot cycle, the heats absorbed at the hot and cold reservoirs are related to each other by the expression

$$\frac{Q_2}{T_2} + \frac{Q_1}{T_1} = 0 \tag{7-111}$$

This relation may be rearranged readily to give

$$\frac{T_2}{T_1} = \frac{|Q_2|}{|Q_1|} \tag{7-112}$$

Clearly, then,

$$\frac{\theta_2}{\theta_1} = \frac{T_2}{T_1} \tag{7-113}$$

or, in other words, $\theta$ is proportional to $T$:

$$\theta = kT \tag{7-114}$$

If we allow $\theta_2$ in Eq. (7-113) to be the temperature of the boiling point of water, $\theta_{\text{b.p.}}$, and $\theta_1$ to be $\theta_{\text{f.p.}}$, then it can be shown readily, by substitution of (7-113) into the expression

$$\theta_{\text{b.p.}} - \theta_{\text{f.p.}} = 100 = T_{\text{b.p.}} - T_{\text{f.p.}} \tag{7-115}$$

that

$$\theta_{\text{f.p.}} = T_{\text{f.p.}} \tag{7-116}$$

This equality establishes the value of the proportionality constant, $k$, in Eq. (7-114) as 1, so that

$$\theta = T \tag{7-117}$$

In other words, the thermodynamic temperature scale is identical with that defined by means of a thermometer containing an ideal gas.

## Value of Absolute Zero

Since the thermodynamic temperature scale is identical with the ideal gas scale, absolute zero may be determined numerically by extrapolation at constant pressure of a volume–temperature (centrigrade) curve for an ideal gas to zero volume. Real determinations, however, depend upon the use of the thermodynamic definition and the equations of the Joule-Thomson process.[16] If we follow the conventional choice of the boiling point and freezing points of water as the fixed points of the thermodynamic (as well as centigrade) temperature scale, then 0°C corresponds to 273.16 ± 0.01°K.

It was pointed out by Kelvin in 1848, and re-emphasized by Giauque in 1939, that it is not necessary to choose two fixed points for the thermodynamic scale. An alternative and preferable procedure is to choose a numerical value for one fixed point, for example the triple point of water, $T_{\text{t.p.}}$ and to define any absolute temperature, $T$, by the relation

$$T = 273.1600 \lim_{P \to 0} \left[ \frac{(PV)_T}{(PV)_{T_{\text{t.p.}}}} \right] \qquad (7\text{-}118)^{17}$$

in which $T_{\text{t.p.}}$ has been assigned the value of 273.1600°K. The triple point, at which ice, water, and water vapor are in equilibrium (in the absence of air), is preferred to the ice point, at which ice is in equilibrium with water saturated with dissolved air, because possible complications due to variations in the amount of dissolved air with varying pressure are avoided. The Kelvin-Giauque proposal has now been adopted by international agreement.[18] The ice point, 0°C, is related, therefore, to the thermodynamic

[16] P. S. Epstein, *Textbook of Thermodynamics*, Wiley, New York, 1937, pp. 74–76.
[17] Compare this relation with Eq. (3-1).
[18] H. G. Stimson, *Am. J. Phys.*, **23**, 614 (1955).

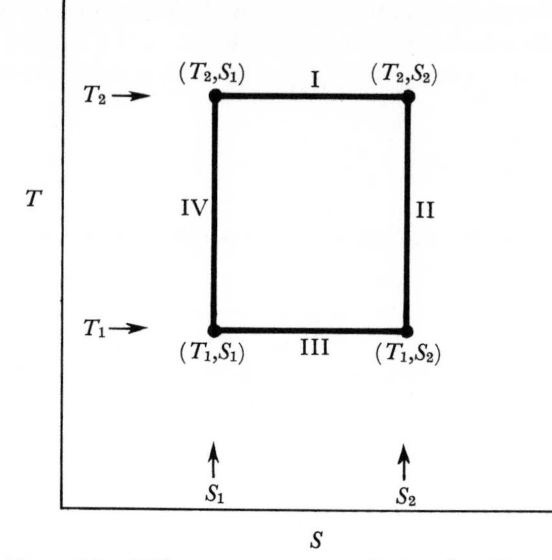


***Figure 7-7*** *Gibbs temperature-entropy diagram for a Carnot cycle.*

scale by the equation,

$$0°C = 273.150°K \tag{7-119}$$

since the ice point is experimentally 0.010° lower than the triple point.

## 7-11 TEMPERATURE–ENTROPY DIAGRAM

In making diagrams of various reversible cycles, it is a common practice to plot pressure as a function of volume, because the area under the curve, $\int P\,dV$, gives the work done in any step. We have used, instead, temperature and volume as coordinates, because a diagram on this basis emphasizes the constancy of temperature in an isothermal process. However, it suffers the disadvantage that the area is not related to the work. Gibbs[19] pointed out that a diagram using temperature and entropy as coordinates is a particularly useful one, since it illustrates graphically not only the work involved in a reversible cycle but also the heats. In addition, this type of diagram emphasizes the isentropic nature of an adiabatic reversible process as well as the constancy of temperature in isothermal stages. A typical diagram—for a simple Carnot cycle—is illustrated in Figure 7-7. The

[19] *The Collected Works of J. Willard Gibbs*, Vol. I, Longmans, Green, New York, 1931, p. 9.

four stages in a forward cycle are labeled by the Roman numerals. In step I the temperature is constant, heat $Q_2$ is absorbed by the working substance, and the entropy increases from $S_1$ to $S_2$. Since this stage is reversible and isothermal,

$$\frac{Q_2}{T_2} = \Delta S = S_2 - S_1 \tag{7-120}$$

and

$$Q_2 = T_2(S_2 - S_1) = \text{area under line I} \tag{7-121}$$

In step II there is a drop in temperature in the adiabatic reversible expansion, but no change in entropy. The isentropic nature of II is emphasized by the vertical line. In step III we have an isothermal reversible compression with a heat numerically equal to $Q_1$ being evolved. Since this step is reversible and isothermal,

$$\frac{Q_1}{T_1} = \Delta S = S_1 - S_2 = -(S_2 - S_1) \tag{7-122}$$

and

$$Q_1 = -T_1(S_2 - S_1) = \text{negative of area under line III} \tag{7-123}$$

In the fourth step, which is adiabatic and reversible, there is no entropy change, but the temperature rises to the initial value, $T_2$. Since the cycle has been completed,

$$\Delta E = 0 \tag{7-124}$$

and

$$Q_2 + Q_1 = W \tag{7-125}$$

Therefore

$$\begin{aligned} W &= T_2(S_2 - S_1) - T_1(S_2 - S_1) \\ &= (T_2 - T_1)(S_2 - S_1) = \text{area enclosed by cycle} \end{aligned} \tag{7-126}$$

Thus the work and heats involved in the cycle are clearly illustrated by a $T$-$S$ diagram, and the nature of the isothermal and isentropic steps is strongly emphasized.

## Exercises

**1.** A mole of an ideal monatomic gas ($C_v = \frac{3}{2}R$) at a pressure of 1 atm and a temperature of 273.1°K is to be transformed to a pressure of 0.5 atm and a temperature of 546.2°K. The change may be brought about in an infinite variety of ways. Consider the following four reversible paths, each consisting of two parts:

(1) Isothermal expansion and isobaric temperature rise.
(2) Isothermal expansion and isochoric temperature rise.
(3) Adiabatic expansion and isobaric temperature rise.
(4) Adiabatic expansion and isochoric temperature rise.

(a) Determine $P$, $V$, and $T$ of the gas after the initial step of each of the four paths.

*Table 7-7*

| $V$, liters | $P$, atm | $T$, °K |
|---|---|---|
| 22.41 | 1.0000 | 273.1 |
| | 0.5000 | |
| 44.82 | 0.3150 | 172.0 |
| 67.23 | 0.1603 | 131.3 |
| 89.65 | | |

Represent the paths on a $T$-$V$ diagram. To facilitate plotting, some of the necessary data for the adiabatic expansions are presented in Table 7-7. Supply the additional data required for the completion of the adiabatic curve.

(b) Calculate for each portion of each path and for each complete path the following: $W$, the work done by the gas; $Q$, the heat absorbed by the gas; $\Delta E$ of the gas; $\Delta H$ of the gas; $\Delta S$ of the gas. Assemble your results in tabular form.

(c) Note which functions in (b) have values that are independent of the path used in the transformation.

**2.** An ideal gas is carried through a Carnot cycle. Draw diagrams of this cycle using each of the following sets of coordinates:

(a) $P, V$ (d) $E, S$
(b) $T, P$ (e) $S, V$
(c) $T, S$ (f) $T, H$

**3.** (a) By a procedure analogous to that used to obtain Eq. (7-102), show that

$$\left(\frac{\partial S}{\partial V}\right)_T = \frac{P + (\partial E/\partial V)_T}{T} \tag{7-127}$$

(b) Starting with Eq. (7-127) let us demonstrate the validity of Eq. (7-103). Rearrange (7-127) to

$$P = T\left(\frac{\partial S}{\partial V}\right)_T - \left(\frac{\partial E}{\partial V}\right)_T \tag{7-128}$$

Differentiate with respect to temperature at constant volume to obtain

$$\left(\frac{\partial P}{\partial T}\right)_V = \left(\frac{\partial S}{\partial V}\right)_T + T\frac{\partial^2 S}{\partial V\,\partial T} - \frac{\partial^2 E}{\partial V\,\partial T} \tag{7-129}$$

Show also that appropriate differentiation of Eq. (7-102) leads to the relation

$$\frac{\partial^2 S}{\partial V\,\partial T} = \frac{1}{T}\frac{\partial^2 E}{\partial V\,\partial T} \tag{7-130}$$

and proceed to obtain

$$\left(\frac{\partial S}{\partial V}\right)_T = \left(\frac{\partial P}{\partial T}\right)_V \tag{7-103}$$

(c) Combining the results of parts (a) and (b) show that

$$\left(\frac{\partial E}{\partial V}\right)_T = T\left(\frac{\partial P}{\partial T}\right)_V - P \tag{7-131}$$

(d) Prove that $(\partial E/\partial V)_T = 0$ for any gas obeying a general gas law of the form

$$P\,f(V) = RT$$

where $f(V)$ is any continuous function of volume.

(e) Derive the expression

$$\left(\frac{\partial E}{\partial V}\right)_P = C_v\left(\frac{\partial T}{\partial V}\right)_P + T\left(\frac{\partial P}{\partial T}\right)_V - P \tag{7-132}$$

**4.** A gas obeys the equation of state

$$Pv = RT + BP$$

where $B$ is a constant at all temperatures.

(a) Show that the internal energy, $E$, is a function of the temperature only.

(b) Find $(\partial E/\partial V)_P$. Compare with the value obtained for this same partial derivative for an ideal gas.

(c) Derive an equation for the entropy of this gas which is analogous to Eq. (7-98) for the ideal gas.

**5.** Complete the steps missing between Eqs. (7-115) and (7-116).

**6.** Show that the efficiency of a Carnot cycle in which any step is carried out irreversibly cannot be greater than that of a reversible Carnot cycle.

**7.** Gibbs[20] has suggested that the equation

$$E = \exp(S/C_v)\; V^{-R/C_v} \tag{7-133}$$

($C_v$ and $R$ being constants) be regarded as the fundamental thermodynamic equation of an ideal gas. With the aid of the two laws of thermodynamics show that Eqs. (6-1) and (6-2) are contained implicitly in Eq. (7-133).

**8.** A (reversible) Joule cycle consists of the following four steps: isobaric increase in volume; adiabatic expansion; isobaric decrease in volume; adiabatic compression. Helium gas with the equation of state

$$Pv = RT + BP \tag{7-134}$$

(where $B = 15$ cm$^3$ mole$^{-1}$) is carried through a Joule cycle. Draw diagrams of this cycle using each of the following sets of coordinates:

(a) $P,V$
(b) $E,V$
(c) $T,S$

**9.** A (reversible) Sargent cycle consists of the following four steps: isochoric increase in pressure; adiabatic expansion; isobaric decrease in volume; adiabatic compression. A gas obeying Eq. (7-134) is carried through a Sargent cycle. Draw diagrams of this cycle using each of the following sets of coordinates:

(a) $P,V$ (d) $S,V$
(b) $T,V$ (e) $S,T$
(c) $E,V$ (f) $H,T$

[20] *The Collected Works of J. Willard Gibbs*, Vol. I, Longmans, Green, New York, 1931 p. 13.

**10.** A (reversible) cycle may also be completed in three steps, for example, the following: isothermal expansion (at $T_2$) from $V_1$ to $V_2$; cooling (at constant $V_2$) from $T_2$ to $T_1$; adiabatic compression back to initial state.

(a) Draw a diagram of this cycle using $T$ and $V$ as coordinates.

(b) A nonideal gas obeying Eq. (7-134) is carried through this cycle. Compute $\Delta S$ for each step and show that $\oint dS = 0$ for this nonideal gas in this cycle. Assume that $C_v$ for this gas is a constant. Some of its other characteristics in an adiabatic process have been worked out as Exercise 4, Chapter 6.

**11.** In Figure 7-8 are drawn a series of adiabatic reversible paths, $1 \rightarrow 2$, $1' \rightarrow 2'$, etc., each one starting at the temperature $T_2$ and ending at the temperature $T_1$. The points 1, 1′, etc., are labeled in an order such that for a process proceeding to the right along the isothermal $T_2$ (e.g., $1' \rightarrow 1$) heat is absorbed by the system.

An essential step in the Caratheodory formulation of the second law of thermodynamics is a proof of the following statement: two adiabatics (such as $a$ and $b$ in Figure 7-8) cannot intersect.

Prove that $a$ and $b$ cannot intersect.

(*Suggestion:* assume $a$ and $b$ do intersect at the temperature $T_1$ and show that this assumption permits you to violate the Kelvin statement of the second law.)

**12.** For an isolated (adiabatic) system, $\Delta S > 0$ for any natural (spontaneous) process from state $a$ to state $b$, as has been proved on pp. 126–128. An alternative and probably simpler proof of this proposition may be obtained if one uses a temperature entropy diagram (Figure 7-9) instead of Figure 7-6. In Figure 7-9 is shown a *reversible* adiabatic process, represented as a vertical line since $\Delta S = 0$ for this process. In terms of Figure 7-9, we may state our proposition as follows: for an isolated system, a spontaneous process from $a$ to $b$ must lie to the right of the reversible one, since $\Delta S = S_b - S_a > 0$.

Prove that $b$ cannot be to the left of $b'$, i.e., that $\Delta S$ cannot be negative for the isolated spontaneous process.

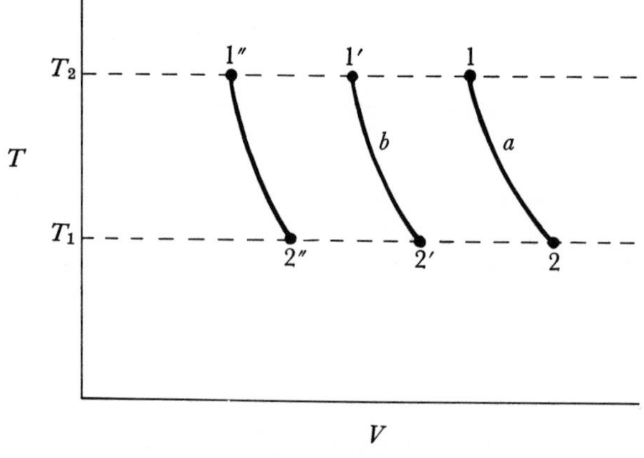


*Figure 7-8*

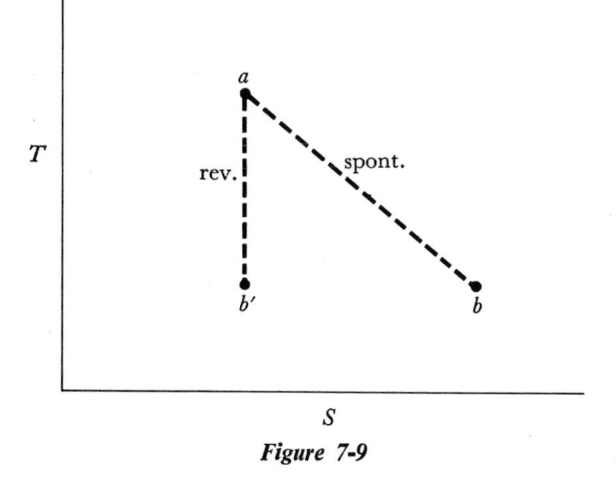


*Figure 7-9*

(*Suggestion:* assume that $b$ is to the left of $b'$, and then complete a suitable cycle back to $a$ which allows you to violate the Kelvin statement of the second law.)

**13.** A spring is placed in a large thermostat at 27°C and stretched isothermally and reversibly from its equilibrium length $L_0$ to $10L_0$. During this reversible stretching 1.00 cal of heat was absorbed by the spring. The stretched spring, still in the constant-temperature thermostat, is then released without any restraining back-tension and allowed to jump back to its initial length $L_0$; during this spontaneous process the spring *evolves* 2.50 cal of heat.

(a) What is the entropy change for the stretching of the spring?

(b) What is the entropy change for the collapse of the spring?

(c) What is the entropy change for the universe (spring + surrounding thermostat) for the total process, stretching plus return collapse to initial $L_0$?

(d) How much work was done on the spring in the stretching process?

# 8 The Free-Energy Functions

## 8-1 PURPOSE OF THE NEW FUNCTIONS

In Chapter 7 we formulated the second basic postulate of thermodynamics and derived from it a useful thermodynamic function, the entropy. In examining the properties of this new thermodynamic function we found that it has the very desirable characteristic of being a criterion of the spontaneity of a chemical or physical transformation. When the change in entropy of the substances involved in a transformation *and of their surrounding environment* is positive, the reaction is irreversible. A reaction with positive $\Delta S$ may (or may not) occur spontaneously; a reaction with negative $\Delta S$ (total) will never occur spontaneously.

Thus in principle we have attained our primary objective in chemical thermodynamics; the establishment of a criterion of spontaneity. Nevertheless, for practical purposes the criterion in its present form is generally an inconvenient one, since it requires a knowledge of the properties of the environment, as well as of the substances which are of primary interest. A modification of this criterion which does not deal directly with the environment would be much more useful. After several trials a suitable modification was proposed which introduced certain new thermodynamic quantities known as the free-energy functions. In addition to acting as criteria of spontaneity, these free-energy functions have been found to have the very useful properties of predicting the maximum yields obtainable in equilibrium reactions and the maximum work that may be obtained from a particular transformation.

## 8-2 DEFINITIONS

Two free-energy functions are in common use. The *Helmholtz free energy*, $A$, is defined by the relation

$$A = E - TS \tag{8-1}$$

The *Gibbs free energy*, $G$,[1] is defined by the expression

$$G = H - TS \tag{8-2}$$

For most chemical problems the Gibbs free energy is the more useful, for reasons which will be evident shortly. Because of the much greater use of the Gibbs free-energy function, the term "free energy" without any name prefixed is frequently used to designate $G$, and will be so used in this text.

## 8-3 CONSEQUENCES OF DEFINITIONS AND DERIVED RELATIONS

### Free Energy a Thermodynamic Property

Since both $G$ and $A$ are defined by an explicit equation, in terms of variables which depend only upon the state of a system, it is evident that both of these new functions are thermodynamic properties. Hence their differentials are exact and we may write the expressions

$$\oint dG = 0 \tag{8-3}$$

$$\oint dA = 0 \tag{8-4}$$

### Relation between $G$ and $A$

From the definitions of these functions [Eqs. (8-1) and (8-2)] it is clear that

$$G = H - TS = E + PV - TS = E - TS + PV \tag{8-5}$$

or

$$G = A + PV \tag{8-6}$$

### Free-Energy Functions for Isothermal Conditions

Transformations at constant temperature are of very frequent interest in chemical problems. For finite changes at a fixed temperature $T (= T_2 = T_1)$,

[1] The letter $F$ has also been commonly used for the Gibbs energy, particularly in the United States. Most tabulations of chemical thermodynamic data use $F$ for the function of Eq. (8-2).

Eq. (8-2) becomes

$$\begin{aligned}\Delta G = G_2 - G_1 &= (H_2 - T_2 S_2) - (H_1 - T_1 S_1) \\ &= H_2 - H_1 - (T_2 S_2 - T_1 S_1) \\ &= H_2 - H_1 - T(S_2 - S_1) \\ &= \Delta H - T \Delta S \end{aligned} \tag{8-7}$$

Similarly, for an infinitesimal change under isothermal conditions ($dT = 0$)

$$\begin{aligned} dG &= dH - T\,dS - S\,dT \\ &= dH - T\,dS \end{aligned} \tag{8-8}$$

The equations for $A$ can be derived in an analogous fashion:

$$\Delta A = \Delta E - T \Delta S \tag{8-9}$$

$$dA = dE - T\,dS \tag{8-10}$$

## Equations for Total Differentials

Since the procedure is the same for both free-energy functions, we shall consider in detail the derivation only for the Gibbs free energy, $G$. Starting with the definition given by Eq. (8-2)

$$G = H - TS \tag{8-2}$$

we may differentiate to obtain

$$dG = dH - T\,dS - S\,dT \tag{8-11}$$

Since the enthalpy has been defined by the expression

$$H = E + PV \tag{8-12}$$

it follows that $dH$ is given by the relation

$$dH = dE + P\,dV + V\,dP \tag{8-13}$$

hence

$$dG = dE + P\,dV + V\,dP - T\,dS - S\,dT \tag{8-14}$$

Considering a substance or a system which is doing no work except mechanical (that is, $P\,dV$ work), we may substitute for $dE$ from the first law of thermodynamics,

$$dE = DQ - P\,dV \tag{8-15}$$

and obtain

$$dG = DQ + V\,dP - T\,dS - S\,dT \tag{8-16}$$

When the change in $G$ is due to some reversible transformation, then the definition of entropy,

$$dS = \frac{DQ}{T} \tag{8-17}$$

may be rearranged to

$$DQ = T\,dS \tag{8-18}$$

which, upon substitution into Eq. (8-16), leads to the equation for $dG$:

$$dG = V\,dP - S\,dT \tag{8-19}$$

By an entirely analogous procedure it is possible to show that the total differential of the Helmholtz free energy is given by the expression

$$dA = -P\,dV - S\,dT \tag{8-20}$$

## Pressure and Temperature Coefficients of the Free Energy

If we consider Eq. (8-19), it is obvious that if the temperature is maintained constant, the second term on the right-hand side of the expression disappears and the equation may be rearranged to

$$\left(\frac{\partial G}{\partial P}\right)_T = V \tag{8-21}$$

Thus we find that the pressure coefficient of the free energy of a substance depends directly upon the volume of the substance.

More often we shall be interested in the change in $\Delta G$ of a chemical reaction, rather than merely in $G$, with variation in pressure. The required relation may be derived readily from Eq. (8-21). To be definite, let us represent the chemical transformation by the simple equation

$$A + B = C + D \tag{8-22}$$

For each one of these substances we may write an equation corresponding to (8-21):

$$\left(\frac{\partial G_A}{\partial P}\right)_T = V_A \tag{8-23}$$

$$\left(\frac{\partial G_B}{\partial P}\right)_T = V_B \tag{8-24}$$

$$\left(\frac{\partial G_C}{\partial P}\right)_T = V_C \tag{8-25}$$

$$\left(\frac{\partial G_D}{\partial P}\right)_T = V_D \tag{8-26}$$

Subtracting the sum of the pressure coefficients for the reactants from that for the products, we obtain the desired relation:

$$\left(\frac{\partial G_C}{\partial P}\right)_T + \left(\frac{\partial G_D}{\partial P}\right)_T - \left(\frac{\partial G_A}{\partial P}\right)_T - \left(\frac{\partial G_B}{\partial P}\right)_T = V_C + V_D - V_A - V_B \tag{8-27}$$

or

$$\left(\frac{\partial \Delta G}{\partial P}\right)_T = \Delta V \tag{8-28}$$

Turning now to the temperature coefficient of the free energy, we may proceed in a manner analogous to that used to derive the equation for the derivative with respect to pressure. It is clear from Eq. (8-19) that if the pressure is maintained constant, the first term on the right-hand side drops out, and the expression may be rearranged to read

$$\left(\frac{\partial G}{\partial T}\right)_P = -S \tag{8-29}$$

For a chemical transformation accompanied by a change in free energy, $\Delta G$, it can be shown by a procedure similar to that outlined by Eqs. (8-22) to (8-28) that

$$\left(\frac{\partial \Delta G}{\partial T}\right)_P = -\Delta S \tag{8-30}$$

Since the derivations of the volume and temperature coefficients of the Helmholtz free energy are so similar to those just illustrated for the Gibbs free energy, only the final results will be recorded:

$$\left(\frac{\partial A}{\partial V}\right)_T = -P \tag{8-31}$$

$$\left(\frac{\partial \Delta A}{\partial V}\right)_T = -\Delta P \tag{8-32}$$

$$\left(\frac{\partial A}{\partial T}\right)_V = -S \tag{8-33}$$

$$\left(\frac{\partial \Delta A}{\partial T}\right)_V = -\Delta S \tag{8-34}$$

## Equations Derived from the Reciprocity Relation

Since the free energy, $G(T,P)$, is a thermodynamic property, that is, $dG$ is an exact differential, the reciprocity relation (see Chapter 2) must hold.

Thus we may write

$$dG = \left(\frac{\partial G}{\partial P}\right)_T dP + \left(\frac{\partial G}{\partial T}\right)_P dT \tag{8-35}$$

and

$$\frac{\partial}{\partial T}\frac{\partial G}{\partial P} = \frac{\partial}{\partial P}\frac{\partial G}{\partial T} \tag{8-36}$$

But from previous considerations we have obtained

$$dG = V\,dP - S\,dT \tag{8-19}$$

A comparison of Eqs. (8-19) and (8-35) shows that

$$\left(\frac{\partial G}{\partial P}\right)_T = V \tag{8-21}$$

and

$$\left(\frac{\partial G}{\partial T}\right)_P = -S \tag{8-29}$$

Hence

$$\frac{\partial}{\partial T}\frac{\partial G}{\partial P} = \left(\frac{\partial V}{\partial T}\right)_P = \frac{\partial}{\partial P}\frac{\partial G}{\partial T} = -\left(\frac{\partial S}{\partial P}\right)_T \tag{8-37}$$

or

$$\left(\frac{\partial S}{\partial P}\right)_T = -\left(\frac{\partial V}{\partial T}\right)_P \tag{8-38}$$

By a similar set of operations on the $A$ function, we can show that

$$\left(\frac{\partial S}{\partial V}\right)_T = \left(\frac{\partial P}{\partial T}\right)_V \tag{8-39}$$

## 8-4 CRITERIA OF NATURE OF CHEMICAL CHANGE

Having considered the definitions of the free-energy functions and having derived some useful equations expressing their properties, we must proceed now on our primary course of relating the free-energy change to the nature of the physical or chemical transformation. We wish to find first a relation between $\Delta G$ and the spontaneity or lack of spontaneity of a transformation.

### Criteria of Equilibrium

***At constant pressure and temperature.*** Let us consider a group of substances at equilibrium at a fixed temperature and subject to no external forces except the constant pressure of the surrounding environment (Figure 8-1). For substances plus environment we may write

$$\Delta S_{\substack{\text{isolated} \\ \text{system}}} = 0 \tag{8-40}$$

since we have concluded in Chapter 7 that at equilibrium the entropy change of an isolated system is zero. But

$$\Delta S_{\substack{\text{isol} \\ \text{sys}}} = \Delta S_{\text{substances}} + \Delta S_{\text{environment}} = 0 \tag{8-41}$$

Furthermore,

$$\Delta S_{\text{environment}} = -\Delta S_{\text{subs}} = \frac{-Q_{\text{subs}}}{T} = \frac{-\Delta H_{\text{subs}}}{T} \tag{8-42}$$

the last two equalities arising from the constancy of temperature and of pressure, respectively. Consequently, Eq. (8-41) may be rewritten

$$\Delta S_{\text{subs}} - \frac{\Delta H_{\text{subs}}}{T} = 0 \tag{8-43}$$

or

$$T\Delta S - \Delta H = -\Delta G_{P,T} = 0 \tag{8-44}$$

where $\Delta S$, $\Delta H$, and $\Delta G$ refer to the substances alone, not the environment.

If we had started with Eq. (8-40) in the infinitesimal form

$$dS_{\substack{\text{isol} \\ \text{sys}}} = 0 \tag{8-45}$$

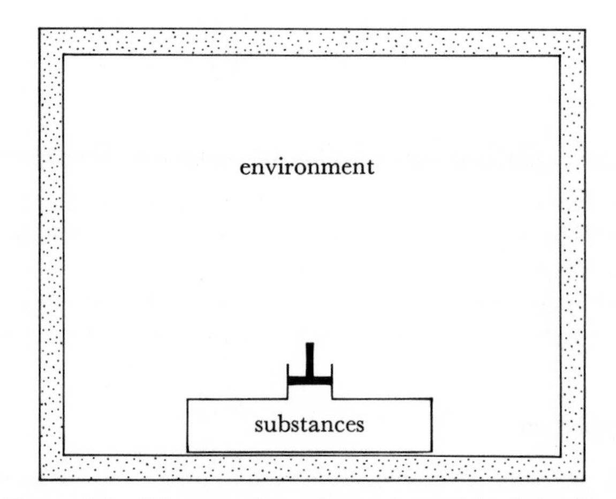


***Figure 8-1*** *Substances plus environment comprising isolated system.*

we could have proved, in steps corresponding to Eqs. (8-41)–(8-43), that

$$dG_{P,T} = 0 \tag{8-46}$$

is an equivalent criterion of equilibrium.

Let us consider the import of Eq. (8-46) for a concrete example. Suppose the "substances" container of Figure 8-1 has in it some liquid water in equilibrium with its vapor (at a fixed temperature):

$$H_2O(l) = H_2O(g) \tag{8-47}$$

Let $n$ represent the number of moles of $H_2O(g)$, but let $G$ and $V$, which are extensive quantities, represent the total free energy and the total volume of the contents of this container. Then what Eq. (8-46) says is that, if equilibrium exists,

$$\left(\frac{\partial G}{\partial n}\right)_{P,T} = 0 \tag{8-48}$$

In the derivation of Eq. (8-44) we have assumed for simplicity that the pressure and temperature are maintained constant throughout the macroscopic change. Actually it is merely necessary that the pressure and temperature at the beginning of the change be the same as that at the end; for $\Delta G$ depends only upon the initial and final states of a system. Hence if the $\Delta G$ is zero for the isothermal, isobaric transformation, it is also zero for any other path which has the same end points.

Thus we have arrived at a very simple criterion of physical or chemical equilibrium. For a system at equilibrium, and subject to no external forces except the pressure of the surroundings, the change in free energy is zero for any transformation in which the initial temperature and pressure are the same as the respective final values.

It should be emphasized that in this new criterion expressed by Eq. (8-44), no mention is made of the environment. Thus we have been able to overcome the disadvantage of the entropy criterion. In reality, what we have done is to substitute for the entropy criterion, which is conveniently applicable to an isolated system of fixed volume and internal energy, a new criterion which is applicable under conditions more commonly characteristic of chemical (or physical) transformations—a nonisolated system or group of substances at fixed pressure and temperature.

It is of interest to consider also the change in the Helmholtz free energy, $A$, under the conditions just specified. Since the temperature is constant and the process is a reversible one,

$$dA_{P,T} = dE - T\,dS = DQ - P\,dV - T\,dS = T\,dS - P\,dV - T\,dS \tag{8-49}$$

or

$$dA_{P,T} = -P\,dV \tag{8-50}$$

and

$$\Delta A_{P,T} = -P\,\Delta V \tag{8-51}$$

The quantity $P\,dV$ is the work necessary to push back the atmosphere during the infinitesimal transformation of the system at equilibrium. Clearly, then, $\Delta A_{P,T}$ is the negative of this work quantity for a macroscopic change, namely, $-P\,\Delta V$.

***At constant volume and temperature.*** Another set of conditions frequently encountered in chemical transformations is that of fixed volume and constant temperature. For these conditions it turns out that the $A$ function is the most suitable criterion of equilibrium. By a procedure similar to that used to derive Eq. (8-44), we can show that

$$\Delta A_{V,T} = 0 \tag{8-52}$$

Likewise we could prove readily (see Exercise 12, p. 170) that, for a group of substances at equilibrium, an equation corresponding to (8-48) is valid:

$$\left(\frac{\partial A}{\partial n}\right)_{V,T} = \left(\frac{\partial G}{\partial n}\right)_{P,T} = 0 \tag{8-53}$$

## Criteria of Spontaneity

Having established criteria of equilibrium, we may proceed to a consideration of the nature of $\Delta G$ and $\Delta A$ when transformations can occur spontaneously.

***Constant pressure and temperature.*** Again we consider a group of substances at constant pressure and temperature (Figure 8-1) but this time a group in which a transformation may occur spontaneously. Again we specify that the only restraint on the substances is that of the constant pressure of the environment; in other words no net useful work, such as electrical work is being done. Such conditions are the ones of primary interest to the chemist, since generally he wants information on the feasibility of a given reaction if it is carried out in an apparatus open to the atmosphere (or at some fixed pressure).

Referring to Figure 8-1, we may now state, since a spontaneous change can occur, that

$$\Delta S_{\substack{\text{isol}\\ \text{sys}}} = \Delta S_{\text{subs}} + \Delta S_{\text{environment}} > 0 \tag{8-54}$$

Furthermore

$$Q_{\text{environment}} = -Q_{\text{subs}} \tag{8-55}$$

and since the transformation occurs at constant temperature and pressure

$$\Delta S_{\text{environment}} = -\frac{Q_{\text{subs}}}{T} = -\frac{\Delta H_{\text{subs}}}{T} \qquad (8\text{-}56)^2$$

Therefore, for a spontaneous change it follows from Eq. (8-54) that

$$\Delta S_{\text{subs}} - \frac{\Delta H_{\text{subs}}}{T} > 0 \qquad (8\text{-}57)$$

or that

$$\Delta G_{P,T} < 0 \qquad (8\text{-}58)$$

where $\Delta G$ refers to the substances only, and not to the environment.

Thus for a spontaneous change occurring at constant pressure and temperature and subject only to the restraint of environmental pressure, there must be a decrease in free energy of the participating substances. We thus have the complementary relation to Eq. (8-44), the criterion for equilibrium.

***Constant volume and temperature.*** By a procedure analogous to that used to derive Eq. (8-58), we can show readily that

$$\Delta A_{V,T} < 0 \qquad (8\text{-}59)$$

for a spontaneous change at constant volume and temperature, again with only the pressure of the environment as a restraint.

## Heat of Reaction as an Approximate Criterion of Spontaneity

For many years it was thought, purely on an empirical basis, that if the enthalpy change for a given reaction was negative, that is, if heat were evolved at constant pressure, the transformation could occur spontaneously. This rule was verified for many reactions. Nevertheless, there are numerous exceptions, one of which was cited in the preceding chapter.

It is of interest to see under what conditions the enthalpy change might be a reliable criterion of spontaneity. Since we are generally interested in isothermal processes, we may refer to Eq. (8-7) for the free-energy change at constant temperature. It is evident from this expression that if $T\,\Delta S$ is small with respect to $\Delta H$, there will be little difference between $\Delta H$ and $\Delta G$. Usually $T\,\Delta S$ is of the order of magnitude of a few thousand calories. Evidently, then, if $\Delta H$ is sufficiently large, perhaps above 10 kcal, the sign of $\Delta H$ will be the same as that of $\Delta G$. For such relatively large values of the heat of a reaction (at constant pressure), $\Delta H$ is a reliable criterion of spontaneity, since if $\Delta H$ were negative, $\Delta G$, the fundamental criterion, would

[2] The student should recall that the change in state of the environment for an absorption of heat $Q$ is the same whether $Q$ is generated by the working substances reversibly or irreversibly. Hence $\Delta S_{\text{environment}} = Q_{\text{environment}}/T$.

probably be negative also. It should be recognized, however, that $\Delta H$ is not the fundamental criterion, and judgments based on its sign may frequently be misleading, particularly when the magnitudes involved are small.

## 8-5 FREE ENERGY AND THE EQUILIBRIUM CONSTANT

In the preceding sections we have established the properties of the free-energy functions as criteria of equilibrium and spontaneity of transformations. From the sign of $\Delta G$ it is thus possible to predict whether a given chemical transformation can proceed spontaneously. Further considerations show that $\Delta G$ is capable of giving even more information. In particular, from the value of the free-energy change under certain standard conditions it is possible to calculate the equilibrium constant for a given reaction. First, however, we must define our standard conditions.

### Definitions

It is evident that $\Delta G$ for a given reaction depends upon the state of the reactants and products. If we are to tabulate values of the change in free energy for chemical transformations, it will be necessary to agree on certain standard conditions to which this $\Delta G$ shall refer, since it would be of little use to have free-energy tables in which no two values referred to substances under the same conditions. The standard states which have been agreed upon by convention are assembled in Table 8-1.

In addition to standard states we shall speak of the *standard free energy of formation*, $\Delta Gf^\circ$, of a substance (Table 8-2). By this we shall mean *the change in free energy accompanying the formation of a substance in its standard state from its elements in their standard states, all of the substances being at the specified temperature*. For example, the standard free energy of formation of $CO_2$ refers to

***Table 8-1***

*Standard states for free energies of reaction*

| | |
|---|---|
| Standard state of solid | Pure solid in most stable form at 1 atm pressure and the specified temperature |
| Standard state of liquid | Pure liquid in most stable form at 1 atm pressure and the specified temperature |
| Standard state of gas | Pure gas at unit fugacity[a]; for ideal gas fugacity is unity when the pressure is 1 atm |

[a] The term *fugacity* has yet to be defined. Nevertheless, it is used in this table because of reference to it in future problems. For the present the standard state of a gas may be considered to be that of an ideal gas—1 atm pressure.

*Table 8-2*

*Standard free energies of formation*[a] *at 25°C*

| Substance | $\Delta Gf°$, kcal mole$^{-1}$ | Substance | $\Delta Gf°$, kcal mole$^{-1}$ |
|---|---|---|---|
| H(*g*) | 48.575 | Methane(*g*) | −12.140 |
| O(*g*) | 54.994 | Ethane(*g*) | −7.860 |
| Cl(*g*) | 25.192 | Propane(*g*) | −5.614 |
| Br(*g*) | 19.69 | *n*-Butane(*g*) | −4.10 |
| $Br_2$(*g*) | 0.751 | Ethylene(*g*) | 16.282 |
| I(*g*) | 16.766 | Propylene(*g*) | 14.990 |
| $I_2$(*g*) | 4.63 | *l*-Butene(*g*) | 17.09 |
| $H_2O$(*g*) | −54.6357 | Acetylene(*g*) | 50.000 |
| $H_2O$(*l*) | −56.6902 | Benzene(*g*) | 30.989 |
| HF(*g*) | −64.7 | Toluene(*g*) | 29.228 |
| HCl(*g*) | −22.769 | *o*-Xylene(*g*) | 29.117 |
| HBr(*g*) | −12.72 | *m*-Xylene(*g*) | 28.405 |
| HI(*g*) | 0.31 | *p*-Xylene(*g*) | 28.952 |
| ICl(*g*) | −1.32 | Methanol(*l*) | −39.73 |
| NO(*g*) | 20.719 | Ethanol(*l*) | −41.77 |
| CO(*g*) | −32.8079 | Glycine(*s*) | −88.61 |
| $CO_2$(*g*) | −94.2598 | Acetic acid(*l*) | −93.8 |
| | | Taurine(*s*) | −136.7 |

[a] Selected from "Selected Values of Chemical Thermodynamic Properties," *Natl. Bur. Standards* (*U.S.*) *Cir. 500* (1952), and *Selected Values of Physical and Thermodynamic Properties of Hydrocarbons,* Am. Petroleum Inst. Project 44, 1953.

the reaction

$$\text{C(graphite, 1 atm)} + O_2(g, \text{ 1 atm}) = CO_2(g, \text{ 1 atm})$$
$$\Delta G = \Delta Gf° = -94.2598 \text{ kcal mole}^{-1} \qquad (8\text{-}60)$$

It is a consequence of our definition that $\Delta Gf°$ for any element is zero.

We may also speak of the *standard free-energy change*, $\Delta G°$, for *any* reaction. Obviously we are referring to *the change in free energy accompanying the conversion of reactants in their standard states to products in their standard states.* It can be shown by simple additivity rules that, since the free energy is a thermodynamic property and hence does not depend upon the path used to carry out a chemical transformation,

$$\Delta G° = \sum \Delta Gf°(\text{products}) - \sum \Delta Gf°(\text{reactants}) \qquad (8\text{-}61)$$

## Relation between $\Delta G^\circ$ and the Equilibrium Constant

Having established the requisite definition of $\Delta Gf^\circ$, we may proceed to derive the important expression relating the standard free energy of a reaction to its equilibrium constant. For the present we shall restrict our discussion to pure, ideal gases or to pure liquids and solids, because we are not yet in a position to consider the form of the free-energy functions for real gases.

For an ideal gas we may derive readily an equation for the change in free energy in an isothermal expansion by recognizing that Eq. (8-19) reduces to the following at fixed temperature ($dT = 0$):

$$dG = V\,dP \tag{8-62}$$

For an ideal gas,

$$V = \frac{nRT}{P} \tag{8-63}$$

and hence

$$dG = \frac{nRT}{P}\,dP \tag{8-64}$$

$$\Delta G = nRT \ln \frac{P_2}{P_1} \tag{8-65}$$

This expression will be essential to the following derivation.

Let us represent a chemical transformation by the equation (where lower-case letters represent the number of moles):

$$aA(g, P_A) + bB(g, P_B) = cC(g, P_C) + dD(g, P_D) \tag{8-66}$$

For the present, each substance is assumed to be a pure ideal gas at a given partial pressure. This reaction will be accompanied by a free-energy change, $\Delta G$. Suppose we wish to calculate $\Delta G^\circ$ for reaction (8-66). We may proceed to do so by adding suitable equations to Eq. (8-66), so that each substance is carried from its partial pressure to a pressure of 1 atm, and then adding the free-energy changes accompanying these reactions to $\Delta G$ for Eq. (8-66). Thus we would add the following:

$$aA\,(P_A) + bB\,(P_B) = cC\,(P_C) + dD\,(P_D) \qquad \Delta G \tag{8-66}$$

$$aA\,(P_A' = 1) = aA\,(P_A) \qquad \Delta G = aRT \ln\left(\frac{P_A}{1}\right) \tag{8-67}$$

$$bB\,(P_B' = 1) = bB\,(P_B) \qquad \Delta G = bRT \ln\left(\frac{P_B}{1}\right) \tag{8-68}$$

$$cC\,(P_C) = cC\,(P_C' = 1) \qquad \Delta G = cRT \ln \left(\frac{1}{P_C}\right) \tag{8-69}$$

$$dD\,(P_D) = dD\,(P_D' = 1) \qquad \Delta G = dRT \ln \left(\frac{1}{P_D}\right) \tag{8-70}$$

---

$$aA\,(P_A' = 1) + bB\,(P_B' = 1) = cC\,(P_C' = 1) + dD\,(P_D' = 1)$$

$$\Delta G^\circ = \Delta G + aRT \ln P_A + bRT \ln P_B + cRT \ln \left(\frac{1}{P_C}\right) + dRT \ln \left(\frac{1}{P_D}\right) \tag{8-71}$$

Equation (8-71) can be simplified by combining logarithmic terms to yield

$$\Delta G^\circ = \Delta G + RT \ln \frac{(P_A)^a(P_B)^b}{(P_C)^c(P_D)^d} \tag{8-72}$$

Inversion of the ratio leads to

$$\Delta G^\circ = \Delta G - RT \ln \frac{(P_C)^c(P_D)^d}{(P_A)^a(P_B)^b} \tag{8-73}$$

If the pressures in Eq. (8-66) correspond to equilibrium values, then since we are dealing with an isothermal, isobaric[3] transformation (with the only restraint being the pressure of the environment),

$$\Delta G = 0 \tag{8-74}$$

By definition, the ratio of the *equilibrium* pressures is symbolized by $K$:

$$\left[\frac{(P_C)^c(P_D)^d}{(P_A)^a(P_B)^b}\right]_{\text{equil}} = K \tag{8-75}$$

Equation (8-73) thus becomes

$$\Delta G^\circ = -RT \ln K \tag{8-76}$$

Evidently, then, $K$ must be a constant, because it is proportional to the antilogarithm of $\Delta G^\circ$; and since $\Delta G^\circ$ is the change in free energy under certain specified conditions (substances in their standard states), it must have a fixed value at a given temperature. $K$ is commonly called the *thermodynamic equilibrium constant* and is truly a constant. Obviously, it can be evaluated numerically from Eq. (8-76) if the standard free energy for

[3] It should be emphasized that $\Delta G$ for Eq. (8-66) refers to the change in free energy when pure $A$ at a *fixed* pressure of $P_A$ and pure $B$ at a *fixed* pressure of $P_B$ react to give pure $C$ at a *fixed* pressure of $P_C$ and pure $D$ at a *fixed* pressure of $P_D$, although the individual pressures are not necessarily the same for each gas.

the reaction is known. Perhaps it should be emphasized that, although $K$ refers to equilibrium pressures, it is calculated by means of Eq. (8-76) from data for $\Delta G^\circ$ referring to the reaction occurring between gases at individual pressures of 1 atm.

## Dependence of $K$ on the Temperature

From the value of $\Delta G^\circ$ at a single temperature it is possible to calculate the equilibrium constant, $K$. It is desirable, in addition, to be able to calculate $K$ as a function of the temperature, so that it should not be necessary to have extensive tables of $\Delta G^\circ$ at frequent temperature intervals. The derivation of the necessary functional relationship requires a direct relation between $\Delta G$ and $\Delta H$.

***Direct relation between $\Delta G$ and $\Delta H$.*** Starting from the fundamental definition

$$G = H - TS \tag{8-2}$$

we may obtain

$$\frac{G}{T} = \frac{H}{T} - S \tag{8-77}$$

which may be differentiated at constant pressure to give

$$\begin{aligned}\left(\frac{\partial(G/T)}{\partial T}\right)_P &= \left(\frac{\partial(H/T)}{\partial T}\right)_P - \left(\frac{\partial S}{\partial T}\right)_P \\ &= H\left(\frac{\partial(1/T)}{\partial T}\right)_P + \frac{1}{T}\left(\frac{\partial H}{\partial T}\right)_P - \left(\frac{\partial S}{\partial T}\right)_P \end{aligned} \tag{8-78}$$

Each of these three terms may be reduced further to give the following expressions:

$$H\left(\frac{\partial(1/T)}{\partial T}\right)_P = -\frac{H}{T^2} \tag{8-79}$$

$$\frac{1}{T}\left(\frac{\partial H}{\partial T}\right)_P = \frac{C_p}{T} \tag{8-80}$$

$$dS_P = \frac{DQ_P}{T} = \frac{C_p\,dT}{T} \tag{8-81}$$

or

$$\left(\frac{\partial S}{\partial T}\right)_P = \frac{C_p}{T} \tag{8-82}$$

Substitution of Eqs. (8-79), (8-80), and (8-82) into Eq. (8-78) leads to

$$\left(\frac{\partial(G/T)}{\partial T}\right)_P = -\frac{H}{T^2} \tag{8-83}$$

It is obvious that by a procedure analogous to that used to derive Eq. (8-28), we may obtain the following from Eq. (8-83):

$$\left(\frac{\partial(\Delta G/T)}{\partial T}\right)_P = -\frac{\Delta H}{T^2} \tag{8-84}$$[4]

***$\Delta G$ as a function of temperature.*** We have shown in Chapter 5 that a general expression for $\Delta H$ as a function of temperature may be written in the form

$$\Delta H = \Delta H_0 + \int \Delta C_p \, dT \tag{8-85}$$

If the heat capacities of the substances involved in the transformation can be expressed in the form of a simple power series,

$$C_p = a + bT + cT^2 + \cdots \tag{8-86}$$

where $a$, $b$, and $c$ are constants, then Eq. (8-85) takes the form

$$\Delta H = \Delta H_0 + \Delta aT + \frac{\Delta b}{2} T^2 + \frac{\Delta c}{3} T^3 + \cdots \tag{8-87}$$

where the $\Delta$'s refer to the sums of the coefficients for the products minus the sums of the coefficients for the reactants. Equation (8-87), in turn, may be inserted into (8-84), which may then be integrated, constant pressure being assumed [and terms higher than $T^3$ in Eq. (8-84) being dropped in this example]:

$$\int d\frac{\Delta G}{T} = -\int \frac{\Delta H}{T^2} \, dT = -\int \left(\frac{\Delta a}{T} + \frac{\Delta b}{2} + \frac{\Delta c}{3} T + \frac{\Delta H_0}{T^2}\right) dT \tag{8-88}$$

If we represent the constant of integration by $I$, the preceding expression may be written

$$\frac{\Delta G}{T} = I - \Delta a \ln T - \frac{\Delta b}{2} T - \frac{\Delta c}{6} T^2 + \frac{\Delta H_0}{T} \tag{8-89}$$

which leads finally to an equation explicit in $\Delta G$.

$$\Delta G = \Delta H_0 - \Delta a T \ln T + IT - \frac{\Delta b}{2} T^2 - \frac{\Delta c}{6} T^3 \tag{8-90}$$[5]

[4] This equation is also valid if the free-energy change under discussion is $\Delta G^\circ$. In this case, however, $\Delta H^\circ$ is the enthalpy change at zero pressure for gases and at infinite dilution for substances in solution. For a rigorous discussion of these relationships between standard states, see Chapter 19.

[5] Strictly speaking, this equation is valid for $\Delta G^\circ$ only if the heat capacities and the enthalpy change are those for the gases at zero pressure (see Chapter 19).

The constant $\Delta H_0$ may be evaluated as described in Chapter 5 if one value of the heat of reaction is known. Similarly, the constant $I$ may be determined if $\Delta H_0$ and one value of $\Delta G$ are known.

The use of Eq. (8-90) may be illustrated best by a specific example. Consider the reaction

$$\text{C(graphite)} + \text{O}_2(g) = \text{CO}_2(g) \tag{8-91}$$

From the heat-capacity equations and $\Delta Hf^\circ$, we have shown in Chapter 5, page 72, that

$$\Delta H = -94{,}218.3 + 1.331T - 3.357 \times 10^{-3}\, T^2 + 25.70 \times 10^{-7}\, T^3 \tag{8-92}$$

Substituting into Eq. (8-88) and integrating, we obtain the following expression for $\Delta G/T$:

$$\frac{\Delta G}{T} = I - 1.331 \ln T + 3.357 \times 10^{-3}\, T - 12.85 \times 10^{-7}\, T^2 - \frac{94{,}218.3}{T}$$

(8-93)[6]

At 298.15°K the standard free energy of formation of $CO_2$, $\Delta G^\circ$, is $-94{,}259.8$ cal mole$^{-1}$ (Table 8-2). Using this value for $\Delta G$ in Eq. (8-93), we can evaluate the integration constant, $I$:

$$I = 15.208 \tag{8-94}$$

Thus the explicit equation for the standard free-energy change in reaction (8-91) becomes

$$\Delta G^\circ = 15.208T - 3.065T \log_{10} T + 3.357 \times 10^{-3}\, T^2 - 12.85 \times 10^{-7}\, T^3 - 94{,}218.3 \tag{8-95}$$

***K* as a function of the temperature.** The equilibrium constant can be related to the temperature through either of two thermodynamic functions.

*The differential relation.* It is evident that the substitution of Eq. (8-76) into (8-84) leads to

$$\left(\frac{\partial(\Delta G^\circ/T)}{\partial T}\right)_P = -\frac{\Delta H^\circ}{T^2} = \left(\frac{\partial(-RT \ln K/T)}{\partial T}\right)_P = -R\left(\frac{\partial \ln K}{\partial T}\right)_P \tag{8-96}$$

From this equation we may obtain, upon rearrangement,

$$\frac{d \ln K}{dT} = \frac{\Delta H^\circ}{RT^2}$$

(8-97)[7]

[6] Strictly speaking, this equation is valid for $\Delta G^\circ$ only if the heat capacities and the enthalpy change are those for the gases at zero pressure. In the present example, the differences in $C_p$'s between zero and 1 atm pressure have been neglected.

[7] Since $\Delta G^\circ$ does not depend on pressure, $K$ does not depend on pressure. Hence we need not use partial derivative notation in this equation.

*The integral relation.* If the heat capacities fit the power series specified in (8-86), $\Delta G$ may be expressed by Eq. (8-90). Obviously, then, making use of Eq. (8-76), we obtain, in place of Eq. (8-90),

$$\ln K = -\frac{\Delta H_0}{RT} + \frac{\Delta a}{R} \ln T - \frac{I}{R} + \frac{\Delta b}{2R} T + \frac{\Delta c}{6R} T^2 \tag{8-98}$$

In the general case, when a function for the heat capacities is unavailable, it is necessary to integrate Eq. (8-97):

$$\int_{T_1}^{T_2} d \ln K = \int_{T_1}^{T_2} \frac{\Delta H^\circ}{RT^2}\, dT \tag{8-99}$$

# 8-6 USEFUL WORK AND FREE ENERGY

So far we have considered situations where the only restraint upon a system is the constant pressure of the environment. Such situations are of primary interest in connection with the general problem of spontaneity or equilibrium in chemical reactions. Nevertheless, we must give some attention also to systems which are so arranged that they can produce work other than that against the atmosphere. Although in most cases we shall consider only electrical manifestations of such additional work, it should be pointed out that other restraints such as the tension of a spring or magnetic, centrifugal, or surface forces may also assume significance in many problems.

## Some Characteristics of Isothermal Transformations

Practicable relations between free energy and useful work are obtainable only for isothermal processes. Let us examine some thermodynamic quantities for isothermal changes particularly to compare irreversible with reversible processes.

For concreteness let us keep a specific example in mind, for example, the formation of 1 mole of aqueous HCl from the gaseous elements $H_2$ and $Cl_2$:

$$\tfrac{1}{2}H_2(g) + \tfrac{1}{2}Cl_2(g) = HCl(aq) \tag{8-100}$$

If the gaseous mixture is exposed to a photochemical stimulus, the reaction proceeds spontaneously. Since such a system is under no restraint other than constant atmospheric pressure and since the temperature may be maintained constant,

$$dG_{P,T} < 0 \tag{8-101}$$

Furthermore, since no net *useful* work (that is, none other than that against

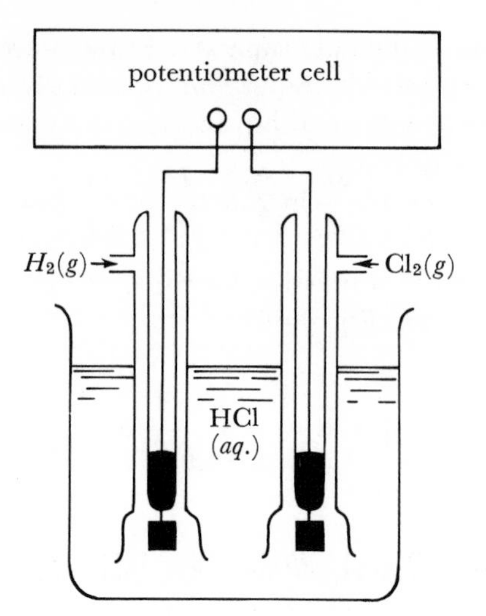


***Figure 8-2*** *Formation of aqueous HCl in a reversible manner.*

the atmosphere) can be obtained under the conditions described, we may also write

$$DW_{\text{net}} = 0 \tag{8-102}$$

On the other hand, the chemical transformation may be carried out reversibly, as in the cell illustrated by Figure 8-2. The $H_2$ and $Cl_2$ electrodes are connected to a potentiometer.[8] If the electromotive force of the cell is opposed by the emf of the potentiometer maintained at an infinitesimally lower value than that of the $H_2$-$Cl_2$ cell, then the conversion to HCl can be carried out reversibly, though it would take an infinitely long time to obtain 1 mole. In either this reversible or the explosively spontaneous path for carrying out the transformation of Eq. (8-100) the change in free energy is the same if the states of the initial and of the final substances are the same in both methods. The amount of useful (electrical) work is very different, however, and in the reversible path

$$DW_{\text{net}} \neq 0 \tag{8-103}$$

[8] For the purposes of the present discussion, the conventional potentiometer cannot be used, for the rate of discharge of the operating battery is only slightly decreased or increased, *but is not reversed* when the potential of the potentiometer is made slightly below, or above, that of the $H_2$-$Cl_2$ cell. Thus the common potentiometer is not operated in a reversible fashion. For the present discussion, therefore, we shall assume that the potential of the $H_2$-$Cl_2$ cell is opposed by a working battery, which we shall call a *potentiometer-cell,* whose voltage, near that of the $H_2$-$Cl_2$ cell, can be varied by changes in pressure. Such a potentiometer-cell can be operated in a reversible manner.

The potentiometer may also be kept at a finitely lower potential than the cell and then reaction (8-100) would also proceed spontaneously; the electrical work obtained in this situation, as we shall see shortly, would be less than in the reversible discharge.

In each process, reversible or spontaneous, we shall start with the same initial state [e.g., $H_2$ and $Cl_2$ in (8-100)] and conclude with the equivalent final state [e.g., HCl in (8-100)]. All these isothermal changes may be represented in a diagram such as Figure 8-3, *a* being the initial state, *b* the final. We shall now proceed to prove directly from the second law of thermodynamics that *in an isothermal process, the reversible work is the maximum work.*

Our proof will depend upon a procedure used frequently in Chapter 7 for entropy. We shall consider two possible methods of going from state *a* to state *b* (Figure 8-3) in an isothermal fashion: (1) a reversible process and (2) an irreversible process. For each path the first law of thermodynamics must be valid.

$$\Delta E_{\text{rev}} = Q_{\text{rev}} - W_{\text{rev}} \tag{8-104}$$

$$\Delta E_{\text{irrev}} = Q_{\text{irrev}} - W_{\text{irrev}} \tag{8-105}$$

Since $E$ is a function of the state only and since both processes have the same starting and end points,

$$\Delta E_{\text{rev}} = \Delta E_{\text{irrev}} \tag{8-106}$$

or

$$Q_{\text{rev}} - W_{\text{rev}} = Q_{\text{irrev}} - W_{\text{irrev}} \tag{8-107}$$

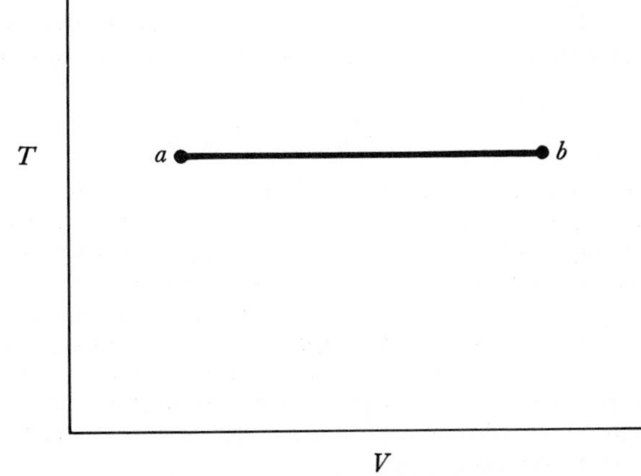


***Figure 8-3*** *An isothermal process.*

***Table 8-3***

*Isothermal cycle*

| | Irreversible process (forward) | Reversible process (backward) | Net for both processes |
|---|---|---|---|
| Heat absorbed | $Q_{irrev}$ | $-Q_{rev}$ | $Q_{irrev} - Q_{rev} > 0$ |
| Work done | $W_{irrev}$ | $-W_{rev}$ | $W_{irrev} - W_{rev} > 0$ |

Let us *assume* now that the irreversible process gives more work than the reversible one. In that case

$$W_{irrev} > W_{rev} \tag{8-108}$$

Hence[9]

$$Q_{irrev} > Q_{rev} \tag{8-109}$$

Let us use the irreversible process (*which goes in only one direction*) to carry the system from state *a* to state *b* and the reversible process to return the system to its initial state. As in previous proofs, we may construct a table for the various steps (Table 8-3). The net result, as we can see from Table 8-3, is that a positive amount of heat has been absorbed and a positive amount of work has been done in an isothermal cycle. However, such a consequence is in contradiction to our alternative statement of the second law of thermodynamics [Chapter 7 (p. 117)], which denies the possibility of converting heat from a reservoir at constant temperature into work without some accompanying changes in the reservoir or its surroundings. In our postulated cyclical process no such accompanying changes have occurred. Hence our process cannot occur, and consequently the isothermal irreversible work cannot be greater than the reversible work. We may conclude then that[10]

$$\underset{\text{isothermal}}{W_{irrev}} < \underset{\text{isothermal}}{W_{rev}} \tag{8-110}$$

[9] If this consequence does not seem obvious when expressed in these general terms, it is suggested that a few numerical values be chosen for $W_{irrev}$, $W_{rev}$, and $Q_{rev}$ [consistent with Eq. (8-108)] and that values of $Q_{irrev}$ then be calculated from Eq. (8-107). The validity of Eq. (8-109) will soon become apparent.

[10] The equality sign is ruled out, since in any isothermal process for which $W = W_{rev}$, it follows (since $\Delta E = \Delta E_{rev}$) that $Q = Q_{rev}$. Hence the entropy change for the substance must be $(Q_{rev}/T)$, and that for the surroundings $(-Q/T)$. For the system as a whole, then, $\Delta S = 0$, which means that we must be dealing with a reversible change. Thus whenever $W = W_{rev}$, the process in which the work $W$ was done must be reversible.

Having proved that the reversible work is the maximum work in an isothermal transformation, let us also compare the values of other thermodynamic quantities for reversible vs. irreversible processes over the same end points. In this comparison it will help to keep in mind a specific example, such as the reaction of Eq. (8-100).

From the first law of thermodynamics, which is applicable to either reversible or irreversible processes, it follows that

$$\Delta E_{\text{rev}} = \Delta E_{\text{irrev}} \tag{8-106}$$

$$Q_{\text{rev}} - W_{\text{rev}} = Q_{\text{irrev}} - W_{\text{irrev}} \tag{8-107}$$

Since we have demonstrated the validity of Eq. (8-110), the following relation must also be true:

$$Q_{\text{irrev}} < Q_{\text{rev}} \tag{8-111}$$

Since entropy is a function of the state, or in other words, from the second law of thermodynamics

$$\Delta S_{\text{rev}} = \Delta S_{\text{irrev}} \tag{8-112}$$

For the reversible (isothermal) process

$$\Delta S_{\text{rev}} = \frac{Q_{\text{rev}}}{T} \tag{8-113}$$

For an explosively irreversible process in which no useful work (other than expansion work) is done, but which is carried out isobarically, we may also state

$$Q_{\text{irrev}} = \Delta H_{\text{irrev}} \tag{8-114}$$

Of course, since $H$ is a function of state, the following is also true:

$$\Delta H_{\text{rev}} = \Delta H_{\text{irrev}} \tag{8-115}$$

At first glance one might feel that Eq. (8-115) contradicts (8-111) and (8-114). One should note in passing, therefore, that

$$Q_{\text{rev}} \neq \Delta H_{\text{rev}} \tag{8-116}$$

even if the process is isobaric; for the original proof of the equality of $DQ$ and $dH$ at constant pressure required that no work be done except that given by the $P\,dV$ term (see p. 50)[11]. Finally we should write

$$\Delta G_{\text{rev}} = \Delta G_{\text{irrev}} \tag{8-117}$$

and

$$\Delta A_{\text{rev}} = \Delta A_{\text{irrev}} \tag{8-118}$$

[11] The student is also reminded that

$$DQ_{\text{rev}} \neq dE_{\text{rev}}$$

because nonmechanical work is produced when this process is carried out reversibly.

since $G$ and $A$ are also thermodynamic functions of state and independent of the path.

## Relation between $\Delta G$ and Net Useful Work at Constant Pressure and Temperature

We shall direct our attention once again to the example cited previously, the formation of a mole of aqueous HCl from the gases $H_2$ and $Cl_2$:

$$\tfrac{1}{2}H_2(g) + \tfrac{1}{2}Cl_2(g) = HCl(aq) \tag{8-100}$$

From the reversible discharge of the $H_2$-$Cl_2$ cell with the emf of the potentiometer-cell kept opposed to, but infinitesimally below, the potential of the cell, some useful (electrical) work is obtained other than that expended against the atmosphere. This electrical work is used to charge the potentiometer-cell. We shall call this work $W_{\text{net, rev}}$. Clearly

$$DW_{\text{total}} = DW_{\text{net, rev}} + P\,dV \tag{8-119}$$

Since the process is one at constant pressure and temperature, we may write

$$dG = dH - T\,dS = dE + P\,dV - T\,dS \tag{8-120}$$

According to the first law of thermodynamics,

$$dE = DQ - DW \tag{8-121}$$

We now have, in view of Eq. (8-119),

$$dE = DQ - DW_{\text{net, rev}} - P\,dV \tag{8-122}$$

The substitution of Eq. (8-122) into (8-120) leads to

$$dG = DQ - DW_{\text{net, rev}} - T\,dS \tag{8-123}$$

Since the process under discussion is being carried out in a reversible fashion,

$$DQ = T\,dS \tag{8-124}$$

Hence

$$dG_{P,T} = -DW_{\text{net, rev}} \tag{8-125}$$

Thus we have derived the very significant consequence that the change in free energy is the negative of the net (that is, nonatmospheric), reversible work available in a transformation at constant pressure and temperature. Since in isothermal processes the reversible work is the maximum work, it is evident that the free-energy change gives the negative of the maximum possible net work available from a specified reaction. For any real process at constant pressure and temperature,

$$DW_{\text{net, irrev}} < dW_{\text{net, rev}} \tag{8-126}$$

Therefore

$$DW_{\text{net, irrev}} < -dG_{P,T} \tag{8-127}$$

Thus the free-energy change gives the limit which may be approached in obtaining net useful work in any real process at constant temperature and pressure.

## Relation between $\Delta A$ and Total Work at Constant Temperature

For the reversible process just considered in connection with the Gibbs free energy, it is evident that the Helmholtz free energy must obey the following relations under isothermal conditions:

$$\begin{aligned} dA &= dE - T\,dS \\ &= DQ - DW_{\text{total, rev}} - T\,dS \\ &= T\,dS - DW_{\text{total, rev}} - T\,dS \end{aligned} \tag{8-128}$$

or

$$dA_T = -DW_{\text{total, rev}} \tag{8-129}$$

Thus the change in Helmholtz free energy in an isothermal transformation is the negative of the maximum total work (that is, net useful work as well as that against the atmosphere) available from a specified reaction.

## Gibbs-Helmholtz Equation

We have seen that, at constant pressure and a fixed temperature, $-\Delta G$ is a measure of the maximum net work available from a chemical reaction. The particular value obtained for $\Delta G$, however, depends upon the specific temperature at which the isothermal transformation is carried out. Thus $\Delta G_{P,T}$ may differ at different temperatures, varying perhaps in a fashion such as is indicated in Figure 8-4.

Knowing a value of $\Delta G_{P,T}$ at one temperature, we may wish to calculate it at another. The required relation may be derived readily from expressions available already.

For an isothermal reaction,

$$\Delta G = \Delta H - T\,\Delta S \tag{8-7}$$

But we have also proved that at fixed pressure

$$\Delta S = -\left(\frac{\partial \Delta G}{\partial T}\right)_P \tag{8-30}$$

Hence it follows that

$$\Delta G_{P,T} = \Delta H_{P,T} + T\left(\frac{\partial \Delta G_{P,T}}{\partial T}\right)_P \tag{8-130}$$

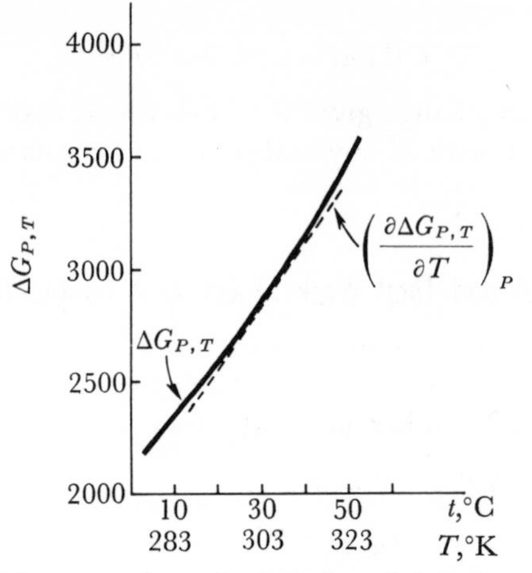


***Figure 8-4*** *Standard free-energy change for the isothermal, isobaric reaction*

$$HSO_4^-(aq) = H^+(aq) + SO_4^{=}(aq)$$

*as a function of the temperature. The broken line gives the slope, or derivative, at 25°C.*

Equation (8-130) frequently is called the *Gibbs-Helmholtz equation.* Clearly the temperature coefficient of the free-energy change, $(\partial \Delta G_{P,T}/\partial T)_P$, can be obtained if $\Delta G$ and $\Delta H$ are known.

When electrical work is obtained from the reaction, the Gibbs-Helmholtz equation is generally used in a modified form. If the electrical work is obtained under reversible conditions, that is, against a counterpotential only infinitesimally smaller than that of the cell, then

$$W_{\text{elec}} = W_{\text{net, rev}} = (\text{potential}) \times (\text{charge})$$
$$= (\mathscr{E})\,(n\mathscr{F}) \tag{8-131}$$

where $\mathscr{E}$ is the potential obtained from the cell under reversible conditions, $\mathscr{F}$ is the number of charges in 1 faraday of electricity, and $n$ is the number of faradays of charge which have passed from the cell. It follows from the integrated equivalent of Eq. (8-125) that

$$\Delta G = -n\mathscr{F}\mathscr{E} \tag{8-132}$$

By differentiation we obtain

$$\left(\frac{\partial \Delta G}{\partial T}\right)_P = -\,n\mathscr{F}\left(\frac{\partial \mathscr{E}}{\partial T}\right)_P \tag{8-133}$$

since $n$ and $\mathscr{F}$ are temperature-independent quantities. Substitution of the preceding two expressions into Eq. (8-130) leads to

$$-n\mathscr{F}\mathscr{E} = \Delta H - n\mathscr{F}T\left(\frac{\partial \mathscr{E}}{\partial T}\right)_P \tag{8-134}$$

or, upon rearrangement, to a somewhat more familiar form of the Gibbs-Helmholtz equation,

$$\Delta H = n\mathscr{F}\left[T\left(\frac{\partial \mathscr{E}}{\partial T}\right)_P - \mathscr{E}\right] \tag{8-135}$$

## Relation between $\Delta H_P$ and $Q_P$ When Useful Work is Done

We have repeatedly made use of the relation

$$\Delta H_P = Q_P \tag{8-136}$$

with the very careful stipulation that not only must the pressure on the system be constant, but also there must be no work other than expansion work. Such are the conditions under which most chemical reactions are carried out, and hence the enthalpy change has been of much value as a measure of the heat of a reaction. It should be emphasized, however, that if nonatmospheric work is also being obtained, for example in the form of electrical work, Eq. (8-136) is no longer valid. That such must be the case is readily evident from the following considerations. According to the first law of thermodynamics,

$$dE = DQ - DW_{\text{total}} \tag{8-137}$$

which we may now write as

$$dE = DQ - DW_{\text{net}} - P\,dV \tag{8-138}$$

Since at constant pressure

$$dH_P = dE + P\,dV \tag{8-139}$$

we may substitute Eq. (8-138) into (8-139) and obtain

$$dH_P = DQ_P - DW_{\text{net}} \tag{8-140}$$

or

$$\Delta H_P = Q_P - W_{\text{net}} \tag{8-141}$$

Thus we see that in general the enthalpy change under isobaric conditions equals the heat absorbed *minus* the net useful (nonatmospheric) work. Only when $W_{\text{net}}$ is zero do we get the common expression given by Eq. (8-136).

## Exercises

**1.** Prove the validity of Eqs. (8-20), (8-31) through (8-34), and (8-39).

**2.** Derive the following expressions:

(a)
$$\left(\frac{\partial(\Delta G/T)}{\partial(1/T)}\right)_P = \Delta H \tag{8-142}$$

(b)
$$dG = V\left(\frac{\partial P}{\partial V}\right)_T dV + \left[V\left(\frac{\partial P}{\partial T}\right)_V - S\right] dT \tag{8-143}$$

**3.** (a) Rearrange the definition of $A$ to read

$$E = A + TS$$

Then prove that

$$\left(\frac{\partial E}{\partial V}\right)_T = -P + T\left(\frac{\partial P}{\partial T}\right)_V$$

which has also been proved as Eq. (7-131).

(b) With similar operations on $G$ show that

$$\left(\frac{\partial H}{\partial P}\right)_T = V - T\left(\frac{\partial V}{\partial T}\right)_P$$

This relation will be useful later as Eq. (12-18).

**4.** If a rubber band is stretched, the reversible work is given by

$$DW = -\tau\, dL$$

where $\tau$ is the tension on the band and $L$ its length.

(a) If the stretching is carried out at constant pressure show that

$$dG = \tau\, dL - S\, dT$$

(b) Show further that

$$\left(\frac{\partial G}{\partial L}\right)_T = \tau$$

(c) Prove that

$$\left(\frac{\partial \tau}{\partial T}\right)_L = -\left(\frac{\partial S}{\partial L}\right)_T$$

(d) Assuming that the volume of the rubber band does not change during stretching, derive the following equation from fundamental thermodynamic principles:

$$\left(\frac{\partial E}{\partial L}\right)_T = \tau + T\left(\frac{\partial S}{\partial L}\right)_T = \tau - T\left(\frac{\partial \tau}{\partial T}\right)_L$$

(e) For an ideal gas it can be shown that

$$\frac{1}{P}\left(\frac{\partial P}{\partial T}\right)_V = \frac{1}{T}$$

Show that the corresponding equation for an "ideal" rubber band is

$$\frac{1}{\tau}\left(\frac{\partial \tau}{\partial T}\right)_L = \frac{1}{T}$$

**5.** One mole of an ideal gas at 273.15°K is allowed to expand isothermally from a pressure of 100 atm to 10 atm.

(a) Calculate (and arrange in tabular form) the values of $W$, $Q$, $\Delta E$, $\Delta H$, $\Delta S$, $\Delta G$, and $\Delta A$ of the gas if the expansion is reversible.

(b) Calculate (and arrange in tabular form adjacent to the preceding table) the values of $W$, $Q$, $\Delta E$, $\Delta H$, $\Delta S$, $\Delta G$, and $\Delta A$ of the entire isolated system (gas plus its environment) if the expansion is reversible.

(c) Calculate (and arrange in tabular form adjacent to the preceding tables) the values of the same thermodynamic quantities for the gas if it is allowed to expand freely so that no work whatever is done by it.

(d) Calculate (and arrange in tabular form adjacent to the preceding tables) the values of the same thermodynamic quantities for the entire isolated system if the expansion is free.

**6.** A mole of steam is condensed reversibly to liquid water at 100°C and 760 mm (constant) pressure. The heat of vaporization of water is 539.4 cal $g^{-1}$. Assuming that steam behaves as an ideal gas, calculate $W$, $Q$, $\Delta E$, $\Delta H$, $\Delta S$, $\Delta G$, and $\Delta A$ for the condensation process.

**7.** Using thermal data available in this and preceding chapters, find an expression for $\Delta G°$ as a function of temperature for the reaction

$$CO(g) + \tfrac{1}{2}O_2(g) = CO_2(g)$$

**8.** If the heat capacities of reactants and products are expressed by equations of the form

$$C_p = a + bT - \frac{c'}{T^2}$$

where $a$, $b$, and $c'$ are constants, what will be the form of the equation for $\Delta G$ as a function of temperature?

**9.** Consider a reaction such as (8-66) in which $A$ is a pure solid at 1 atm pressure, and the other substances are as indicated in the text. Derive an expression corresponding to Eq. (8-73).

**10.** In theories of electrolytes, it is customary to regard the free energy of the solution as composed of two parts: $G_u$, the free energy the particles would have if uncharged, and $G_e$, the additional free energy resulting from charging the particles to form ions.

$G_e$ can be shown to be given by the equation

$$G_e = -\frac{2\pi^{1/2}N_1^{3/2}\epsilon^3V(\nu_+Z_+^2 + \nu_-Z_-^2)^{3/2}}{3D^{3/2}(kT)^{1/2}} \qquad (8\text{-}144)$$

where $N_1$ = number of molecules per unit volume of solution
$\epsilon$ = charge on electron
$V$ = volume of solution
$\nu_+$ = number of positive ions per molecule
$Z_+$ = number of charges on each positive ion
$\nu_-$ = number of negative ions per molecule
$Z_-$ = number of charges on each negative ion
$D$ = dielectric constant of solution
$k$ = Boltzmann constant
$T$ = absolute temperature

(a) Assume that $V$ and $D$ do not change with temperature. Show that

$$H_e = \tfrac{3}{2}G_e$$

and that

$$S_e = \frac{G_e}{2T}$$

(b) It is obvious from (8-144) that $G_e$ is a negative quantity. Hence $S_e$ must be negative. What does this mean about the degree of order in a solution of ions as compared to that in an equivalent solution of uncharged particles? How would you interpret this difference in terms of the molecular structure of the solution?

**11.** A spring obeys Hooke's law $\tau = Kx$ where $\tau$ is the tension and $x$ the displacement from the equilibrium position. For a particular spring at 25°C, $K = 2.0 \times 10^{-3}$ dyne cm$^{-1}$ and $dK/dT = -1.0 \times 10^{-5}$ dyne cm$^{-1}$ deg$^{-1}$.

(a) The spring is placed in a thermostat at 25°C and stretched in a reversible manner from $x = 0$ to $x = 10$ cm. How much heat is given to or absorbed from the thermostat by the spring?

(b) The spring is then allowed to snap back to its original position without doing any work. How much heat would it deliver into the thermostat?

**12.** Consider as an example the equilibrium

$$H_2O(l) = H_2O(g)$$

at some fixed temperature. Let $n$ represent the number of moles of $H_2O(g)$, but let $G$ and $V$ represent the total free energy and the total volume of all the substances involved. Equilibrium exists if

$$\left(\frac{\partial G}{\partial n}\right)_P = 0$$

(a) Show that

$$\left(\frac{\partial G}{\partial n}\right)_V = \left(\frac{\partial G}{\partial n}\right)_P + \left(\frac{\partial G}{\partial P}\right)_n \left(\frac{\partial P}{\partial n}\right)_V$$

(b) Prove therefrom that

$$\left(\frac{\partial A}{\partial n}\right)_{V,T} = \left(\frac{\partial G}{\partial n}\right)_{P,T}$$

**13.** For stretching a film of water at constant pressure and temperature, until its area is increased by 1 cm$^2$, the free-energy change, $\Delta G$, is given by the equation

$$\Delta G = 75.64 - 0.14t \quad \text{(in ergs)}$$

where $t$ is the temperature at which the stretching is carried out, in °C. When the film is stretched the total volume of the water is not changed measurably.

(a) How much work must be done to increase the area of the film *reversibly* by 1 cm$^2$ at 10°C?

(b) How much heat will be absorbed in the process in (a)?

(c) What are $\Delta E$, $\Delta H$, $\Delta S$, $\Delta A$ for (a)?

(d) After the film has been stretched 1 cm$^2$ reversibly, it is allowed to contract spontaneously and irreversibly to its original area. No work is regained in this process. What is $\Delta G$ for this step?

(e) Find $Q$, $\Delta E$, $\Delta H$, $\Delta S$, and $\Delta A$ for the process in (d).

**14.** In the historical development of thermodynamics, functions other than those of Gibbs and Helmholtz have also been worked with. Thus

$$J = -\frac{E}{T} + S$$

is called the Massieu function, and

$$K = -\frac{H}{T} + S$$

is known as the Planck function. Show that

$$dJ = \frac{E}{T^2}\,dT + \frac{P}{T}\,dV$$

and

$$dK = \frac{H}{T^2}\,dT - \frac{V}{T}\,dP$$

**15.** An electrochemical cell is placed in a thermostated bath at 25°C and 1 atm pressure, under which conditions it produces an emf of 0.100 volt. For this cell $\partial\mathscr{E}/\partial T$ is $1 \times 10^{-4}$ volt $\text{deg}^{-1}$.

(a) If electrical work is done on this cell and it is charged reversibly until 1 faraday of charge has been stored in it, how much heat is given to or absorbed from the thermostat?

(b) If the charged cell is short-circuited, so that no electrical work is obtained from it, and allowed to return to its initial state in (a), how much heat is given to or absorbed from the thermostat?

# 9 Application of the Free-Energy Function to some Phase Changes

Having established convenient criteria for equilibrium and for spontaneity, we are now in a position to apply the fundamental laws of thermodynamics to problems that occur in chemistry. We shall direct our attention first to transformations involving merely phase changes.

## 9-1 TWO PHASES AT EQUILIBRIUM AT GIVEN PRESSURE AND TEMPERATURE

The familiar equations describing equilibrium conditions between two phases of a specified substance are readily derivable from the two laws of thermodynamics, with the aid of the new functions which we have defined in the preceding chapter.

Let us represent the equilibrium at any given temperature and pressure by the equation

$$\text{state } A \rightleftharpoons \text{state } B \tag{9-1}$$

Since the system is in equilibrium,

$$\Delta G_{P,T} = G_B - G_A = 0 \tag{9-2}$$

The temperature is now changed by an amount $dT$. If the system is to be maintained in equilibrium, the pressure must be altered by some quantity, $dP$. Nevertheless, if equilibrium is maintained at the new temperature, $T'$,

$$T' = T + dT \tag{9-3}$$

then

$$\Delta G'_{P',T'} = G'_B - G'_A = 0 \tag{9-4}$$

Obviously, then,

$$d(\Delta G) = d(G_B - G_A) = 0 \tag{9-5}$$

and

$$dG_B = dG_A \tag{9-6}$$

## Clapeyron Equation

From the preceding chapter we may adopt the general equation for the total differential, $dG$, and write

$$dG_A = V_A\,dP - S_A\,dT \tag{9-7}$$

$$dG_B = V_B\,dP - S_B\,dT \tag{9-8}$$

Setting up the equality demanded by (9-6), we obtain

$$V_B\,dP - S_B\,dT = V_A\,dP - S_A\,dT \tag{9-9}$$

which can be rearranged to give

$$(V_B - V_A)\,dP = (S_B - S_A)\,dT \tag{9-10}$$

and, consequently,

$$\frac{dP}{dT} = \frac{S_B - S_A}{V_B - V_A} \tag{9-11}$$

We are interested in the value of this derivative, $dP/dT$, at a specified temperature and pressure such as is indicated by point *a* in Figure 9-1. For an isothermal, reversible (that is, equilibrium) condition at constant pressure,

$$S_B - S_A = \Delta S = \int \frac{DQ_P}{T} = \frac{1}{T}\int DQ_P = \frac{\Delta H}{T} \tag{9-12}$$

Therefore Eq. (9-11) may be converted to

$$\frac{dP}{dT} = \frac{\Delta H}{T\,\Delta V} \tag{9-13}$$

which is generally known as the *Clapeyron equation.*

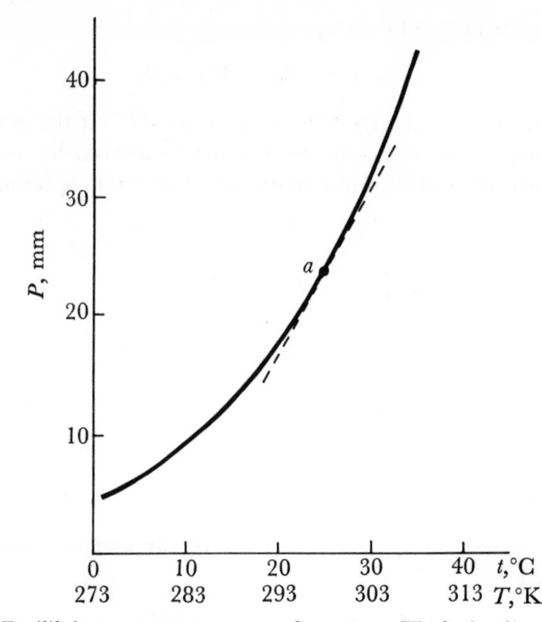


***Figure 9-1*** *Equilibrium vapor-pressure curve for water. The broken line gives the slope at a specified pressure and temperature.*

So far we have made no special assumptions as to the nature of the phases $A$ and $B$ in deriving Eq. (9-13). Evidently, then, the Clapeyron equation is applicable to equilibrium between any two phases of one component.

## Clausius-Clapeyron Equation

The Clapeyron equation can be reduced to a particularly convenient form if we restrict the equilibrium between $A$ and $B$ to that of a gas and condensed phase (liquid or solid). In this situation

$$V_B - V_A = V_{\text{gas}} - V_{\text{cond}} \tag{9-14}$$

In general, the volume of a given weight of a gas, $V_{\text{gas}}$, is much larger than that of a corresponding weight of the condensed phase, $V_{\text{cond}}$:

$$V_{\text{gas}} \gg V_{\text{cond}} \tag{9-15}$$

When Eq. (9-15) is valid, $V_{\text{cond}}$ may be neglected[1] with respect to $V_{\text{gas}}$ in

[1] For example, the molal volume of liquid $H_2O$ near the boiling point is about 18 cc, whereas that for water vapor is near 30,000 cc.

Eq. (9-14). Furthermore, if we approximate the volume of the gas by the ideal gas law,

$$V_{\text{gas}} = \frac{RT}{P} \tag{9-16}$$

then we may use Eq. (9-16) to substitute for $\Delta V$ in Eq. (9-13) and obtain

$$\frac{dP}{dT} = \frac{\Delta H}{T(RT/P)} = \frac{P(\Delta H)}{RT^2} \tag{9-17}$$

It follows that

$$\frac{1}{P}\frac{dP}{dT} = \frac{d \ln P}{dT} = \frac{\Delta H}{RT^2} \tag{9-18}$$

For many substances, over not too large a region of temperature, the heat of vaporization is substantially constant. Equation (9-18) may then be integrated readily as follows:

$$d \ln P = \frac{\Delta H}{R}\frac{dT}{T^2} = -\frac{\Delta H}{R} d\left(\frac{1}{T}\right) \tag{9-19}$$

$$\ln \frac{P_2}{P_1} = -\frac{\Delta H}{R}\left[\frac{1}{T_2} - \frac{1}{T_1}\right] \tag{9-20}$$

or

$$\log P = -\frac{\Delta H}{2.303R}\frac{1}{T} + \text{constant} \tag{9-21}$$

Any one of the Eqs. (9-18)–(9-21) is known as the *Clausius-Clapeyron equation* and may be used either to obtain $\Delta H$ from known values of the vapor pressure as a function of temperature or, vice versa, to predict vapor pressures of a liquid (or a solid) when the heat of vaporization (or sublimation) and one vapor pressure are known.

## 9-2 THE EFFECT OF AN INERT GAS ON VAPOR PRESSURE

Another situation of interest occurs in liquid–vapor equilibria in which the system is exposed to the atmosphere (Figure 9-2). We shall assume that the air is essentially insoluble in the liquid phase and that atmospheric pressure is some given value, $P$. The partial pressure of the vapor, $p$, can be shown to differ from that of the saturation vapor pressure of the liquid in the absence of any foreign gas such as air.

Since the liquid and vapor are in equilibrium at a given temperature and total pressure $P$, we may write

$$G_{\text{gas}} = G_{\text{liquid}} \tag{9-22}$$

Let us assume that the vapor behaves as an ideal gas, even in the presence

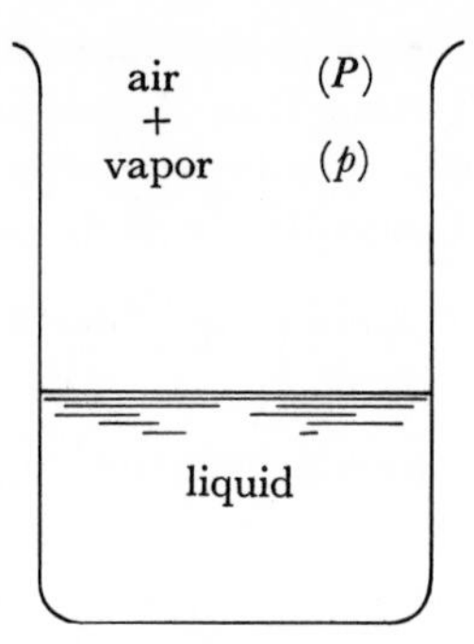


***Figure 9-2*** *Liquid-vapor equilibrium in the presence of an inert gas.*

of the foreign gas. It has been shown in Chapter 8, Eq. (8-64), that for 1 mole of an ideal gas

$$dG_{\text{gas}} = \frac{RT}{P}\,dP \tag{9-23}$$

Integration of this equation from any pressure, $p$, to the standard state for an ideal gas, a pressure of 1 atm,

$$\int_{G}^{G^\circ} dG_{\text{gas}} = \int_{p}^{1} RT\,d\ln P \tag{9-24}$$

leads to

$$G_{\text{gas}} = G^\circ_{\text{gas}} + RT\ln p \tag{9-25}$$

where $G^\circ_{\text{gas}}$ is the standard free energy of the vapor at 1 atm pressure and the given temperature.

If we use Eq. (9-25) to substitute for $G_{\text{gas}}$ in Eq. (9-22) we can rearrange the resultant to

$$RT\ln p = G_{\text{liquid}} - G^\circ_{\text{gas}} \tag{9-26}$$

It follows, therefore, that

$$R\ln p = \frac{G_{\text{liquid}}}{T} - \frac{G^\circ_{\text{gas}}}{T} \tag{9-27}$$

## Variable Total Pressure at Constant Temperature

Under these conditions we may differentiate Eq. (9-27) as follows:

$$R\left(\frac{\partial \ln p}{\partial P}\right)_T = \frac{1}{T}\left(\frac{\partial G_{\text{liquid}}}{\partial P}\right)_T - \frac{1}{T}\left(\frac{\partial G^\circ_{\text{gas}}}{\partial P}\right)_T \tag{9-28}$$

But $G^\circ_{gas}$ is independent of pressure since it is the standard free energy at a definite, fixed pressure—1 atm. Thus the second term on the right-hand side of Eq. (9-28) drops out. The first term on the right can be evaluated readily from Eq. (8-21). Consequently from Eq. (9-28) we obtain

$$\left(\frac{\partial \ln p}{\partial P}\right)_T = \frac{V_{liquid}}{RT} \tag{9-29}$$

where $V_{liquid}$ is the molal volume of the liquid phase.

The change of vapor pressure with change in total pressure of an inert atmosphere is actually small. For example, for water, where $V_{liquid}$ is 18 cm³, the right-hand side of Eq. (9-29) reduces to less than 0.001 at room temperature (for $R = 82$ cm³-atm mole⁻¹ deg⁻¹ and $T = 298°$).

## Variable Temperature at Constant Total Pressure

The Clausius-Clapeyron equation (9-18) gives the temperature dependence of the vapor pressure for a liquid in equilibrium with pure vapor. It is of interest to consider the situation of a liquid in equilibrium with its vapor in the presence of air, at a fixed atmospheric pressure.

Under these circumstances, if the temperature is varied we may differentiate Eq. (9-27) as follows:

$$R\left(\frac{\partial \ln p}{\partial T}\right)_P = \left(\frac{\partial (G_{liquid}/T)}{\partial T}\right)_P - \left(\frac{\partial (G^\circ_{gas}/T)}{\partial T}\right)_P \tag{9-30}$$

From Chapter 8, Eq. (8-83), we may substitute for each term on the right-hand side of Eq. (9-30) to obtain

$$R\left(\frac{\partial \ln p}{\partial T}\right)_P = -\frac{H_{liquid}}{T^2} + \frac{H^\circ_{gas}}{T^2} \tag{9-31}$$

The enthalpy $H^\circ_{gas}$ is independent of pressure, however, since the vapor is assumed to behave as an ideal gas [see Eq. (6-16)]. Consequently the enthalpy terms of Eq. (9-31) may be combined into the heat of vaporization, $\Delta H = H_{gas} - H_{liquid}$, and hence we obtain

$$\left(\frac{\partial \ln p}{\partial T}\right)_P = \frac{\Delta H}{RT^2} \tag{9-32}$$

a result comparable to Eq. (9-18).

# 9-3 TEMPERATURE DEPENDENCE OF HEAT OF PHASE TRANSITION

We are accustomed to think of the temperature coefficient of $\Delta H$ as given by

$$\left(\frac{\partial \Delta H}{\partial T}\right)_P = \Delta C_p \tag{9-33}$$

In, for example, a vaporization or sublimation, however, the vapor pressure does not remain constant as the temperature is varied. Hence to obtain $(d\,\Delta H/dT)_{\text{sat}}$, the temperature coefficient of the latent heat in the presence of saturated vapor at every temperature, we must find the dependence of $\Delta H$ on vapor pressure as well as temperature. Thereafter, since vapor pressure is also a function of the temperature, we can obtain $(d\,\Delta H/dT)_{\text{phase equil}}$.

Let us start then with an equation for the total differential

$$d(\Delta H) = \left(\frac{\partial\,\Delta H}{\partial T}\right)_P dT + \left(\frac{\partial\,\Delta H}{\partial P}\right)_T dP \tag{9-34}$$

$$= \Delta C_p\, dT + \left(\frac{\partial H_B}{\partial P} - \frac{\partial H_A}{\partial P}\right)_T dP \tag{9-35}$$

where the subscripts $A$ and $B$ refer to the two phases at equilibrium. It is not difficult to show from the free-energy function (see Exercise 3, Chapter 8) that

$$\left(\frac{\partial H}{\partial P}\right)_T = V - T\left(\frac{\partial V}{\partial T}\right)_P \tag{9-36}$$

With this relation, Eq. (9-35) may be converted into

$$d(\Delta H) = \Delta C_p\, dT + \left[\Delta V - T\left(\frac{\partial\,\Delta V}{\partial T}\right)_P\right] dP \tag{9-37}$$

Since $dT$ and $dP$ are not independent if equilibrium between phases is maintained, we may use the Clapeyron equation (9-13) to substitute for $dP$ and obtain

$$d(\Delta H) = \Delta C_p\, dT + \left[\Delta V - T\left(\frac{\partial \Delta V}{\partial T}\right)_P\right] \frac{\Delta H}{T\Delta V}\, dT \tag{9-38}$$

From this it follows that

$$\frac{d(\Delta H)}{dT} = \Delta C_p + \frac{\Delta H}{T} - \Delta H\left(\frac{\partial \ln \Delta V}{\partial T}\right)_P \tag{9-39}$$

So far in our derivation we have made no assumption as to the nature of phase $A$ or $B$, and hence Eq. (9-39) is applicable to all types of phase transition. In practice, when both $A$ and $B$ are condensed phases, the third term on the right-hand side of Eq. (9-39) is small compared with its predecessors and hence the equation reduces to

$$\frac{d(\Delta H)}{dT} = \Delta C_p + \frac{\Delta H}{T} \tag{9-40}$$

If the phase transition is a vaporization or sublimation an alternative approximation applies:

$$\Delta V \simeq V_{\text{gas}} = \frac{RT}{P} \tag{9-41}$$

Thereupon it follows that the third term of Eq. (9-39) cancels the second and hence

$$\frac{d(\Delta H)}{dT} \simeq \Delta C_p \tag{9-42}$$

Although Eqs. (9-33) and (9-42) are formally alike they refer to different types of processes. The former is strictly true for a process occurring at a constant pressure throughout a range of temperature. Vaporization or sublimation does not fulfill this restriction, but, nevertheless, Eq. (9-42) is approximately correct because the molal volume of the condensed phase is small compared to that of the gas.

## 9-4 CALCULATION OF $\Delta G$ FOR SPONTANEOUS PHASE CHANGE

So far we have considered problems in phase changes in which equilibrium is maintained. It is also pertinent to describe some procedures for the calculation of the change in free energy in transformations that are known to be spontaneous. For example, we might consider the freezing of supercooled water at $-10°C$:

$$H_2O(l, -10°C) = H_2O(s, -10°C) \tag{9-43}$$

At 0°C and 1 atm pressure of air, the process is at equilibrium. Hence

$$\Delta G_{0°C} = 0 \tag{9-44}$$

At $-10°C$, the supercooled water may freeze spontaneously. Therefore we can say immediately that

$$\Delta G_{-10°C} < 0 \tag{9-45}$$

Nevertheless, we still wish to evaluate $\Delta G$ numerically.

### Arithmetic Method

The simplest procedure to calculate the free-energy change at $-10°C$ makes use of the relation

$$\Delta G = \Delta H - T\Delta S \tag{9-46}$$

for any isothermal process. $\Delta H$ and $\Delta S$ at $-10°C$ $(T_2)$ are calculated from the known values at 0°C $(T_1)$ and from the temperature coefficients of these thermodynamic quantities. Since the procedure may be represented by the sum of a series of equations, the method may be called an arithmetic one. The series of equations are given in Table 9-1. From the values calculated for $\Delta H$ and $\Delta S$, it is evident that

$$\Delta G = -1343 + (263.15)(4.910) = -51 \text{ cal mole}^{-1} \tag{9-47}$$

## Analytic Method

The proposed problem could also be solved in a straightforward manner by integration of the equation derived in the preceding chapter,

$$\left(\frac{\partial (\Delta G/T)}{\partial T}\right)_P = -\frac{\Delta H}{T^2} \tag{9-48}$$

***Table 9-1***

*Free energy for freezing of supercooled water*

|  |  |
|---|---|
| $H_2O(l, 0°C) = H_2O(s, 0°C)$ | $\Delta H = -1436 \text{ cal mole}^{-1}$ |
| | $\Delta S = \dfrac{-1436}{273.15} = -5.257 \text{ cal mole}^{-1} \text{ deg}^{-1}$ |
| $H_2O(s, 0°C) = H_2O(s, -10°C)$ | $\Delta H = \int_{T_1}^{T_2} C_p\, dT = 8.7\,(-10)$ |
| | $= -\ 87 \text{ cal mole}^{-1}$ |
| | $\Delta S = \int_{T_1}^{T_2} \dfrac{C_p}{T}\, dT = C_p \ln \dfrac{T_2}{T_1}$ |
| | $= -0.324 \text{ cal mole}^{-1} \text{ deg}^{-1}$ |
| $H_2O(l, -10°C) = H_2O(l, 0°C)$ | $\Delta H = \int_{T_2}^{T_1} C_p'\, dT = 18(10)$ |
| | $= 180 \text{ cal mole}^{-1}$ |
| | $\Delta S = \int_{T_2}^{T_1} \dfrac{C_p'}{T}\, dT = 0.671 \text{ cal mole}^{-1} \text{ deg}^{-1}$ |
| $H_2O(l, -10°C) = H_2O(s, -10°C)$ | $\Delta H = -1343 \text{ cal mole}^{-1}$ |
| | $\Delta S = -4.910 \text{ cal mole}^{-1} \text{ deg}^{-1}$ |

As in the arithmetic method, we may assume that the heat capacities of ice and water, respectively, are substantially constant over the small temperature range under consideration. Thus from the relation

$$\left(\frac{\partial \Delta H}{\partial T}\right)_P = \Delta C_p \tag{9-49}$$

we obtain, upon integration,

$$\Delta H = \Delta H_0 + \int (C_{p(\text{ice})} - C_{p(\text{water})})\, dT$$

$$= \Delta H_0 - 9.3T \tag{9-50}$$

Since at 0°C, $\Delta H$ is $-1436$ cal mole$^{-1}$, we can determine $\Delta H_0$:

$$\Delta H_0 = -1436 + 9.3\,(273.15) = 1104.39 \qquad (9\text{-}51)^2$$

Hence

$$\Delta H = 1104.39 - 9.3T \tag{9-52}$$

and

$$\frac{\Delta G}{T} = -\int \frac{(1104.39 - 9.3T)}{T^2}\, dT$$

$$= \frac{1104.39}{T} + 9.3 \ln T + I \tag{9-53}$$

where $I$ is a constant. Rearrangement leads to

$$\Delta G = 1104.39 + 9.3T \ln T + IT \tag{9-54}$$

Since $\Delta G$ is known to be zero at 0°C, the constant $I$ may be evaluated:

$$I = \frac{-1104.39 - 9.3\,(273.15)\,(2.303)\log(273.15)}{273.15}$$

$$= -\,56.226 \qquad (9\text{-}55)^2$$

Thus we have an explicit equation for $\Delta G$ as a function of temperature:

$$\Delta G = 1104.39 + 9.3T \ln T - 56.226T \tag{9-56}$$

At $-10$°C this equation leads to

$$\Delta G_{-10°\text{C}} = -51 \text{ cal mole}^{-1} \tag{9-57}$$

This is the same result as was obtained by the arithmetic method.

Other methods, depending upon other expressions for $\Delta G$, may be used also. However, the preceding procedures are among the simplest and most direct.

[2] More significant figures are retained in these numbers than may be justified by the precision of the data upon which they are based. Such a procedure is necessary, however, in calculations involving small differences between large numbers.

## Exercises

**1.** Examine each of the following seven transformations:

(a) $H_2O(s, -10°C, 1 \text{ atm}) \rightarrow H_2O(l, -10°C, 1 \text{ atm})$;
(*Note:* No specification is made that this process is carried out isothermally, isobarically, or reversibly.)

(b) same as part (a), but restricted to a reversible change;

(c) same as part (a), but restricted to isothermal and isobaric conditions;

(d) the two-step, isobaric, reversible transformation
$H_2O(l, 25°C, 1 \text{ atm}) \rightarrow H_2O(l, 100°C, 1 \text{ atm})$
$H_2O(l, 100°C, 1 \text{ atm}) \rightarrow H_2O(g, 100°C, 1 \text{ atm})$;

(e) ideal gas (25°C, 100 atm) → ideal gas (25°C, 1 atm), reversible;

(f) ideal gas (25°C, 100 atm) → ideal gas (25°C, 10 atm), no work done;

(g) adiabatic reversible expansion of a perfect gas from 100 to 10 atm.

Consider each of the following equations:

(1) $\int \frac{DQ}{T} = \Delta S$

(2) $Q = \Delta H$

(3) $\frac{\Delta H}{T} = \Delta S$

(4) $-\Delta G$ = actual net work

(5) $-\Delta G$ = maximum net work

For each transformation, list the equations of the group (1) to (5) that are valid. If your decision depends upon the existence of conditions not specified, state what these conditions are.

**2.** Calculate $\Delta G°$ for each of the following transformations:

(a) $H_2O(l, 100°C) \rightarrow H_2O(g, 100°C)$.

(b) $H_2O(l, 25°C) \rightarrow H_2O(g, 25°C)$. The vapor pressure of $H_2O$ at 25°C is 0.0313 atm.

**3.** The vapor pressure of pure bromine at 25°C is 0.280 atm. The vapor pressure of bromine in a dilute aqueous solution at 25°C obeys the equation $p = 1.45m$, where $m$ is its molality.

(a) Calculate $\Delta G$ for the transformation

$$Br_2(l, 25°C) \rightarrow Br_2(0.01m, \text{aq. soln.}, 25°C).$$

(b) What would be the molal concentration of bromine in a saturated solution in water at 25°C?

**4.** An equation for $\Delta G$ for the freezing of supercooled water may be obtained also by integration of the equation

$$\left(\frac{\partial \Delta G}{\partial T}\right)_P = -\Delta S$$

An expression for $\Delta S$ as a function of temperature, for substitution into the preceding equation, may be derived from

$$\left(\frac{\partial \Delta S}{\partial T}\right)_P = \frac{\Delta C_p}{T}$$

(a) Show that

$$\Delta G = I' - \Delta C_p(T \ln T) + (\Delta C_p - \Delta S_0)T$$

where $I'$ and $\Delta S_0$ are constants.

(b) Evaluate the constants from data for the freezing process at 0°C.

(c) Calculate $\Delta G$ at $-10$°C and compare the result with the values calculated by the methods described in the text.

**5.** The transition

$$\text{sulfur (rhombic)} = \text{sulfur (monoclinic)}$$

is at equilibrium (at 1 atm pressure) at 95.5°C. The entropies (in cal mole$^{-1}$ deg$^{-1}$) of the allotropic forms are the following functions of temperature:

$$S_{\text{rh}} = -14.61 + 3.58 \ln T + 6.24 \times 10^{-3} T$$

$$S_{\text{mono}} = -14.55 + 3.56 \ln T + 6.96 \times 10^{-3} T$$

Compute the free-energy change for this allotropic transition at 25°C.

***Table 9-2***

| | Graphite | Diamond |
|---|---|---|
| $\Delta Gf^{\circ}_{298}$ (cal mole$^{-1}$) | 0 | 685.0 |
| $S^{\circ}_{298}$ (cal mole$^{-1}$ deg$^{-1}$) | 1.3609 | 0.5829 |
| Density (g cm$^{-3}$) | 2.22 | 3.51 |

**6.** By convention the free energy of formation, $\Delta Gf^{\circ}$, of graphite is assigned the value of zero. On this basis, $\Delta Gf^{\circ}_{298}$ of diamond is 685.0 cal mole$^{-1}$. Entropies and densities are also listed in Table 9-2. Assuming that the entropies and densities are approximately constant, determine the possibilities for the manufacture of diamonds from graphite by the use of high temperatures and pressures. [Cf. F. P. Bundy, H. T. Hall, H. M. Strong, and R. H. Wentorf, Jr., *Nature*, **176**, 51 (1955).]

**7.** The melting points of carbon tetrachloride at various pressures are given in Table 9-3, together with $\Delta V$ of fusion. Find $\Delta H$ and $\Delta S$ of fusion at (a) 1 atm; (b) 6000 atm.

***Table 9-3***

| $P$, atm | $t$, °C | $\Delta V$, cm$^3$ mole$^{-1}$ |
|---|---|---|
| 1 | $-22.6$ | 3.97 |
| 1000 | $-15.3$ | 3.06 |
| 2000 | 48.9 | 2.51 |
| 5000 | 130.8 | 1.52 |
| 7000 | 176.2 | 1.08 |

**8.** For liquid thiacyclobutane the vapor pressure, in millimeters, may be expressed by the equation [D. W. Scott, H. L. Finke, W. N. Hubbard, J. P. McCullough, C. Katz, M. E. Gross, J. F. Messerly, R. E. Pennington, and G. Waddington, *J. Am. Chem. Soc.*, **75**, 2795 (1953)],

$$\log_{10} P = 7.01667 - \frac{1321.331}{t + 224.513}$$

where $t$ is in °C. Calculate $\Delta H$ of vaporization at 298°K.

**9.** The vapor pressure of liquid helium may be expressed by the equation

$$P = AT^{5/2} e^{-[(a/T) + bT^{5.5}]}$$

where $A$, $a$, and $b$ are constants. Find an equation for $\Delta H$ of vaporization as a function of temperature.

**10.** Compute $\Delta G°$ for the transformation

$$H_2O(l, -5°C) = H_2O(s, -5°C)$$

given that the vapor pressure of supercooled liquid water at −5°C is 3.163 mm and that of ice 3.012 mm.

**11.** What would be the form of the integrated Clausius-Clapeyron equation if the heat capacity of the vapor is given by the equation

$$C_p = a + bT$$

and that of the condensed phase by

$$C_p' = a' + b'T$$

where the $a$'s and $b$'s are constants?

# 10 Application of Free Energy to Chemical Reactions

We must direct our attention next to the application of the free-energy criterion to chemical transformations. Since most chemical reactions are carried out at constant pressure and temperature, and with no restraints other than the pressure of the atmosphere, it is the Gibbs free energy, $G$, in which we shall be most interested. For application to chemical transformations, tables of free-energy data generally are assembled in terms of $\Delta G^\circ$, so that the equilibrium constant of a reaction may be calculated.

The standard free-energy change for a specified reaction may be obtained by several procedures. Although most of these have become familiar from elementary work in physical chemistry, it will be convenient to discuss all of them briefly at one point, so that their advantages and limitations may be compared.

## 10-1 ADDITION OF KNOWN $\Delta G^\circ$'s FOR SUITABLE CHEMICAL EQUATIONS LEADING TO THE DESIRED EQUATION

Since the free energy is a thermodynamic property, values of $\Delta G$ depend only upon the initial and final states and not upon the particular path used to go from one set of substances to another. Hence values of $\Delta G^\circ$ do not

*Table 10-1*

*Summation of $\Delta G^\circ$'s*

|  |  |
|---|---|
| $CO_2(g) + 4H_2(g) = CH_4(g) + 2H_2O(g)$ | $\Delta G^\circ_{298} = -27{,}150$ cal |
| $CH_4(g) = C(\text{graphite}) + 2H_2(g)$ | $\Delta G^\circ_{298} = 12{,}140$ cal |
| $C(\text{graphite}) + \frac{1}{2}O_2(g) = CO(g)$ | $\Delta G^\circ_{298} = -32{,}807.9$ cal |
| $2H_2O(g) = 2H_2O(l)$ | $\Delta G^\circ_{298} = -4109.6$ cal |
| $H_2O(l) = H_2(g) + \frac{1}{2}O_2(g)$ | $\Delta G^\circ_{298} = 56{,}689.9$ cal |
| $CO_2(g) + H_2(g) = H_2O(l) + CO(g)$ | $\Delta G^\circ = 4762$ cal mole$^{-1}$ |

depend upon the intermediate chemical reactions which have been used to transform a set of reactants, under specified conditions, to a series of products. Thus one may add known free energies to obtain values for reactions for which direct data are not available.

This method is illustrated best, perhaps, by a specific example. Let us consider as a problem[1] the determination of $\Delta G^\circ_{298}$ for the reaction

$$CO_2(g) + H_2(g) = H_2O(l) + CO(g) \tag{10-1}$$

We shall assume that the standard free energies of formation of $CO(g)$, $CH_4(g)$, and $H_2O(l)$, respectively, are known and also that standard free energies are available for the condensation of water vapor at 25°C and for the reaction

$$CO_2(g) + 4H_2(g) = CH_4(g) + 2H_2O(g) \tag{10-2}$$

The solution of our problem may then be obtained by the summation process in Table 10-1.

Once the standard free-energy change is known, it is of course possible to calculate the equilibrium constant for reaction (10-1):

$$\Delta G^\circ = -RT \ln K$$

$$4762 = -(1.987)(298.15)(2.303) \log K \tag{10-3}$$

$$K = 3.24 \times 10^{-4}$$

[1] In problems involving gases, the student is expected at this point to think of ideal gases only, for which the standard state is the gas at a pressure of 1 atm. For a real gas, the standard state is that of the gas at unit fugacity. All the statements of this chapter apply to a real gas at unit fugacity, as well as to an ideal gas in its standard state (see Chapter 15).

## 10-2 DETERMINATION OF $\Delta G°$ FROM EQUILIBRIUM MEASUREMENTS

Frequently the standard free energies required to calculate $\Delta G°$ for a specified reaction are not available. It is necessary then to resort to more direct relations between $\Delta G°$ and experimental measurements.

One of these direct methods depends upon the determination of the equilibrium constant of a given reaction. As an example we shall consider the dissociation of isopropyl alcohol:

$$(CH_3)_2CHOH(g) = (CH_3)_2CO(g) + H_2(g) \tag{10-4}$$

With a suitable catalyst, equilibrium pressures can be measured for this dissociation. At 452.2°K and a total pressure, $P$, of 0.947 atm, the degree of dissociation, $\alpha$, at equilibrium has been found[2] to be 0.564.

If we start with 1 mole of isopropyl alcohol, $\alpha$ moles each of acetone and hydrogen are formed. The quantity of alcohol remaining at equilibrium must be $1 - \alpha$. The total number of moles of all three gases is

$$\text{total moles} = (1 - \alpha) + \alpha + \alpha = 1 + \alpha \tag{10-5}$$

Hence the mole fraction, $N$, of each substance is

$$N_{(CH_3)_2CHOH} = \frac{1 - \alpha}{1 + \alpha} \tag{10-6}$$

$$N_{(CH_3)_2CO} = \frac{\alpha}{1 + \alpha} \tag{10-7}$$

$$N_{H_2} = \frac{\alpha}{1 + \alpha} \tag{10-8}$$

The equilibrium constant, $K$, being a function of the equilibrium partial pressures,[3] is given by

$$K = \frac{P_{(CH_3)_2CO}P_{H_2}}{P_{(CH_3)_2CHOH}} = \frac{[\alpha/(1 + \alpha)]\,P\,[\alpha/(1 + \alpha)]\,P}{[(1 - \alpha)/(1 + \alpha)]\,P} = \frac{\alpha^2}{1 - \alpha^2}P \tag{10-9}$$

$$K = 0.444 \tag{10-10}$$

The standard free-energy change may then be calculated from Eq. (10-3):

$$\Delta G°_{452.2°K} = -RT\ln(0.444) = 730 \text{ cal mole}^{-1} \tag{10-11}$$

[2] H. J. Kolb and R. L. Burwell, Jr., *J. Am. Chem. Soc.*, **67**, 1084 (1945).

[3] We are still using the assumption that the behavior of these gases may be described adequately by the ideal gas law. For precise formulations one must substitute fugacity of the gas in place of pressure. In problems involving solutions, it will be necessary to use a relative fugacity called the "activity" (see Chapter 19).

This is an appropriate occasion to emphasize that a positive value of $\Delta G^\circ$ does not imply that the reaction under consideration may not proceed spontaneously under any conditions. $\Delta G^\circ$ refers to the reaction

$$(CH_3)_2CHOH(g, P = 1 \text{ atm}) = (CH_3)_2CO(g, P = 1 \text{ atm}) + H_2(g, P = 1 \text{ atm}) \qquad (10\text{-}12)$$

where each substance is in its standard state, that is, at a partial pressure of 1 atm. Under these conditions the positive value of $\Delta G^\circ$ allows us to state categorically that reaction (10-12) will not proceed spontaneously. On the other hand, if we were to start with isopropyl alcohol at a partial pressure of 1 atm and no acetone or hydrogen, the alcohol might decompose spontaneously at 452.2°K, because, as the value of the equilibrium constant and the experimental data upon which it is based indicate, over 50 per cent dissociation may occur in the presence of a suitable catalyst. Yields can be made even greater if one of the products is removed continually.

We might also calculate $\Delta G$ for one set of conditions with the substances not all in their standard states, e.g.,

$$(CH_3)_2CHOH(g, P = 1 \text{ atm}) = (CH_3)_2CO(g, P = 0.1 \text{ atm}) + H_2(g, P = 0.1 \text{ atm}) \qquad (10\text{-}13)$$

For this computation we must refer back to Eq. (8-73) which relates $\Delta G$ under any pressure conditions to $\Delta G^\circ$ and the corresponding $P$'s and which, rearranged, reads

$$\Delta G = \Delta G^\circ + RT \ln \frac{(P_C)^c(P_D)^d}{(P_A)^a(P_B)^b} \qquad (10\text{-}14)$$

Applied to our present reaction [Eq. (10-13)], this relation gives

$$\Delta G = 730 + RT \ln \frac{(0.1)^2}{1} = -3710 \text{ cal mole}^{-1} \qquad (10\text{-}15)$$

Thus, if one is considering a given reaction in connection with the preparation of some substance, it is important not to be misled by positive values of $\Delta G^\circ$, for $\Delta G^\circ$ refers to the reaction under standard conditions. It is quite possible that appreciable yields can be obtained, even though a reaction may not go to *completion*. Such a case is illustrated well by the example of isopropyl alcohol just cited. Only if the values of $\Delta G^\circ$ are very large positive ones, perhaps greater than 10 kcal, can one be assured without calculations of the equilibrium constant that no significant degree of transformation can be obtained.

In addition, it is worth while to emphasize again that, although the standard free-energy change, $\Delta G^\circ$, refers to reactions with every substance under standard conditions, for example reaction (10-12), the equilibrium constant, $K$, calculated from Eq. (10-3) refers to the equilibrium state:

$$(CH_3)_2CHOH(g, P_{equil}) = (CH_3)_2CO(g, P_{equil}) + H_2(g, P_{equil}) \qquad (10\text{-}16)$$

For reaction (10-16), $\Delta G = 0$, according to the criterion developed in Chapter 8. Nevertheless, the equilibrium constant for (10-16) can be calculated from $\Delta G^\circ$ for reaction (10-12).

## 10-3 DETERMINATION FROM MEASUREMENTS OF ELECTROMOTIVE FORCE

This method, like the one just described, depends upon the ability of the system to undergo a transformation *reversibly* in an electrical cell. In this case the system will be opposed by a counter electromotive force just sufficient to balance the electromotive force (emf) obtained in the electrical cell. The emf observed under such circumstances is related to the free-energy change for the reaction by the expression derived in Chapter 8:

$$\Delta G = -n\mathcal{F}\mathcal{E} \qquad (10\text{-}17)$$

If the substances involved in the transformation are in their standard states,[4] then the measured emf, called $\mathcal{E}^\circ$, may be used to calculate the standard free-energy change, $\Delta G^\circ$:

$$\Delta G^\circ = -n\mathcal{F}\mathcal{E}^\circ \qquad (10\text{-}18)$$

A very simple example of a reaction to which this method is applicable is

$$\tfrac{1}{2}H_2(g) + AgCl(s) = HCl(aq) + Ag(s) \qquad (10\text{-}19)$$

From measurements of the emf of a cell containing hydrogen and silver-silver chloride electrodes, respectively, dipping into a solution of hydrochloric acid, it is possible to calculate that $\mathcal{E}^\circ$ is 0.022239 volt. Hence

$$\Delta G^\circ = -(1)\,(96{,}487)\,(0.22239)\ \text{volt-coulomb}$$

or

$$\Delta G^\circ = -5160\ \text{cal mole}^{-1} \qquad (10\text{-}20)$$

## 10-4 CALCULATION FROM THERMAL DATA AND THE THIRD LAW OF THERMODYNAMICS

The methods described so far depend directly or indirectly upon the reversible character of at least one reaction for every substance of interest.

[4] Actually, the measurements need not be made with every substance in its standard state. Methods of calculating $\mathcal{E}^\circ$ from emf measurements are described in Chapters 20 and 21.

For some time it was a challenge to theoretical chemists to devise some method of calculation of free energies from thermal data alone (that is, enthalpies and heat capacities) so that the need for experiments under equilibrium conditions might be avoided. One of the equations for $\Delta G$ derived in Chapter 8 is

$$\Delta G = \Delta H - T\Delta S \tag{10-21}$$

applicable to any isothermal reaction. Clearly, if it were possible to obtain $\Delta S$ from thermal data alone, it would be a simple matter to calculate $\Delta G$. The calculation of $\Delta S$ from thermal data alone, however, cannot be made without the introduction of a new assumption beyond the first two laws of thermodynamics. We shall discuss the nature of this new assumption and the consequences of it in the following chapter.

## 10-5 CALCULATION FROM SPECTROSCOPIC DATA AND STATISTICAL MECHANICS

Many free-energy changes, particularly for gaseous reactions, may be calculated from theoretical analyses of vibrational and rotational energies of molecules. The parameters used in these calculations are obtained from spectroscopic data. This method, however, depends upon assumptions beyond those of classical chemical thermodynamics and hence will not be described in this textbook. The results of these calculations can be used, nevertheless, even prior to an understanding of the methods by which they have been obtained.

## Exercises

**1.** According to D. P. Stevenson and J. H. Morgan [*J. Am. Chem. Soc.*, **70**, 2773 (1948)] the equilibrium constant, $K$, for the isomerization reaction

$$\text{cyclohexane}(l) = \text{methylcyclopentane}(l)$$

may be expressed by the equation

$$\ln K = 4.814 - \frac{2059}{T}$$

(a) Derive an equation for $\Delta G°$ as a function of $T$.
(b) Find $\Delta H°$ and $\Delta S°$ at 25°C.
(c) Find $\Delta H°$ and $\Delta S°$ at 0°C.
(d) Find $\Delta C_p^\circ$.

**2.** According to J. L. Hales and E. F. G. Herington, [*Trans. Faraday Soc.*, **53**, 616 (1957)] the equilibrium constant, $K$, for the hydrogenation of pyridine to piperidine,

$$C_5H_5N(g) + 3H_2(g) = C_5H_{11}N(g)$$

over the temperature range of 140 to 260°C may be expressed by the equation

$$\log_{10} K_p = -20.281 + \frac{10{,}560}{T}$$

Find $\Delta H^\circ$, $\Delta S^\circ$, and $\Delta C_p^\circ$ at 200°C.

**3.** Energy changes for the conversion of the chair to the boat conformation of the cyclohexane ring may be estimated from a study of the equilibrium between *cis*- and *trans*-1,3-di-*t*-butylcyclohexane. Some analytical results of N. L. Allinger and L. A. Freiberg [*J. Am. Chem. Soc.*, **82**, 2393 (1960)] are listed below:

| $T$,°K | 492.6 | 522.0 | 555.0 | 580.0 | 613.0 |
|---|---|---|---|---|---|
| % *trans* | 2.69 | 3.61 | 5.09 | 6.42 | 8.23 |

(a) Compute the equilibrium constant for *cis* ⇌ *trans* at each temperature.
(b) Draw a graph of log $K$ vs. $T$, and of log $K$ vs. $1/T$.
(c) Find $\Delta H^\circ$ and $\Delta S^\circ$ for the conformational change.

**4.** The standard potentials for a galvanic cell in which the reaction

$$\tfrac{1}{2}H_2(g) + AgCl(s) = Ag(s) + HCl(aq)$$

is being carried on are given in Table 2-2.

(a) By graphical differentiation, find the curve for $(\partial \mathscr{E}^\circ/\partial T)_P$ as a function of temperature.

(b) Calculate $\Delta G^\circ$, $\Delta H^\circ$, and $\Delta S^\circ$ at 0, 25, and 60°C, respectively. Tabulate the values you obtain.

(c) The empirical equation for $\mathscr{E}^\circ$ as a function of temperature is

$$\mathscr{E}^\circ = 0.22239 - 645.52 \times 10^{-6}\,(t - 25) - 3.284 \times 10^{-6}\,(t - 25)^2 + 9.948 \times 10^{-9}\,(t - 25)^3$$

where $t$ is centigrade temperature. Using this equation, determine $\Delta G^\circ$, $\Delta H^\circ$, and $\Delta S^\circ$ at 60°C. Compare with the values obtained by the graphical method.

**5.** It is of interest to obtain an equation for $\Delta G$ for a transformation in which concentrations are changing during the course of the reaction. For example, let us consider a case which may be represented as

$$A \rightarrow B$$

in which initially the concentration of $(A) = n$ and that of $(B) = 0$. At any time during the reaction, if $x$ represents the mole fraction of $B$ formed, then $(A) = (1 - x)n$ and $(B) = xn$. At any fraction of conversion $x$, it follows from Eq. (10-14) that

$$\Delta G = \Delta G^\circ + RT \ln \frac{xn}{(1 - x)n} \quad \text{per mole}$$

or

$$\Delta G = \left[\Delta G^\circ + RT \ln \frac{x}{1 - x}\right] m$$

for $m$ moles. Thus if $dA$ moles of $A$ are converted to $dB$ mo les of $B$

$$d(\Delta G) = \left[\Delta G^\circ + RT \ln \frac{x}{1 - x}\right] dB$$

(a) Show that $\Delta G$ for raising the mole fraction of $B$ from 0 to $x$ is given by

$$\int_0^x d(\Delta G) = nx\,\Delta G^\circ + nRT\left[x \ln \frac{x}{1-x} + \ln(1-x)\right]$$

(b) Prove that to reach the equilibrium state, $x_{\text{equil}}$,

$$\Delta G = -nRT \ln(K+1)$$

where $K$ is the equilibrium constant for the reaction.

# 11 The Third Law of Thermodynamics

## 11-1 PURPOSE OF THE THIRD LAW

As was pointed out in the preceding chapter, if it were possible to calculate $\Delta S^\circ$ for a reaction from thermal data alone, it would be a simple matter to evaluate $\Delta G^\circ$ from the relation

$$\Delta G^\circ = \Delta H^\circ - T\Delta S^\circ \tag{11-1}$$

For example, we might wish to determine $\Delta G^\circ_{298}$ for the reaction

$$\text{C(graphite)} + 2H_2(g) = CH_4(g) \tag{11-2}$$

It is obvious that $\Delta H^\circ$ can be determined from the following heats of combustion:

$$CH_4(g) + 2O_2(g) = CO_2(g) + 2H_2O(l) \qquad \Delta H^\circ_{\text{combustion of } CH_4} \tag{11-3}$$

$$CO_2(g) = \text{C (graphite)} + O_2(g) \qquad -\Delta H^\circ_{\text{combustion of C}} \tag{11-4}$$

$$2H_2O(l) = 2H_2(g) + O_2(g) \qquad -2\Delta H^\circ_{\text{combustion of } H_2} \tag{11-5}$$

---

$$CH_4(g) = \text{C (graphite)} + 2H_2(g)$$

$$\Delta H^\circ = \Delta H^\circ_{CH_4} - \Delta H^\circ_{C} - 2\Delta H^\circ_{H_2} \tag{11-6}$$

Clearly, $\Delta H^\circ$ for reaction (11-2) is merely the negative of that for reaction (11-6). It remains, however, to calculate $\Delta S^\circ_{298}$.

The problem of calculating $\Delta S^\circ_{298}$ can be reduced to an alternative problem by the following considerations. Let us assume for the moment that $\Delta S^\circ_{0^\circ K}$ is known. It is evident that we could add the following equations, for each of which $\Delta S$ at a pressure of 1 atm can be determined from thermal data alone, to lead to $\Delta S^\circ_{298}$:[1]

$$C\,(\text{graphite}, 0^\circ K) + 2H_2(s, 0^\circ K) = CH_4(s, 0^\circ K) \qquad \Delta S_{0^\circ K} \qquad (11\text{-}7)^2$$

$$CH_4(s, 0^\circ K) = CH_4(s, T_{mp}) \qquad \Delta S_1 = \int_0^{T_{mp}} \frac{(C_p)_1\, dT}{T} \qquad (11\text{-}8)$$

$$CH_4(s, T_{mp}) = CH_4(l, T_{mp}) \qquad \Delta S_2 = \frac{\Delta H_{\text{fusion}}}{T_{mp}} \qquad (11\text{-}9)$$

$$CH_4(l, T_{mp}) = CH_4(l, T_{bp}) \qquad \Delta S_3 = \int_{T_{mp}}^{T_{bp}} \frac{(C_p)_2\, dT}{T} \qquad (11\text{-}10)$$

$$CH_4(l, T_{bp}) = CH_4(g, T_{bp}) \qquad \Delta S_4 = \frac{\Delta H_{\text{vaporization}}}{T_{bp}} \qquad (11\text{-}11)$$

$$CH_4(g, T_{bp}) = CH_4(g, 298.15^\circ) \qquad \Delta S_5 = \int_{T_{bp}}^{298.15^\circ} \frac{(C_p)_3\, dT}{T} \qquad (11\text{-}12)$$

$$2H_2(s, T'_{mp}) = 2H_2(s, 0^\circ K) \qquad \Delta S_6 = \int_{T'_{mp}}^{0^\circ} \frac{2(C_p)_4\, dT}{T} \qquad (11\text{-}13)$$

$$2H_2(l, T'_{mp}) = 2H_2(s, T'_{mp}) \qquad \Delta S_7 = \frac{-2\Delta H'_{\text{fusion}}}{T'_{mp}} \qquad (11\text{-}14)$$

$$2H_2(l, T'_{bp}) = 2H_2(l, T'_{mp}) \qquad \Delta S_8 = \int_{T'_{bp}}^{T'_{mp}} \frac{2(C_p)_5\, dT}{T} \qquad (11\text{-}15)$$

$$2H_2(g, T'_{bp}) = 2H_2(l, T'_{bp}) \qquad \Delta S_9 = \frac{-2\Delta H'_{\text{vaporization}}}{T'_{bp}} \qquad (11\text{-}16)$$

[1] In this introductory discussion, it is assumed that $CH_4$ and $H_2$ behave as ideal gases at 298°K, and hence the calculation has been outlined for a pressure of 1 atm, that of the standard state of an ideal gas. Methods of making corrections for deviations from ideal behavior are described later in this chapter.

[2] Note that at 0°K hydrogen and methane would be in the solid state.

$$2H_2(g, 298.15^\circ) = 2H_2(g, T'_{bp}) \qquad \Delta S_{10} = \int_{298.15^\circ}^{T'_{bp}} \frac{2(C_p)_6\, dT}{T} \qquad (11\text{-}17)$$

$$C\,(\text{graphite}, 298.15^\circ) = C\,(\text{graphite}, 0^\circ K) \qquad \Delta S_{11} = \int_{298.15^\circ}^{0^\circ} \frac{(C_p)_7\, dT}{T} \qquad (11\text{-}18)$$

---

$$C\,(\text{graphite}, 298.15^\circ) + 2H_2(g, 298.15^\circ) = CH_4(g, 298.15^\circ)$$

$$\Delta S^\circ_{298} = \Delta S^\circ_{0^\circ K} + \sum_1^{11} \Delta S_i \qquad (11\text{-}19)$$

The determination of the sum, $\Sigma_1^{11}\Delta S_i$, requires only a knowledge of heat capacities, heats of fusion and vaporization, and the respective transition temperatures. If the solids existed in more than one crystalline form, it would be necessary to know also the heats and temperatures of such transitions. Nevertheless, all these data are merely thermal data. If, then, we can obtain some information on $\Delta S_{0^\circ K}$ without introducing nonthermal data, we shall have fulfilled our present objective.

The first and second laws of thermodynamics give no indication of the value of $\Delta S_{0^\circ K}$. Apparently it will be necessary to obtain a new principle, formulated from experimental observations, in order to solve this problem.

## 11-2 FORMULATION OF THE THIRD LAW

We have pointed out previously that for many reactions the contribution of the $T\,\Delta S$ term in Eq. (11-1) is relatively small, even at room temperatures, so that $\Delta G$ and $\Delta H$ are frequently close in value even at relatively high temperatures. In a comprehensive series of experiments on galvanic cells, Richards[3] showed, furthermore, that as the temperature decreases, $\Delta G$ approaches $\Delta H$ more and more closely, in the manner indicated in Figure 11-1. Although these results are really only fragmentary evidence, they did furnish the clues which led Nernst to the first formulation of the third law of thermodynamics.

### Nernst Heat Theorem

The trend of $\Delta G$ and $\Delta H$ toward each other may be expressed in mathematical form as follows:

$$\lim_{T\to 0}\,(\Delta G - \Delta H) = 0 \qquad (11\text{-}20)$$

[3] T. W. Richards, *Z. Physik. Chem.*, **42,** 129 (1902).

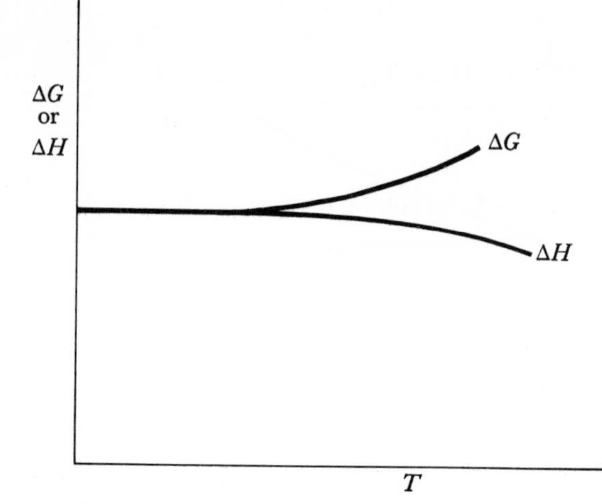


***Figure 11-1*** *Limiting approach of $\Delta G$ and of $\Delta H$ as the temperature approaches absolute zero.*

It is evident from a rearrangement of Eq. (11-1),

$$\Delta G - \Delta H = -T\,\Delta S \tag{11-21}$$

that the relation expressed by Eq. (11-20) may follow simply because as $T$ approaches zero, so must $T\,\Delta S$, as long as $\Delta S$ is finite. Nernst, however, made the additional assumption, based on the appearance of Richards' curves (Figure 11-1), that the limiting value of $\Delta S$ was not only finite but actually zero for all condensed systems:

$$\lim_{T\to 0}\,(-\Delta S) = \lim_{T\to 0}\left(\frac{\partial\,\Delta G}{\partial T}\right)_P = 0 \tag{11-22}$$

In essence, this assumption amounts to saying not only that $\Delta G$ approaches $\Delta H$ as $T$ approaches 0°K, but also that the $\Delta G$ curve (Figure 11-1) approaches a horizontal limiting tangent.

It is conceivable, of course, that Eq. (11-20) may be valid and yet that expression (11-22) will not be fulfilled. This situation would occur if the limiting value of $\Delta S$ were some finite number but not zero, and would correspond graphically to the curve illustrated in Figure 11-2, where $\Delta G$ and $\Delta H$ approach each other at absolute zero but where the limiting slope of $\Delta G$ is finite. In fact, Richards suggested that some of his data be extrapolated to give a graph such as shown in Figure 11-2. Thus from the data available to Nernst there was no assurance of the validity of Eq. (11-22).

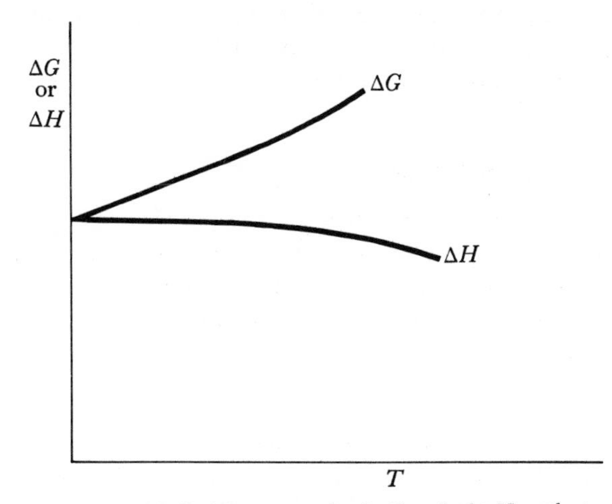


***Figure 11-2*** *A conceivable limiting approach of $\Delta G$ and of $\Delta H$ as the temperature approaches absolute zero.*

Nevertheless, numerous experiments since then have confirmed this postulate, if it is limited to perfect crystalline systems. *Apparent* exceptions have been accounted for satisfactorily. The term "perfect" implies that we are dealing with a single, pure substance. There are other restrictions implied by this term, but they will be discussed later.

## Planck's Formulation

In Nernst's statement of the third law no comment is made on the value of the absolute entropy at 0°K, although it must be finite or zero if $\Delta S_{0°\mathrm{K}}$ is to be finite for a reaction involving condensed phases. Planck[4] extended Nernst's assumption by making the additional postulate that *the absolute value of the entropy of a pure solid or a pure liquid approaches zero at 0°K:*

$$\lim_{T \to 0} S = 0 \tag{11-23}$$

If Eq. (11-23) is assumed, Nernst's theorem, Eq. (11-22), follows immediately for pure solids and liquids. Planck's formulation is also consistent with the treatment of entropy which is introduced in statistical mechanics.

Planck's statement asserts that $S_{0°\mathrm{K}}$ is zero only for *pure solids and pure*

[4] M. Planck, *Thermodynamik*, 3d ed., Veit & Co., Leipzig, 1911, p. 279.

*liquids*, whereas Nernst assumed that his theorem was applicable to *all condensed phases*, including solutions. According to Planck, solutions at 0°K have a positive entropy equal to the entropy of mixing.[5]

## Statement of Lewis and Randall

Lewis and Gibson[6] also emphasized the positive entropy of solutions at 0°K and in addition pointed out that supercooled liquids, such as glasses, even when composed of a single element (for example, sulfur), probably retain positive entropies even as the temperature approaches absolute zero. For these reasons Lewis and Randall[7] proposed the following statement of the third law of thermodynamics:

> *If the entropy of each element in some crystalline state be taken as zero at the absolute zero of temperature: every substance has a finite positive entropy, but at the absolute zero of temperature the entropy may become zero, and does so become in the case of perfect crystalline substances.*

It is this statement which we shall adopt as our working form of the third law of thermodynamics. From a practical standpoint of the chemist, that is, in making free-energy calculations, this statement is the most convenient formulation. Nevertheless, it should be realized that from a theoretical point of view more elegant formulations have been suggested.[8]

As has been mentioned, the above statement of the third law has been formulated to exclude solutions and glasses from the class of substances assumed to have zero entropy at 0°K. We might examine, therefore, one example of each exclusion to see that this limitation is essential.

For the mixing process

$$\mathrm{AgCl}(s, 0°\mathrm{K}) + \mathrm{AgBr}(s, 0°\mathrm{K}) = \text{solid solution}(s, 0°\mathrm{K}) \qquad (11\text{-}24)$$

the entropy change may be represented as

$$\Delta S_{0°\mathrm{K}} = S_{\substack{\text{solid}\\ \text{sol}}} - S_{\mathrm{AgBr}} - S_{\mathrm{AgCl}} \qquad (11\text{-}25)$$

and may be computed from the experimentally known $\Delta S_{298°}$ for the same

[5] An equation for the entropy of mixing in ideal solutions is derived in Chapter 17.

[6] G. N. Lewis and G. E. Gibson, *J. Am. Chem. Soc.*, **42,** 1529 (1920).

[7] G. N. Lewis and M. Randall, *Thermodynamics*, McGraw-Hill, New York, 1923, p. 448.

[8] O. Stern, *Ann. Physik*, **49,** 823 (1916). E. D. Eastman and R. T. Milner, *J. Chem. Phys.*, **1,** 444 (1933). R. H. Fowler and E. A. Guggenheim, *Statistical Thermodynamics*, Macmillan, New York, 1939, p. 224. P. C. Cross and H. C. Eckstrom *J. Chem. Phys.*, **10,** 287 (1942). F. E. Simon, *Physica*, **4,** 1089 (1937).

mixing reaction plus heat capacity data from near 0° to 298°K for each of the three solids.[9]

For the formation of 1 mole of a particular solid solution $\Delta S_{0°K}$ turns out to be 1.03 eu. Hence if $S_{AgBr}$ and $S_{AgCl}$ are each taken as zero at 0°K, the entropy of the solid solution at 0°K is not zero but 1.03 gibbs/mole. It is of interest that this value is close to that, 1.16 gibbs/mole, which one would calculate for the entropy of mixing to form an ideal solution. In any event a solid solution does not obey the third law.

Likewise glasses do not fit the third law, that is, $\Delta S_{0°K}$ is not zero for a transition such as

$$\text{glycerol (crystalline, 0°K)} = \text{glycerol (glass, 0°K)} \qquad (11\text{-}26)$$

To calculate $\Delta S$ for this transition it is necessary to have heat capacity data for both solid forms of glycerol from near 0°K to the melting point, plus the heat of fusion of crystals. Such data[10] lead to a $\Delta S$ for Eq. (11-26) of 4.6 eu. Thus it follows that glassy glycerol cannot be assigned zero entropy at 0°K, but possesses a residual entropy of 4.6 gibbs/mole, and hence it too does not obey the third law.

Having mentioned some exclusions from the third law, we should also comment on a situation not outside the law which the unwary student might place in that omitted class. There are many substances which may exist in two (or more) different crystalline forms at low temperatures. One form is, of course, more stable than the other. Nevertheless, if each is a *perfect crystalline substance*, its entropy at 0°K will turn out to be zero. For example, for the transition

$$\text{sulfur (monoclinic, 0°K)} = \text{sulfur (rhombic, 0°K)} \qquad (11\text{-}27)$$

$\Delta S_{0°K}$ may be computed from heat capacity measurements[11] for each crystalline form from near 0°K to the transition temperature (368.6°K) plus the heat of transition. The result obtained is zero within experimental error. Hence both rhombic and monoclinic sulfur are assigned zero entropy at 0°K.

## Unattainability of Absolute Zero

For purposes of computation, the statement of Lewis and Randall will serve us very well. Nevertheless, one should be aware of an alternative statement of the third law (from which in fact the Nernst heat theorem and the Lewis and Randall statement follow as consequences), which is of more general significance and which is in the form of a principle of impotence,

[9] E. D. Eastman and R. T. Milner, *J. Chem. Phys.*, **1,** 444 (1933).
[10] F. Simon and E. Lange, *Z. Physik*, **38,** 227 (1926).
[11] E. D. Eastman and W. C. McGavock, *J. Am. Chem. Soc.*, **59,** 145 (1937).

paralleling our statements of the first two laws:

*It is impossible to attain absolute zero in a finite number of operations.*

Classically in thermodynamics this statement was a trivial one since it was considered a direct consequence of the first two laws of thermodynamics. For example, if we consider an entropy change at constant pressure

$$dS = \frac{DQ_P}{T} = \frac{C_p}{T}\,dT \tag{11-28}$$

In classical mechanics, the specific heat had a finite value at all temperatures; hence

$$\lim_{T\to 0}\left(\frac{\partial S}{\partial T}\right)_P = \lim_{T\to 0}\frac{C_p}{T} = \infty \tag{11-29}$$

Consequently the entropy of any substance should tend toward negative infinity as $T$ approaches absolute zero, and clearly no finite series of processes could reach absolute zero.

In actual fact, however, and as a consequence of quantum behavior of matter, heat capacities tend to zero as $T \to 0°K$ (at a rate proportional to $T$ for metals and to $T^3$ for other solids). Hence unattainability of absolute zero no longer follows from the first two laws of thermodynamics. The entire question of attainability thus becomes a pertinent one.

In actual practice it is a common feature of all low-temperature cooling processes that the lower the temperature attained the harder it is to proceed further down. As with the first and second laws of thermodynamics, therefore, we make a generalized and condensed statement of much experience in the form: *No system can be reduced to* $0°K$.

As in the case of the second law, where the Clausius statement as a principle of impotence was not convenient for the analysis of chemical problems, so the unattainability statement of the third law is not the convenient form for computational purposes. However, it is not difficult to demonstrate that the Lewis and Randall statement follows from the unattainability principle and thus is not an independent theorem.

One can also proceed in the reverse manner and prove that the assumption that $S^\circ_{0°K}$ is zero leads to the unattainability statement.

For this latter purpose let us consider in general terms the problem of cooling a system below any hitherto attainable temperature. The process for doing this might be an allotropic transformation, a change in external magnetic field, a volume change, etc. We shall represent the initial state as $a$ (at temperature $T_1$) and the final state as $b$ (at temperature $T_2$). The process will be carried out adiabatically since any other reservoir available to us is not at a lower temperature than the working system and hence cannot help us achieve a drop in temperature.

The entropies of the substances in states $a$ and $b$ are expressible by the following equations:

$$S_a(T_1) = S_a(0°\mathrm{K}) + \int_0^{T_1} \frac{C_a}{T}\, dT \tag{11-30}$$

$$S_b(T_2) = S_b(0°\mathrm{K}) + \int_0^{T_2} \frac{C_b}{T}\, dT \tag{11-31}$$

The adiabatic transformation may be either reversible or (spontaneously) irreversible. In the former circumstances, since $\Delta S$ is zero, it follows from Eq. (11-30) and (11-31) that

$$S_a(0°\mathrm{K}) + \int_0^{T_1} \frac{C_a}{T}\, dT = S_b(0°\mathrm{K}) + \int_0^{T_2} \frac{C_b}{T}\, dT \tag{11-32}$$

If now we take as our fundamental axiom of the third law the statement

$$S_a(0°\mathrm{K}) = S_b(0°\mathrm{K}) \tag{11-33}$$

then Eq. (11-32) becomes

$$\int_0^{T_1} \frac{C_a}{T}\, dT = \int_0^{T_2} \frac{C_b}{T}\, dT \tag{11-34}$$

The left-hand side of Eq. (11-34) must be positive since $T_1 > 0$ and since $C_a > 0$ for any nonzero temperature. Therefore the right-hand side of Eq. (11-34) must also be positive, and this can only be true if $T_2 \neq 0$, that is, if the cooling process does not attain 0°K.

So far we have discussed only reversible adiabatic processes for going from state $a$ to state $b$. If the process is irreversible and in the direction $a \rightarrow b$, then since $\Delta S > 0$ we must write, in place of Eq. (11-32),

$$S_a(0°\mathrm{K}) + \int_0^{T_1} \frac{C_a}{T}\, dT < S_b(0°\mathrm{K}) + \int_0^{T_2} \frac{C_b}{T}\, dT \tag{11-35}$$

Again if we take Eq. (11-33) as our statement of the third law, if follows that

$$\int_0^{T_1} \frac{C_a}{T}\, dT < \int_0^{T_2} \frac{C_b}{T}\, dT \tag{11-36}$$

Since the left-hand side of Eq. (11-36) is positive, it follows again that the right-hand side, and therefore, $T_2$ is positive. We conclude therefore that absolute zero is unattainable.

## 11-3 THERMODYNAMIC PROPERTIES AT ABSOLUTE ZERO

From the third law of thermodynamics it is possible to derive a number of limiting relationships which must be valid for thermodynamic quantities at the absolute zero of temperature.

### Equivalence of $G$ and $H$

It follows immediately from the Lewis and Randall statement of the third law and the definition of free energy that for any substance

$$G_{0^\circ K} = H_{0^\circ K} - TS_{0^\circ K} = H_{0^\circ K} \tag{11-37}$$

### $\Delta C_p$ in a Chemical Transformation

Starting with the expression (11-22), we can see readily from the Gibbs-Helmholtz relation [Eq. (8-130)],

$$\Delta G = \Delta H + T\left(\frac{\partial \Delta G}{\partial T}\right)_P \tag{11-38}$$

that the following relation must also be valid:

$$\lim_{T\to 0}\left(\frac{\partial \Delta G}{\partial T}\right)_P = \lim_{T\to 0}\frac{\Delta G - \Delta H}{T} = 0 \tag{11-39}$$

A glance at the expression

$$\lim_{T\to 0}\,[(\Delta G - \Delta H)/T]$$

will show that as it stands it is an indeterminate form, since both $(\Delta G - \Delta H)$ and $T$ approach zero. To resolve an indeterminate expression, we may apply the mathematical rule of differentiating numerator and denominator, respectively, with respect to the independant variable, $T$. Carrying out this procedure, we obtain from Eq. (11-39)

$$\lim_{T\to 0}\frac{(\partial \Delta G/\partial T)_P - (\partial \Delta H/\partial T)_P}{1} = 0 \tag{11-40}$$

and

$$\lim_{T\to 0}\left(\frac{\partial \Delta G}{\partial T}\right)_P = \lim_{T\to 0}\left(\frac{\partial \Delta H}{\partial T}\right)_P = \lim_{T\to 0}\Delta C_p \tag{11-41}$$

In view of our fundamental postulate, Eq. (11-22), it follows that

$$\lim_{T\to 0}\Delta C_p = 0 \tag{11-42}$$

Many investigators have shown that $\Delta C_p$ does approach zero as $T$ approaches absolute zero. Nevertheless, these results in themselves do not constitute experimental evidence for the third law, because as long as the limiting value of $(\partial\,\Delta G/\partial T)_P$ is not infinite, it can be shown by a procedure corresponding to Eqs. (11-40) and (11-41) that Eq. (11-42) must be valid.

## Limiting Values of $C_p$ and $C_v$

The third law asserts that the entropy of any substance (referred to the corresponding elements) must be finite or zero at absolute zero. In view of the finite values observed for $\Delta S$ at higher temperatures, it follows that the entropy of a substance must be finite at all (finite) temperatures.

In Chapter 7 it was shown that for a reversible isobaric temperature change in a substance

$$dS_P = \frac{DQ_P}{T} = \frac{C_p\,dT}{T} \tag{11-28}$$

This differential equation may be integrated, *at constant pressure*, to give

$$S = \int_0^T \frac{C_p\,dT}{T} + S_0 \tag{11-43}$$

where $S_0$ represents an integration constant. Since $S$ must be finite at all temperatures, it follows that

$$\lim_{T\to 0} C_p = 0 \tag{11-44}$$

If $C_p$ had a finite value at $T = 0$, it is obvious that the integral in Eq. (11-43) would not converge, since $T$ in the denominator goes to zero, and hence that $S$ would not be finite.

By a completely analogous procedure, we can show that

$$\lim_{T\to 0} C_v = 0 \tag{11-45}$$

## Temperature Coefficients of Pressure and Volume

In view of the statement that

$$\lim_{T\to 0} S = 0 \tag{11-23}$$

it follows that in the limit of absolute zero of temperature the entropy of a perfect crystalline substance must be independent of changes in pressure or volume.[12] Thus

$$\lim_{T\to 0}\left(\frac{\partial S}{\partial P}\right)_T = 0 \tag{11-46}$$

and

$$\lim_{T\to 0}\left(\frac{\partial S}{\partial V}\right)_T = 0 \tag{11-47}$$

In Chapter 8 we showed that

$$\left(\frac{\partial S}{\partial P}\right)_T = -\left(\frac{\partial V}{\partial T}\right)_P \tag{11-48}$$

and

$$\left(\frac{\partial S}{\partial V}\right)_T = \left(\frac{\partial P}{\partial T}\right)_V \tag{11-49}$$

Combining Eqs. (11-46) and (11-48), we obtain the expression

$$\lim_{T\to 0}\left(\frac{\partial V}{\partial T}\right)_P = 0 \tag{11-50}$$

Similarly, Eqs. (11-47) and (11-49) lead to

$$\lim_{T\to 0}\left(\frac{\partial P}{\partial T}\right)_V = 0 \tag{11-51}$$

In other words, the temperature gradients of the pressure and volume vanish as absolute zero is approached.

## 11-4 TABLES OF ENTROPIES AT 298°K

In the statement which we have adopted for the third law, it is assumed (arbitrarily) that the entropy of each element in some crystalline state may be taken as zero at 0°K. For every perfect crystalline substance, then, the entropy is also zero at 0°K. Consequently, we have set $S_0$, the integration constant in Eq. (11-43), equal to zero. Thus we may write

$$S = \int_0^T \frac{C_p\, dT}{T} \tag{11-52}$$

Evidently, then, we can evaluate the entropy of a perfect crystalline solid at any specified temperature by integration of the heat-capacity data.

[12] One may generalize this statement to all the variables, $x_1, x_2, \ldots x_i$, which may determine the state of a substance at the absolute zero and hence conclude that $\lim_{T\to 0} (\partial S/\partial x_i)_T = 0$.

The entropy so obtained is frequently called the "absolute" entropy and is indicated as $S_T^\circ$. In no sense, however, is $S_T^\circ$ truly an absolute entropy, for we must always remember that behind Eq. (11-52) lies the assumption that the entropy of each element in some state at 0°K may be taken as zero. It is clearly recognized that this assumption is merely one of convenience, since entropies associated with the nucleus, for example, are not zero.

Should we be interested in the absolute entropy of a substance at a temperature at which it is no longer a solid, it is necessary merely to add the entropy of transformation to a liquid or gas and the subsequent entropies of warming. The same procedure would apply to a solid which exists in different crystalline forms as the temperature is raised. The procedure may be illustrated best by an outline of some sample calculations.

## Typical Calculations

***For solid or liquid.*** For either of these final states it is necessary to have heat-capacity data for the solid down to temperatures approaching absolute zero. The integration indicated by Eq. (11-52) is then carried out in two steps. From approximately 20°K up, graphical methods may be used. Below 20°K, however, few data are available. It is customary, therefore, to rely on the Debye equation in this region.

*Use of Debye equation at very low temperatures.* It is generally assumed that the Debye equation expresses the behavior of the heat capacity adequately below about 20°K.[13] This relation [Eq. (4-40)],

$$C_p \simeq C_v = 464.5 \frac{T^3}{\theta^3} \text{ cal mole}^{-1} \text{ deg}^{-1} \tag{11-53}$$

contains but one constant, $\theta$, which may be determined from one value of $C_p$ in the region near 20°K or lower. The integral for the absolute entropy then becomes

$$S = \int_0^T \frac{kT^3}{T}\, dT = \int_0^T kT^2\, dT \tag{11-54}$$

where $k$ represents $464.5/\theta^3$.

*Absolute entropy of methylammonium chloride.* Heat capacities for this solid in its various crystalline modifications have been determined[14] very precisely down to 12°K; some of these data are summarized in Figure 11-3. In

[13] Deviations from the $T^3$ law and their significance have been discussed by K. Clusius and L. Schachinger, *Z. Naturforschung*, **2a,** 90 (1947), by G. L. Pickard and F. E. Simon, *Proc. Phys. Soc.*, **61,** 1 (1948), and by A. R. Ubbelohde, *Modern Thermodynamical Principles*, 2nd ed., Clarendon Press, Oxford, 1952, p. 109.

[14] J. G. Aston and C. W. Ziemer, *J. Am. Chem. Soc.*, **68,** 1405 (1946).

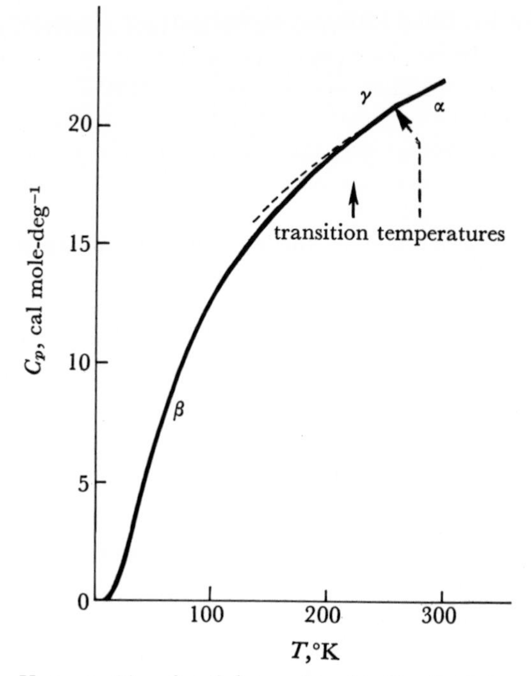


***Figure 11-3*** *Heat capacities of methylammonium chloride. Symbols α, β, and γ indicate the three allotropic forms of the solid.*

this case, where there are three crystalline forms between 0° and 298°K, one can calculate the absolute entropy by integrating Eq. (11-52) for each allotrope in the temperature region in which it is most stable, and by adding to the integrals thus obtained the two entropies of transition. The details as they are carried out in actual practice, at a pressure of 1 atm, may be summarized as follows:

(a) $CH_3NH_3Cl(s, 0°K, \beta \text{ form}) = CH_3NH_3Cl(s, 12.04°K, \beta \text{ form})$

$$\Delta S_1 = \int_{0°K}^{12.04°K} \frac{C_p\,dT}{T} = 0.067 \text{ cal mole}^{-1} \text{ deg}^{-1} \qquad \text{Debye equation with } \theta = 200.5$$

(b) $CH_3NH_3Cl(s, 12.04°, \beta \text{ form}) = CH_3NH_3Cl(s, 220.4°, \beta \text{ form})$

$$\Delta S_2 = \int_{12.04°}^{220.4°} \frac{C_p\,dT}{T} = 22.326 \qquad \text{graphical integration}$$

(c) $CH_3NH_3Cl(s, 220.4°, \beta \text{ form}) = CH_3NH_3Cl(s, 220.4°, \gamma \text{ form})$

$$\Delta S_3 = \frac{\Delta H}{T} = \frac{425.2}{220.4} = 1.929$$

(d) $CH_3NH_3Cl(s, 220.4°, \gamma \text{ form}) = CH_3NH_3Cl(s, 264.5°, \gamma \text{ form})$

$$\Delta S_4 = \int_{220.4°}^{264.5°} \frac{C'_p\, dT}{T} = 3.690 \qquad \text{graphical integration}$$

(e) $CH_3NH_3Cl(s, 264.5°, \gamma \text{ form}) = CH_3NH_3Cl(s, 264.5°, \alpha \text{ form})$

$$\Delta S_5 = \frac{\Delta H'}{T'} = \frac{673.6}{264.5} = 2.547$$

(f) $CH_3NH_3Cl(s, 264.5°, \alpha \text{ form}) = CH_3NH_3Cl(s, 298.15°, \alpha \text{ form})$

$$\Delta S_6 = \int_{264.5°}^{298.15°} \frac{C''_p\, dT}{T} = 2.555 \qquad \text{graphical integration}$$

Addition of Steps (a) to (f) gives

(g) $CH_3NH_3Cl(s, 0°K) = CH_3NH_3Cl(s, 298.15°K)$

$$\Delta S° = \sum_{1}^{6} \Delta S_i = 33.114 \text{ cal mole}^{-1} \text{ deg}^{-1}$$

Thus for methylammonium chloride, $S^{\circ}_{298}$ is 33.114 cal mole$^{-1}$ deg$^{-1}$ (or entropy units).

***For a gas.*** The procedure for the calculation of the absolute entropy of a gas in its standard state is substantially the same as that for a solid or liquid, except that there is one major correction factor necessary for the gas but not for the condensed phases. Since the absolute entropy is calculated from calorimetric heat-capacity data at 1 atm pressure, the result obtained refers, of course, to such a pressure. For most real gases, however, the entropy at 1 atm pressure is not the same as the entropy of the gas in its standard state. Frequently it will be necessary, therefore, to apply a correction to the observed entropy to account for deviations from ideal gas behavior.

*Correction for gas imperfection.* It is perhaps easiest to visualize the derivation of this correction by reference to Figure 11-4. From thermal data one obviously obtains the entropy indicated by line *b*. However, it is the entropy indicated by line *d* that we need for our tables; that is, we want to find the entropy the substance would have if it behaved as an ideal gas at the given temperature and 1 atm pressure.

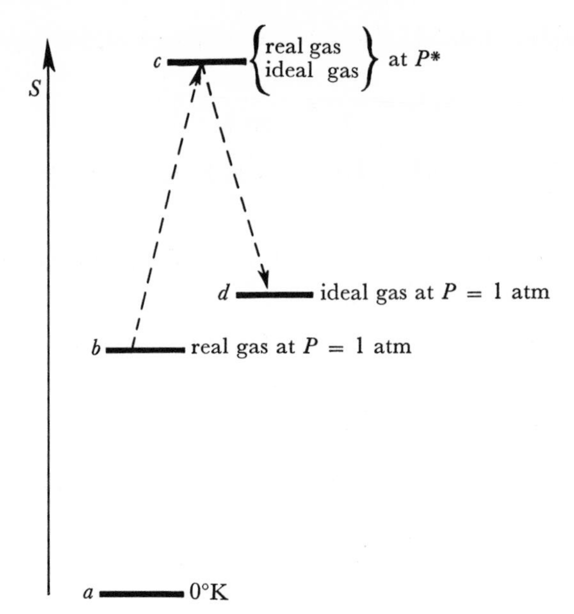


***Figure 11-4*** *Schematic representation of various entropies in connection with correction for gas imperfections.*

At this stage in our discussion of thermodynamic concepts there is no obvious direct method of going from $b$ to $d$. Since entropy is a thermodynamic property, however, we can use any roundabout path to calculate $\Delta S$, so long as the initial and final states are $b$ and $d$, respectively.

If we know $S_{298}$ for the real gas at 1 atm pressure, then we know $\Delta S$ for the reaction

$$A(s, 0°\text{K}) = A(g, P = 1, 298.15°) \qquad \Delta S = S_{298.15} \text{ for } A \quad (11\text{-}55)$$

To this equation we can add the following two transformations:

$$A(g, P = 1, \text{real}, 298.15°) = A(g, P = P^*, \text{real}, 298.15°) \quad (11\text{-}56)$$

$$A(g, P = P^*, \text{ideal}, 298.15°) = A(g, P = 1, \text{ideal}, 298.15°) \quad (11\text{-}57)$$

for each of which $\Delta S$ can be calculated. If $P^*$ is made sufficiently low or, better yet, if $P^*$ approaches zero, then the real gas approaches ideality in its behavior. Hence the right-hand side of Eq. (11-56) is the same as the left-hand side of Eq. (11-57), and addition of Eqs. (11-56) and (11-57) gives

$$A(g, P = 1, \text{real}, 298.15°) = A(g, P = 1, \text{ideal}, 298.15°) \quad (11\text{-}58)$$

The sum of the entropy changes for reactions (11-55) and (11-58) gives us $S^\circ_{298}$ for the gas.

There remains, then, the problem of calculation of the entropy changes for Eqs. (11-56) and (11-57). Since the temperature is fixed, these quantities may be calculated from the relation

$$\left(\frac{\partial S}{\partial P}\right)_T = -\left(\frac{\partial V}{\partial T}\right)_P \tag{11-48}$$

or

$$dS = -\left(\frac{\partial V}{\partial T}\right)_P dP \tag{11-59}$$

Thus, for the transformation indicated in Eq. (11-56),

$$S(P = P^*) - S(P = 1) = -\int_1^{P^*} \left(\frac{\partial V_{\text{real}}}{\partial T}\right)_P dP = +\int_{P^*}^{1} \left(\frac{\partial V}{\partial T}\right)_P dP \tag{11-60}$$

and for that in Eq. (11-57)

$$S_i(P = 1) - S_i(P = P^*) = -\int_{P^*}^{1} \left(\frac{\partial V_{\text{ideal}}}{\partial T}\right)_P dP = -\int_{P^*}^{1} \frac{R}{P}\, dP \tag{11-61}$$

where the subscript $i$ refers to the ideal gas. If $P^*$ is allowed to approach zero pressure, then

$$S_i(P = P^*) = S(P = P^*) \tag{11-62}$$

Hence the correction for gas imperfection becomes

$$S_i(P = 1) - S(P = 1) = \int_{P^*}^{1} \left(\frac{\partial V}{\partial T}\right)_P dP - \int_{P^*}^{1} \frac{R}{P}\, dP \tag{11-63}$$

$$= \int_{P^*}^{1} \left[\left(\frac{\partial V}{\partial T}\right)_P - \frac{R}{P}\right] dP \tag{11-64}$$

Equation (11-64) may be integrated if the value of $(\partial V/\partial T)_P$ is known for the gas under consideration. Generally this coefficient is obtained from the Berthelot equation of state (Chapter 6),

$$P\mathrm{v} = RT\left[1 + \frac{9}{128}\frac{P}{P_c}\frac{T_c}{T}\left(1 - 6\frac{T_c^2}{T^2}\right)\right] \tag{11-65}$$

Differentiation gives readily

$$\left(\frac{\partial V}{\partial T}\right)_P = \frac{R}{P} + \frac{9}{128} R \frac{1}{P_c} T_c \left(12 \frac{T_c^2}{T^3}\right) = \frac{R}{P}\left[1 + \frac{27}{32} \frac{P}{P_c} \frac{T_c^3}{T^3}\right] \tag{11-66}$$

The equation for the correction becomes, therefore,

$$(S_i - S)_{P=1 \text{ atm}} = \int_{P^*}^{1} \frac{27}{32} \frac{R}{P_c} \frac{T_c^3}{T^3} \, dP \tag{11-67}$$

$$= \frac{27}{32} R \frac{P}{P_c} \frac{T_c^3}{T^3}\Bigg]_{P^*}^{P=1} \tag{11-68}$$

If we let $P^*$ approach zero,

$$(S_i - S)_{P=1 \text{ atm}} = \frac{27}{32} \frac{R}{P_c} \frac{T_c^3}{T^3} \tag{11-69}$$

Thus from a knowledge of the critical constants of the gas it is possible now to evaluate the correction in the entropy for deviations from ideal behavior, if the Berthelot equation is applicable.[15]

*Entropy of gaseous cyclopropane at its boiling point.* Heat capacities for cyclopropane have been measured down to temperatures approaching absolute zero by Ruehrwein and Powell.[16] Their calculation of the absolute entropy of the gas at the boiling point, 240.30°, may be summarized as follows:

(a) $C_3H_6(s, 0°K) = C_3H_6(s, 15°K)$
$\Delta S_1 = 0.243$ cal mole$^{-1}$ deg$^{-1}$ Debye equation with $\theta = 130$

(b) $C_3H_6(s, 15°K) = C_3H_6(s, 145.54°K)$ $\Delta S_2 = 15.733$ graphical integration

(c) $C_3H_6(s, 145.54°K) = C_3H_6(l, 145.54°K)$ $\Delta S_3 = \dfrac{\Delta H_{\text{fusion}}}{T} = 8.939$

(d) $C_3H_6(l, 145.54°K) = C_3H_6(l, 240.30°K)$ $\Delta S_4 = 9.176$ graphical integration

(e) $C_3H_6(l, 240.30°K) = C_3H_6(\text{real gas}, 240.30°K)$

$$\Delta S_5 = \frac{\Delta H_{\text{vaporization}}}{T} = 19.946$$

[15] It has been pointed out [J. O. Halford, *J. Chem. Phys.*, **17,** 111, 405 (1949)] that the Berthelot equation may be inadequate for the calculation of entropy corrections due to gas imperfection, especially for vapors such as water and ethyl alcohol.

[16] R. A. Ruehrwein and T. M. Powell, *J. Am. Chem. Soc.*, **68,** 1063 (1946).

Summing steps from (a) to (e), we obtain

(f) $C_3H_6(s, 0°K) = C_3H_6(\text{real gas}, 240.30°K)$

$$\Delta S = \sum_{1}^{5} \Delta S_i = 54.04 \text{ cal mole}^{-1} \text{ deg}^{-1}$$

The correction for deviations from ideality remains to be inserted. The critical constants were taken as 375°K and 50 atm. Hence from Eq. (11-69) we obtain

(g) $C_3H_6(\text{real gas}, 240.30°K) = C_3H_6(\text{ideal gas}, 240.30°K)$

$$\Delta S_6 = 0.13 \text{ cal mole}^{-1} \text{ deg}^{-1}$$

Therefore the absolute entropy, $S^{\circ}_{240.30}$, of cyclopropane in the ideal gas (that is, standard) state is 54.17 eu.

The correction for gas imperfection may often seem small, and there may be a tendency to neglect it. We should keep in mind, therefore, that an error of 0.1 eu affects the free energy by about 30 cal near room temperature, since $\Delta S$ would be multiplied by $T$. An error of 30 cal would change an equilibrium constant of 1.00 to 1.05, a difference of 5 per cent.

## Apparent Exceptions to the Third Law

There are several cases in which calculations of the entropy change of a reaction from values of the absolute entropy obtained from thermal data and the third law are in disagreement with values calculated directly from measurements of $\Delta H^{\circ}$ and determinations of $\Delta G^{\circ}$ from experimental equilibrium constants. For example, for the reaction

$$H_2(g) + \tfrac{1}{2}O_2(g) = H_2O(l) \tag{11-70}$$

$$\Delta S^{\circ} \text{ (thermal data)} = -36.7^{17} \text{ cal mole}^{-1} \text{ deg}^{-1} \tag{11-71}$$

$$\Delta S^{\circ} \text{ (equilibrium)} = \frac{\Delta H^{\circ} - \Delta G^{\circ}}{T} = -39.1 \text{ cal mole}^{-1} \text{ deg}^{-1} \tag{11-72}$$

Thus there is a large discrepancy between the two entropy values.

A satisfactory accounting of this discrepancy was not available until the development of statistical thermodynamics, with its methods of calculating entropies from spectroscopic data, and the discovery of the existence of ortho- and parahydrogen. It was then found that the major portion of the deviation observed between Eqs. (11-71) and (11-72) is due to the

[17] This figure is obtained when values of $S^{\circ}_{298}$ for $H_2$ and $H_2O$ are those determined from calorimetric data alone. Most recent critical tables list values of $S^{\circ}_{298}$ corrected for the effects discussed later in this section. If the latter values are used, $\Delta S^{\circ}$ from the third law turns out to be $-39.0$ cal mole$^{-1}$ deg$^{-1}$.

failure to obtain a true equilibrium between these two forms of $H_2$ molecules, differing in their nuclear spins, during thermal measurements at very low temperatures (Figure 11-5). If true equilibrium were established at all times, more *para*hydrogen would be formed as the temperature is lowered, and at 0°K all the hydrogen molecules would be in the *para* form and the entropy would be zero. In practice, measurements are actually made on a mixture of *ortho/para* of 3:1. This mixture at 0°K has a positive entropy. If the hydrogen were in contact with an appropriate catalyst for *ortho–para* conversion, an equilibrium mixture would be obtained and the entropy could be calculated correctly from the integral giving the area under the equilibrium curve in Figure 11-5.

With the development of statistical thermodynamics and the calculation of the absolute entropies of many substances from spectroscopic data, several other substances in addition to hydrogen have been found to exhibit values of molal entropies in disagreement with those calculated from

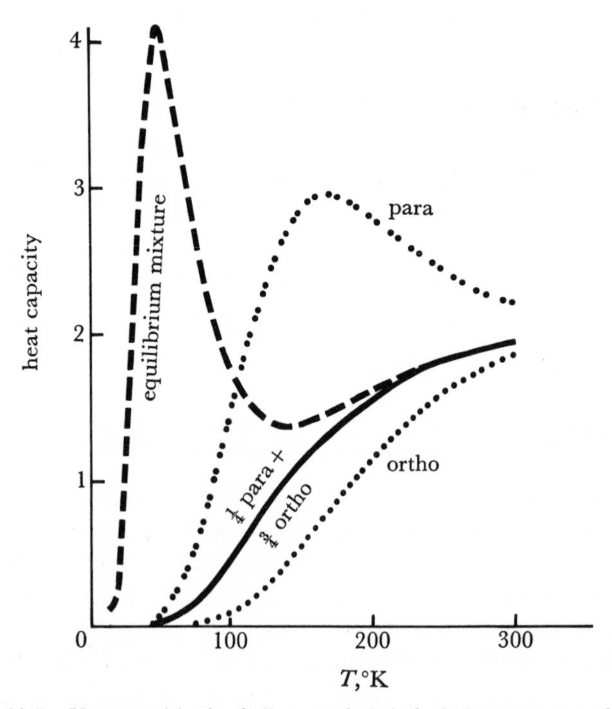


***Figure 11-5*** *Heat capacities (excluding translation) for hydrogen gas as a function of temperature. [Based on data of W. F. Giauque, J. Am. Chem. Soc.,* **52,** 4816 (1930).]

*Table 11-1*

*Molal entropies*

| Substance | Temperature, °K | $S°$ (spectroscopic) | $S°$ (calorimetric) | Deviation |
|---|---|---|---|---|
| CO | 298.1 | 47.313 | 46.2 | 1.11 |
| $COCl_2$ | 280.6 | 68.26 | 66.63 | 1.63 |
| $H_2O$ | 298.1 | 45.10 | 44.28 | 0.82 |
| $N_2O$ | 298.1 | 52.581 | 51.44 | 1.14 |
| NO | 121.4 | 43.75 | 43.0 | 0.75 |
| $ClO_3F$ | 226.48 | 62.59 | 60.17 | 2.42 |

thermal data alone[18] (Table 11-1). Here again the discrepancies may be accounted for on the assumption that even near absolute zero not all the molecules are in the same state and that true equilibrium has not been attained. In the cases of CO, $COCl_2$, $N_2O$, NO, and $ClO_3F$, the close similarity in the sizes of the atoms makes different orientations possible in the crystals, whereas in the case of $H_2O$, hydrogen bonds maintain an irregularity in the distribution of molecules in the crystal. In carbon monoxide, for example, molecules may take up random positions such as CO, OC, in the crystal. Because of these exceptional situations, it is desirable to interpret the term "perfect crystal" as excluding situations in which several orientations of the molecules are present simultaneously.

An exceptional case of a very different type is provided by helium,[19] for which the third law is valid despite the fact that He remains a liquid at 0°K. A phase diagram for helium is shown in Figure 11-6. In this case, in contrast to other substances, the solid–liquid equilibrium line at high pressures does not continue downward at low pressures until it meets the liquid–vapor pressure curve to intersect at a triple point. Rather the solid–liquid equilibrium line takes an unusual turn toward the horizontal as the temperature drops to near 2°K. This change, of course, is due to a surprising metamorphosis in the character of liquid helium as the temperature

[18] W. F. Giauque and H. L. Johnston, *J. Am. Chem. Soc.*, **50,** 3221 (1928). H. L. Johnston and W. F. Giauque, *ibid.*, **51,** 3194 (1929). W. F. Giauque, *ibid.*, **52,** 4816 (1930). J. O. Clayton and W. F. Giauque, *ibid.*, **54,** 2610 (1932). W. F. Giauque and M. F. Ashley, *Phys. Rev.*, **43,** 81 (1933). R. W. Blue and W. F. Giauque, *J. Am. Chem. Soc.*, **57,** 991 (1935). W. F. Giauque and J. W. Stout, *ibid.*, **58,** 1144 (1936). W. F. Giauque and W. M. Jones, *ibid.*, **70,** 120 (1948). J. K. Koehler and W. F. Giauque, *ibid.*, **80,** 2659 (1958). L. Pauling, *Phys. Rev.*, **36,** 430 (1930). L. Pauling, *J. Am. Chem. Soc.*, **57,** 2680 (1935).

[19] For an interesting discussion of the properties of He at very low temperatures, see K. Mendelssohn, *Science,* **127,** 218 (1958).

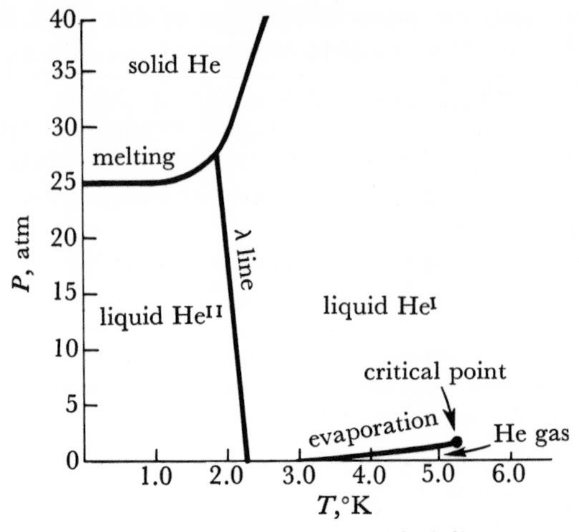


*Figure 11-6 Phase diagram for helium.*

drops below 2.2°K. Below this temperature the liquid has a heat conductivity 100 times greater than that of a metal such as copper or silver, and becomes a *superfluid* in its flow behavior, having a viscosity less than $10^{-9}$ that of a liquid such as water.

This transformed liquid, labeled $He^{II}$, also shows unusual thermal properties. One of these, its entropy, is illustrated in Figure 11-7. For

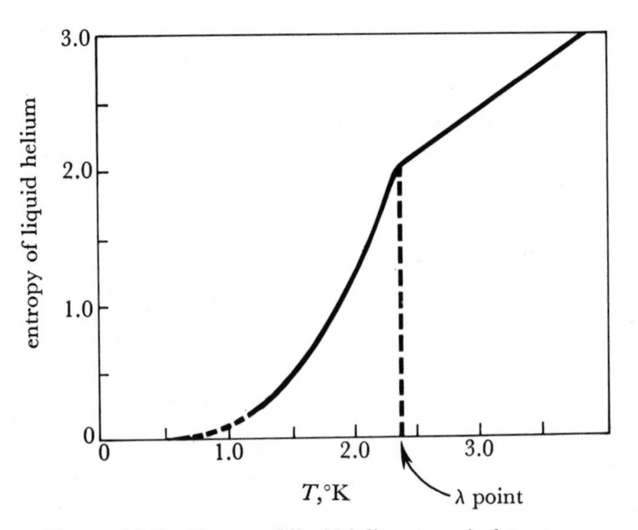


*Figure 11-7 Entropy of liquid helium near absolute zero.*

our present purposes, the important feature of this curve is the approach of $S$ to zero as $T \rightarrow 0$. Thus liquid $He^{II}$ possesses zero entropy at 0°K despite the fact that it is a liquid.

A confirmation of this conclusion is also available if we return to an examination of the solid–liquid equilibrium in the neighborhood of 0°K. As was shown in Chapter 9 [Eq. (9-11)] a two-phase equilibrium obeys the Clapeyron equation

$$\frac{dP}{dT} = \frac{S_{\text{liquid}} - S_{\text{solid}}}{V_{\text{liquid}} - V_{\text{solid}}} \tag{11-73}$$

The densities of liquid and solid helium are different, so that $\Delta V$ of Eq. (11-73) cannot be zero. Yet the horizontal slope of the melting line of the phase diagram shows that $dP/dT$ is zero near 0°K. Hence it is clear that $\Delta S$ of Eq. (11-73) must be zero at 0°K, that is, that $S_{0°\text{K}}$ for liquid He is zero despite the fact that it is a liquid.

The reason why $He^{II}$ is a liquid (high zero-point energy) and the nature of the *order* which leads to zero entropy in the liquid lie deep in quantum mechanics and are beyond the scope of this book. We shall stop with the recognition of the phenomenological aspects of the unique behavior of liquid He.

## Tabulation of Entropy Values

Several sources are available that have critical tabulations of absolute entropies:

*International Critical Tables*, McGraw-Hill, New York, 1933.

Landolt-Börnstein, *Physikalisch-chemische Tabellen*, 5th ed., Springer, Berlin, 1936.

K. K. Kelley, *U.S. Bur. Mines Bull. 477* (1950); K. K. Kelley and E. G. King, *ibid.*, *592* (1961).

W. M. Latimer, *Oxidation Potentials*, 2nd ed., Prentice-Hall, Englewood Cliffs, N.J., 1952.

Selected Values of Chemical Thermodynamic Properties, *Natl. Bur. Std.* (*U.S.*), *Cir. 500*, 1952.

*Selected Values of Physical and Thermodynamic Properties of Hydrocarbons and Related Compounds*, Am. Petrol. Inst. Res. Project 44, Carnegie Press, Pittsburgh, 1953.

Manufacturing Chemists' Assoc., *Selected Values of Properties of Chemical Compounds*, Carnegie Inst. Technol., Pittsburgh, 1955.

*Janaf Thermochemical Tables*, compiled and calculated by the Thermal Laboratory, The Dow Chemical Co., Midland, Mich., 1960.

A few typical values of absolute entropies have been assembled in Table 11-2. Data obtained from spectroscopic studies have been included even though the methods used in their calculation have not been discussed.

***Table 11-2***

*Entropies at 298°K*

| Substance | $S^\circ_{298}$, cal mole$^{-1}$ deg$^{-1}$ | Substance | $S^\circ_{298}$, cal mole$^{-1}$ deg$^{-1}$ |
|---|---|---|---|
| | *Elements*[a,b] | | |
| Al(*s*) | 6.77 | Pb(*s*) | 15.49 |
| Sb(*s*) | 10.92 | Li(*s*) | 6.75 |
| Ar(*g*) | 36.983 | Mg(*s*) | 7.81 |
| As(*s*) | 8.40 | Mn(*s*) | 7.65 |
| Ba(*s*) | 16.0 | Hg(*l*) | 18.17 |
| Be(*s*) | 2.28 | Mo(*s*) | 6.83 |
| Bi(*s*) | 13.58 | Ne(*g*) | 34.948 |
| B(*s*) | 1.403 | Ni(*s*) | 7.14 |
| $Br_2$(*l*) | 36.4 | $N_2$(*g*) | 45.767 |
| Cd(*s*) | 12.37 | $O_2$(*g*) | 49.01 |
| Ca(*s*) | 9.95 | P(red) | 5.46 |
| C(graphite) | 1.3609 | K(*s*) | 15.34 |
| $Cl_2$(*g*) | 53.29 | Rn(*g*) | 42.10 |
| Cr(*s*) | 5.70 | Se(gray) | 10.14 |
| Co(*s*) | 7.18 | Si(*s*) | 4.51 |
| Cu(*s*) | 7.97 | Ag(*s*) | 10.20 |
| $F_2$(*g*) | 48.49 | Na(*s*) | 12.24 |
| Ge(*s*) | 7.43 | S(rhombic) | 7.62 |
| He(*g*) | 30.126 | Sn(white) | 12.29 |
| $H_2$(*g*) | 31.211 | Te(*s*) | 11.88 |
| $D_2$(*g*) | 34.62 | Ti(*s*) | 7.30 |
| $I_2$(*s*) | 27.76 | V(*s*) | 7.02 |
| Fe(*s*) | 6.49 | Xe(*g*) | 40.53 |
| Kr(*g*) | 39.19 | Nz(*s*) | 9.95 |
| | | Zr(*s*) | 9.32 |
| | *Inorganic Compounds*[a] | | |
| BaO(*s*) | 16.8 | $H_2O$(*g*) | 45.11 |
| $BaCl_2 \cdot 2H_2O$(*s*) | 48.5 | HBr(*g*) | 47.48 |
| $BaSO_4$(*s*) | 31.6 | HCl(*g*) | 44.64 |
| $BF_3$(*g*) | 60.70 | HF(*g*) | 41.47 |
| $Ca(OH)_2$(*s*) | 19.93 | HI(*g*) | 49.34 |
| CO(*g*) | 47.31 | ICl(*g*) | 59.12 |
| $CO_2$(*g*) | 51.08 | NO(*g*) | 50.339 |
| CNCl(*g*) | 56.44 | NaCl(*s*) | 17.33 |
| CuO(*s*) | 10.19 | $SO_2$(*g*) | 59.29 |
| $H_2O$(*l*) | 16.73 | $SO_3$(*g*) | 61.24 |

*Table 11-2* (*continued*)

| Substance | $S^{\circ}_{298}$, cal mole$^{-1}$ deg$^{-1}$ | Substance | $S^{\circ}_{298}$, cal mole$^{-1}$ deg$^{-1}$ |
|---|---|---|---|
| | *Organic Compounds*[a,c] | | |
| Methane(*g*) | 44.50 | Acetylene(*g*) | 47.997 |
| Ethane(*g*) | 54.85 | Benzene(*g*) | 64.34 |
| Propane(*g*) | 64.51 | Toluene(*g*) | 76.42 |
| *n*-Butane(*g*) | 74.10 | *o*-Xylene(*g*) | 84.31 |
| Ethylene(*g*) | 52.45 | *m*-Xylene(*g*) | 85.49 |
| Propylene(*g*) | 63.80 | *p*-Xylene(*g*) | 84.23 |
| 1-Butene(*g*) | 73.48 | Cyclohexane(*g*) | 71.28 |

[a] Selected Values of Chemical Thermodynamic Properties, *Natl. Bur. Std.* (*U.S.*), *Circ. 500*, 1952; K. K. Kelley and E. G. King, *U.S. Bur. Mines Bull. 592*, 1961.

[b] D. R. Stull and G. C. Sinke, *Thermodynamic Properties of the Elements*, Am. Chem. Soc., Washington, D.C., 1956.

[c] *Selected Values of Physical and Thermodynamic Properties of Hydrocarbons and Related Compounds*, Am. Petrol. Inst. Res. Project 44, Carnegie Press, Pittsburgh, 1953.

## Exercises

**1.** Assuming that

$$\lim_{T \to 0} \left( \frac{\partial \, \Delta G}{\partial T} \right)_P = 0$$

for reactions involving perfect crystalline solids, prove that

$$\lim_{T \to 0} \left( \frac{\partial \, \Delta A}{\partial T} \right)_V = 0$$

**2.** Prove that $\lim_{T \to 0} \Delta C_v = 0$.

**3.** Assume that the limiting slope, as $T$ approaches zero, of a graph of $\Delta G$ vs. $T$ is a finite value but not zero. Prove that $\Delta C_p$ for the reaction would still approach zero at 0°K.

**4.** It has been suggested [G. J. Janz, *Can. J. Res.*, **25b**, 331 (1947)] that α-cyano-pyridine might be prepared from cyanogen and butadiene by the reaction

$$C_4H_6(g) + C_2N_2(g) = \text{(pyridine ring with N and —CN)}(s) + H_2(g)$$

Pertinent thermodynamic data are given in the Table 11-3. Would you consider it worthwhile, on a thermodynamic basis, to attempt to work out this reaction?

*Table 11-3*

| Substance | $\Delta Hf^\circ_{298}$, cal mole$^{-1}$ | $S^\circ_{298}$, cal mole$^{-1}$ deg$^{-1}$ |
|---|---|---|
| Butadiene($g$) | 26,748 | 66.42 |
| Cyanogen($g$) | 71,820 | 57.64 |
| $\alpha$-Cyanopyridine($s$) | 62,000 | 77.09 |
| Hydrogen($g$) | 0 | 31.21 |

**5.** Methylammonium chloride exists in a number of crystalline forms, as is evident from Figure 11-3. The thermodynamic properties of the $\beta$ and $\gamma$ forms have been investigated by Aston and Ziemer [*J. Am. Chem. Soc.*, **68**, 1405 (1946)] down to temperatures near 0°K, and some of their data are listed below. From the information here given, find the heat of transition from the $\beta$ to the $\gamma$ form at 220.4° K:

$C_p$ for $\beta$ at 12.0°K = 0.202 cal mole$^{-1}$ deg$^{-1}$

$\int C_p \, d \ln T$ from 12.0 to 220.4°K = 22.326 cal mole$^{-1}$ deg$^{-1}$

$C_p$ for $\gamma$ at 19.5°K = 1.426 cal mole$^{-1}$ deg$^{-1}$

$\int C_p \, d \ln T$ from 19.5 to 220.4°K = 23.881 cal mole$^{-1}$ deg$^{-1}$

Normal transition temperature (that is, at $P$ = 1 atm) = 220.4°K

**6.** Cycloheptatriene has two different crystalline forms in the solid state. That labeled I undergoes an entropy change of 27.778 gibbs mole$^{-1}$ on being warmed from 0 to 154°K [H. L. Finke, D. W. Scott, M. E. Gross, J. F. Messerly, and G. Waddington, *J. Am. Chem. Soc.*, **78**, 5469 (1956)]. Some thermal data for form II, the more stable one at very low temperatures, as well as for I are listed below. Is I a "perfect crystalline substance"?

$C_p$ at 12°K for II = 1.08 cal mole$^{-1}$ deg$^{-1}$

$\int C_p \, d \ln T$ from 12–154°K for II = 23.775 cal mole$^{-1}$ deg$^{-1}$

Transition temp. II $\rightarrow$ I = 154°K
$\Delta H$ of transition II $\rightarrow$ I = 561 cal mole$^{-1}$

$\int C_p \, d \ln T$ from 154–198°K for I = 7.455 cal mole$^{-1}$ deg$^{-1}$

Fusion temp. I $\rightarrow$ liquid = 198°K
$\Delta H$ of fusion of I $\rightarrow$ liquid = 277.4 cal mole$^{-1}$

$\int C_p \, d \ln T$ from 198–298°K = 14.669 cal mole$^{-1}$ deg$^{-1}$

Vapor pressure of liquid at 298°K = 23.52 mm

**7.** The equilibrium constant, $K$, for the formation of a deuterium atom from two hydrogen atoms may be defined by the equation

$$2H = D; \qquad K = \frac{p_D}{(p_H)^2}$$

The equation for the temperature dependence of $K$ is

$$\log_{10} K = 20.260 + \tfrac{3}{2} \log_{10} T - \frac{7.04 \times 10^9}{T}$$

(a) Calculate $K$ at a temperature of $10^8$ degrees.

(b) Calculate $\Delta G^\circ$ and $\Delta H^\circ$ at the same temperature.

(c) What is the change in entropy for the conversion of atomic hydrogen into atomic deuterium at a temperature of $10^8$ degrees?

**8.** The heat capacity of $Na_2SO_4 \cdot 10H_2O$ has been measured from 15 to 300°K and $S^\circ_{298.15}$, computed from

$$\int_0^{298} C_p \, d \ln T$$

[G. Brodale and W. F. Giauque, *J. Am. Chem. Soc.*, **80**, 2042 (1958)], found to be 139.95 gibbs mole$^{-1}$. The following thermodynamic data are also known for the hydration reaction:

$$Na_2SO_4(s) + 10H_2O(g) = Na_2SO_4 \cdot 10H_2O(s)$$

$$\Delta G^\circ_{298.15} = -21{,}795 \text{ cal mole}^{-1}$$

$$\Delta H^\circ_{298.15} = -124{,}749 \text{ cal mole}^{-1}$$

Furthermore the entropies, $S^\circ_{298.15}$, for anhydrous $Na_2SO_4$ and for water vapor, are 35.73 and 45.104 gibbs mole$^{-1}$, respectively.

Is $Na_2SO_4 \cdot 10H_2O$ a perfect crystal at 0°K?

**9.** Some thermodynamic information for benzene and its products of hydrogenation are listed in Table 11-4 [G. J. Janz, *J. Chem. Phys.*, **22**, 751 (1954)].

(a) Make a graph of $\Delta G^\circ$ for each compound, relative to benzene, vs. the moles of $H_2$ taken up to form each compound. Show that the diene is thermodynamically unstable relative to any of the other three substances.

(b) If hydrogenation of benzene were carried out over a suitable catalyst so that equilibrium was attained between it and the three products, what would be the relative composition of the mixture at a hydrogen pressure of 1 atm?

***Table 11-4***

| | $\Delta Hf^\circ_{298}$, kcal mole$^{-1}$ | $S^\circ_{298}$, cal mole$^{-1}$ deg$^{-1}$ |
|---|---|---|
| Benzene | 19.82 | 64.3 |
| 1,3-Cyclohexadiene | 25.6 | 68.9 |
| Cyclohexene | − 1.72 | 74.2 |
| Cyclohexane | −29.43 | 71.3 |

*Table 11-5*

| | Crystal I | Crystal II |
|---|---|---|
| $C_p$ at 12.4° | 1.068 cal/mole-deg | 1.571 cal/mole-deg |
| $\int C_p\, d \ln T$ from 12 to 261.6°K (graphical) | 35.398 eu | 36.504 eu |
| $\int C_p\, d \ln T$ from 261.6 to 304.5°K (graphical) | | 5.531 eu |
| $\Delta H$ fusion (at 304.5°K) | | 2826.8 cal/mole |

**10.** Two different crystalline forms of benzothiophene have been described by H. L. Finke, M. E. Gross, J. F. Messerly, and G. Waddington [*J. Am. Chem. Soc.*, **76,** 854 (1954)]. The one which is the stable form at low temperatures is labeled I, the other II. Calorimetric measurements down to 12°K have been made with each crystalline form. At the normal transition temperature, 261.6°K, the enthalpy of transition (I → II) is 720 cal mole$^{-1}$. Some additional thermodynamic data obtained by these investigators are given in Table 11-5. Is crystal II a perfect crystal at 0°K?

**11.** Some thermodynamic data for tin are tabulated below (Table 11-6). It is possible to construct an electrochemical cell

Sn (gray), electrolyte, Sn (white)

in which the following reaction occurs during operation:

$$\text{Sn (gray)} = \text{Sn (white)}$$

(a) Compute the emf of this cell at 25°C and 1 atm.

(b) If the cell is operated reversibly what would be the values of $W_{\text{net}}$, $Q$, $\Delta E$, $\Delta H$, $\Delta S$, and $\Delta G$, respectively, for the conversion of 1 mole of gray tin to white?

(c) If the cell is short circuited so that no electrical work is obtained what would be the values of the thermodynamic quantities listed in (b)?

**12.** The heats of combustion of quinone($s$) and hydroquinone($s$) at 1 atm pressure and 25° are 656.29 and 681.75 kcal mole$^{-1}$, respectively (G. Pilcher and L. E. Sutton, *J. Chem. Soc.*, **1956,** 2695). Entropies have been computed from specific heat data; $S^\circ_{298}$ is 38.55 eu for quinone($s$) and 32.77 for hydroquinone($s$).

(a) Find $\Delta Hf^\circ$ the standard heat of formation for each substance.

(b) Compute $\Delta H^\circ$ for the reduction of quinone to hydroquinone.

(c) Compute $\Delta S^\circ$ and $\Delta G^\circ$ for the reduction.

*Table 11-6*

| | Sn(gray) | Sn(white) |
|---|---|---|
| $\Delta Hf^\circ_{298}$ (cal mole$^{-1}$) | 600 | 0 |
| $S^\circ_{298}$ (gibbs mole$^{-1}$) | 10.7 | 12.3 |
| Density (gm cm$^{-3}$) | 5.75 | 7.31 |

(d) Calculate the $\mathscr{E}^\circ$ for this reaction. The value obtained from electrochemical measurements [J. B. Conant and L. F. Fieser, *J. Am. Chem. Soc.*, **44**, 2480 (1922)] is 0.681 volt.

**13.** We have proved the unattainability statement of the third law by carrying out adiabatic transformations from $a$ to $b$ with substances for which one can state that

$$S_a(0°\text{K}) = 0$$

Suppose state $a$ consists of glassy glycerol, for which $S_a(0°\text{K}) > 0$, and state $b$ of crystalline glycerol. Prove that absolute zero is still unattainable by means of a transformation from the glassy to the crystalline state.

# 12 Standard Free Energies from the Third Law

Having considered the details of the calculation of absolute entropies for standard conditions, let us now turn our attention to their primary use—the calculation of standard free energies.

The methods of estimating thermodynamic functions may be divided into two categories—precise and approximate. Where sufficient data are available, the precise methods are used. In the absence of adequate information, one may still obtain reasonable estimates of entropies, enthalpies, and free energies by having recourse to one or more of the semiempirical approximate methods.

## 12-1 PRECISE METHODS

### Enthalpy Determination

As mentioned in the preceding chapter, it is necessary in all cases to obtain information on the standard enthalpy change for a given reaction before the free-energy change can be calculated from the third law.

$\Delta H_T^\circ$, at some temperature $T$, may be obtained from $\Delta Hf^\circ$ of each of the substances involved in the tranformation. Data on the standard heats of formation are found tabulated in either of two ways. The obvious method is to list $\Delta Hf^\circ$ at some convenient temperature, such as 25°C, or at a series of temperatures. A typical table has been included in Chapter 5. Values at temperatures not listed are generally calculated with the aid of heat-capacity equations.

Under the stimulus of statistical thermodynamics, another method of tabulation, using $H_T^\circ - H_0^\circ$ or $(H_T^\circ - H_0^\circ)/T$, where the subscripts refer to the absolute temperatures, has come into general use. This method of presentation, illustrated in Table 12-1, avoids the inclusion of empirical heat-capacity equations in the results and allows more ready comparison of data from different sources.

The procedure necessary to the calculation of $\Delta Hf^\circ$ at any temperature, $T$, from the new type of table requires a brief discussion. From the definition of the standard heat of formation of a compound, $C$, it is evident that reference is made to the reaction

$$\underset{\left\{\begin{matrix}\text{element in}\\ \text{standard state}\\ \text{at temperature } T\end{matrix}\right\}}{A} + \underset{\left\{\begin{matrix}\text{element in}\\ \text{standard state}\\ \text{at temperature } T\end{matrix}\right\}}{B} + \cdots = \underset{\left\{\begin{matrix}\text{compound in}\\ \text{standard state}\\ \text{at temperature } T\end{matrix}\right\}}{C} \qquad \Delta Hf_T^\circ \qquad (12\text{-}1)$$

Since the enthalpies are available in terms of the function $H_T^\circ - H_0^\circ$, it is apparent that the sum of the following equations gives the desired $\Delta Hf^\circ$:

$$A\,(0^\circ\text{K}) + B\,(0^\circ\text{K}) + \cdots = C\,(0^\circ\text{K}) \qquad \Delta Hf_0^\circ \qquad (12\text{-}2)$$

$$C\,(0^\circ\text{K}) = C\,(T^\circ\text{K}) \qquad \Delta H^\circ = (H_T^\circ - H_0^\circ)_C \qquad (12\text{-}3)$$

$$A\,(T^\circ\text{K}) = A\,(0^\circ\text{K}) \qquad \Delta H^\circ = (H_0^\circ - H_T^\circ)_A = -(H_T^\circ - H_0^\circ)_A \qquad (12\text{-}4)$$

$$B\,(T^\circ\text{K}) = B\,(0^\circ\text{K}) \qquad \Delta H^\circ = (H_0^\circ - H_T^\circ)_B = -(H_T^\circ - H_0^\circ)_B \qquad (12\text{-}5)$$

---

$$A\,(T^\circ\text{K}) + B\,(T^\circ\text{K}) + \cdots = C\,(T^\circ\text{K})$$

$$\Delta Hf_T^\circ = \Delta Hf_0^\circ + (H_T^\circ - H_0^\circ)_{\text{compound}} - \sum (H_T^\circ - H_0^\circ)_{\text{elements}} \qquad (12\text{-}6)$$

Each of the quantities in Eq. (12-6) may be obtained from tables such as Table 12-1.

## Entropy Determination

Standard entropies for many substances are available in tables, such as Table 11-2. Generally the values listed are for 25°C, but many of the original sources, such as the tables of the National Bureau of Standards, give enumerations for other temperatures also. If heat-capacity data are

*Table 12-1*[a]

*Enthalpy function,* $H_T^\circ - H_0^\circ$

| Substance | $\Delta Hf_0^\circ$, kcal mole$^{-1}$ | $H_T^\circ - H_0^\circ$, cal mole$^{-1}$ at $T$°K | | | | | |
|---|---|---|---|---|---|---|---|
| | | 298.16 | 400 | 600 | 800 | 1000 | 1500 |
| $H_2(g)$ | 0 | 2023.81 | 2731.0 | 4,128.6 | 5,537.4 | 6,965.8 | 10,694.2 |
| $O_2(g)$ | 0 | 2069.78 | 2792.4 | 4,279.2 | 5,854.1 | 7,497.0 | 11,776.4 |
| C(graphite) | 0 | 251.56 | 502.6 | 1,198.1 | 2,081.7 | 3,074.6 | 5,814 |
| $CO(g)$ | −27.2019 | 2072.63 | 2783.8 | 4,209.5 | 5,699.8 | 7,256.5 | 11,358.8 |
| $CO_2(g)$ | −93.9686 | 2238.11 | 3194.8 | 5,322.4 | 7,689.4 | 10,222 | 17,004 |
| $H_2O(g)$ | −57.107 | 2367.7 | 3194.0 | 4,882.2 | 6,689.6 | 8,608.0 | 13,848 |
| Methane($g$) | −15.987 | 2397 | 3323 | 5,549 | 8,321 | 11,560 | 21,130 |
| Ethane($g$) | −16.517 | 2856 | 4296 | 8,016 | 12,760 | 18,280 | 34,500 |
| Propane($g$) | −19.482 | 3512 | 5556 | 10,930 | 17,760 | 25,670 | 48,650 |
| Ethylene($g$) | 14.522 | 2525 | 3711 | 6,732 | 10,480 | 14,760 | 27,100 |
| Acetylene($g$) | 54.329 | 2391.5 | 3541.2 | 6,127 | 8,999 | 12,090 | 20,541 |
| Benzene($g$) | 24.000 | 3401 | 5762 | 12,285 | 20,612 | 30,163 | 57,350 |
| Toluene($g$) | 17.500 | 4306 | 7269 | 15,334 | 25,621 | 37,449 | 71,250 |
| *o*-Xylene($g$) | 11.096 | 5576 | 9291 | 19,070 | 31,386 | 45,531 | 85,960 |
| *m*-Xylene($g$) | 10.926 | 5325 | 8925 | 18,563 | 30,817 | 44,933 | 85,330 |
| *p*-Xylene($g$) | 11.064 | 5358 | 8929 | 18,499 | 30,690 | 44,755 | 85,080 |

[a] Taken from Selected Values of Chemical Thermodynamic Properties, *Natl. Bur. Std.* (*U.S.*) *Circ. 500*, 1952; *Selected Values of Physical and Thermodynamic Properties of Hydrocarbons and Related Compounds*, Am. Petrol. Inst. Res. Project 44, Carnegie Press, Pittsburgh, 1953. See also K. K. Kelley, *U.S. Bur. Mines Bull.* 584, 1959.

available, no difficulty is encountered in converting entropy values from one temperature to another by methods analogous to those outlined at the beginning of the preceding chapter. Similar procedures can be used to obtain absolute entropies from heat-capacity data, if the appropriate integrations have not been made in the literature.

It is perhaps trivial to point out that in a reaction such as that represented by Eq. (12-1), the standard entropy change, $\Delta S_T^\circ$, at the temperature $T$, is given by the expression

$$\Delta S_T^\circ = S_{T\,(\text{compound})}^\circ - \sum S_{T\,(\text{elements})}^\circ \tag{12-7}$$

## Change in Standard Free Energy

When adequate enthalpy and entropy data are available, the calculation of $\Delta G_T^\circ$ is simply a matter of substitution into the equation

$$\Delta G_T^\circ = \Delta H_T^\circ - T\,\Delta S_T^\circ \tag{12-8}$$

Generally data on $\Delta H^\circ$ and $\Delta S^\circ$ are available at least at one temperature. The conversion of the free-energy data from one temperature to another can be carried out by the methods outlined in Chapter 8.

With the development of statistical methods and the use of spectroscopic information, an alternative method of presentation of free-energy data as a function of temperature has also come into use. This consists of tabulation of the function $(G_T^\circ - H_0^\circ)/T$, as is illustrated in Table 12-2. This method of tabulation avoids the use of empirical equations, with their associated constants, and allows direct comparison of data from different sources. Although we shall not discuss the methods used for calculating this new function from experimental data, we shall find it simple to use tables of these functions to obtain the free-energy change in a specified reaction.

If, for example, we wish to know the free energy of formation of a specified compound at a given temperature, we can start with Eq. (12-2), that for the formation of the compound at 0°K:

$$A\,(0^\circ\text{K}) + B\,(0^\circ\text{K}) + \cdots = C\,(0^\circ\text{K}) \qquad \Delta G_0^\circ = \Delta Hf_0^\circ \qquad (12\text{-}9)$$

***Table 12-2*** [a]

*Free-energy function,* $(G_T^\circ - H_0^\circ)/T$

| Substance | $(G_T - H_0^\circ)/T$, cal mole$^{-1}$ deg$^{-1}$ at $T$°K | | | | | |
|---|---|---|---|---|---|---|
| | 298.16 | 400 | 600 | 800 | 1000 | 1500 |
| $H_2(g)$ | −24.423 | −26.422 | −29.203 | −31.186 | − 32.738 | − 35.590 |
| $O_2(g)$ | −42.061 | −44.112 | −46.968 | −49.044 | − 50.697 | − 53.808 |
| C(graphite) | − 0.5172 | − 0.8245 | − 1.477 | − 2.138 | − 2.771 | − 4.181 |
| $CO(g)$ | −40.350 | −42.393 | −45.222 | −47.254 | − 48.860 | − 51.864 |
| $CO_2(g)$ | −43.555 | −45.828 | −49.238 | −51.895 | − 54.109 | − 58.481 |
| $H_2O(g)$ | −37.172 | −39.508 | −42.768 | −45.131 | − 47.018 | − 50.622 |
| Methane($g$) | −36.46 | −38.86 | −42.39 | −45.21 | − 47.65 | − 52.84 |
| Ethane($g$) | −45.27 | −48.24 | −53.08 | −57.29 | − 61.11 | − 69.46 |
| Propane($g$) | −52.73 | −56.48 | −62.93 | −68.74 | − 74.10 | − 85.86 |
| Ethylene($g$) | −43.98 | −46.61 | −50.70 | −54.19 | − 57.29 | − 63.94 |
| Acetylene($g$) | −39.976 | −42.451 | −46.313 | −49.400 | − 52.005 | − 57.231 |
| Benzene($g$) | −52.93 | −56.69 | −63.70 | −70.34 | − 76.57 | − 90.45 |
| Toluene($g$) | −61.98 | −66.74 | −75.52 | −83.79 | − 91.53 | −108.75 |
| *o*-Xylene($g$) | −65.61 | −71.74 | −82.81 | −93.01 | −102.46 | −123.30 |
| *m*-Xylene($g$) | −67.63 | −73.50 | −84.20 | −94.18 | −103.48 | −124.11 |
| *p*-Xylene($g$) | −66.26 | −72.15 | −82.83 | −92.76 | −102.02 | −122.59 |

[a] Taken from Selected Values of Chemical Thermodynamic Properties, *Natl. Bur. Std. (U.S.), Circ. 500,* 1952; 44, *Selected Values of Physical and Thermodynamic Properties of Hydrocarbons and Related Compounds,* Am. Petrol. Inst. Res. Project 44, Carnegie Press, Pittsburgh, 1953.

At 0°K the enthalpy of formation of the compound, $\Delta Hf_0^\circ$, equals the free-energy change, since $\Delta S^\circ$ is finite or zero and $T$ is zero. If we add the following equations to (12-9), to bring the reaction up to the temperature $T$, we must also add the accompanying free-energy changes.

$$C\,(0°\text{K}) = C\,(T°\text{K}) \qquad (\Delta G^\circ)_C = (G_T^\circ - G_0^\circ)_C = (G_T^\circ - H_0^\circ)_C \tag{12-10}$$

$$B\,(T°\text{K}) = B\,(0°\text{K}) \qquad (\Delta G^\circ)_B = (G_0^\circ - G_T^\circ)_B = -(G_T^\circ - G_0^\circ)_B$$

$$= -(G_T^\circ - H_0^\circ)_B \tag{12-11}$$

$$A\,(T°\text{K}) = A\,(0°\text{K}) \qquad (\Delta G^\circ)_A = -(G_T^\circ - H_0^\circ)_A \tag{12-12}$$

In each case we make use of the relation

$$G_0^\circ = H_0^\circ \tag{12-13}$$

at 0°K [see Eq. (11-37)]. The summation of Eqs. (12-9) to (12-12) leads to the expression

$$A\,(T°\text{K}) + B\,(T°\text{K}) + \cdots = C\,(T°\text{K})$$

$$\Delta G_T^\circ = \Delta H_0^\circ + (G_T^\circ - H_0^\circ)_{\text{compound}} - \sum (G_T^\circ - H_0^\circ)_{\text{elements}} \tag{12-14}$$

To reduce the range of numerical values, it is convenient to tabulate $(G_T^\circ - H_0^\circ)/T$ instead of $(G_T^\circ - H_0^\circ)$. Hence we have the following expression for the free energy of formation, $\Delta Gf_T^\circ$, of any compound at some specified temperature, $T$:

$$\frac{\Delta Gf_T^\circ}{T} = \left[\frac{\Delta Hf_0^\circ}{T} + \left(\frac{G_T^\circ - H_0^\circ}{T}\right)\right]_{\text{compound}} - \sum \left(\frac{G_T^\circ - H_0^\circ}{T}\right)_{\text{elements}} \tag{12-15}$$

Thus the free energy of formation of a compound can be evaluated from tables of this new function.

It is apparent, of course, that if the free energy of formation of each substance in a reaction is known, it is a simple matter to calculate the free-energy change in any reaction involving these substances, since

$$\Delta G_T^\circ = \sum \Delta Gf_{T\,(\text{products})}^\circ - \sum \Delta Gf_{T\,(\text{reactants})}^\circ \tag{12-16}$$

## 12-2 APPROXIMATE METHODS

Precision data are available for relatively few compounds. In many situations, however, it is desirable to have some idea of the feasibility or impossibility of a given chemical transformation long before the necessary thermodynamic data may become available. To accomplish this purpose, several groups of investigators[1–4] have proposed empirical methods of correlation which allow one to make approximate estimates of the thermodynamic properties required to calculate free energies and equilibrium distributions. We shall consider in some detail only one of these procedures, that of Andersen, Beyer, and Watson, to illustrate the type of approach used in these approximation methods.

## Group-Contribution Method of Andersen, Beyer, and Watson

In common with several other systems, this method is based on the assumption that a given thermodynamic property, such as the entropy, of an organic substance may be resolved into contributions from each of the constituent groups in the molecule. With tables of such group contributions assembled from available experimental data, we can estimate the thermodynamic properties of any molecule by adding the contributions of the constituent groups.

Generally speaking, there are several alternative methods of associating groups into a specified molecule. In the Andersen–Beyer–Watson approach, the thermodynamic properties in *the ideal gaseous state* are estimated by consideration of a given compound as built up from a base group, such as one of those listed in Table 12-3, which has been modified by appropriate substitutions to yield the desired molecule. Thus, aliphatic hydrocarbons may be built up from methane by repeated substitutions of methyl groups for hydrogen atoms. Similarly, any amide may be viewed as a derivative of formamide, any primary amine as a derivative of methylamine.

As the next step in the process of building up larger and more complex molecules, we may consider the changes associated with primary substitutions of $CH_3$ groups in each of the nine base groups listed in Table 12-3. For the first such substitution on a single carbon atom, the changes in thermodynamic properties are listed in Table 12-4. For the cyclic base groups—cyclopentane, benzene, and naphthalene—several carbon atoms are available for successive primary substitutions (no more than one on each carbon atom); the magnitude of the contribution depends upon the number and position of the added methyl groups, as well as on the type of base ring. Benzene and naphthalene may be considered together, but cyclopentane forms a category of its own. In the latter ring system, *ortho* refers to adjacent

[1] G. S. Parks and H. M. Huffman, *The Free Energies of Some Organic Compounds*, Reinhold, New York, 1932.

[2] J. W. Andersen, G. H. Beyer, and K. M. Watson, *Natl. Petrol. News, Tech. Sec.*, **36,** R476 (July 5, 1944).

[3] D. W. Van Krevelen and H. A. G. Chermin, *Chem. Eng. Sci.*, **1,** 66 (1951).

[4] S. W. Benson and J. H. Buss, *J. Chem. Phys.*, **29,** 546 (1958).

***Table 12-3***

*Base group properties*

| Group | $\Delta Hf^\circ_{298.1}$ (g), kcal mole$^{-1}$ | $S^\circ_{298.1}$ (g), cal mole$^{-1}$ deg$^{-1}$ | Heat-capacity constants for ideal gas at $T$°K | | |
|---|---|---|---|---|---|
| | | | $a$ | $b$ (10$^3$) | $c$ (10$^6$) |
| Methane | −17.9 | 44.5 | 3.42 | 17.85 | − 4.16 |
| Cyclopentane | −21.4 | 70.7 | 2.62 | 82.67 | −24.72 |
| Benzene | 18.1 | 64.4 | 0.23 | 77.83 | −27.16 |
| Naphthalene | 35.4 | 80.7 | 3.15 | 109.40 | −34.79 |
| Methylamine | − 7.1 | 57.7 | 4.02 | 30.72 | − 8.70 |
| Dimethylamine | − 7.8 | 65.2 | 3.92 | 48.31 | −14.09 |
| Trimethylamine | −10.9 | | 3.93 | 65.85 | −19.48 |
| Dimethyl ether | −46.0 | 63.7 | 6.42 | 39.64 | −11.45 |
| Formamide | −49.5 | | 6.51 | 25.18 | − 7.47 |

***Table 12-4***

*Contributions of primary $CH_3$ substitution groups replacing hydrogen*

| Base group | $\Delta(\Delta Hf^\circ_{298.1})$ (g), kcal mole$^{-1}$ | $\Delta S^\circ_{298.1}$ (g), cal mole$^{-1}$ deg$^{-1}$ | Heat-capacity constants for ideal gas at $T$°K | | |
|---|---|---|---|---|---|
| | | | $\Delta a$ | $\Delta b$(10$^3$) | $\Delta c$(10$^6$) |
| Methane | − 2.2 | 10.4 | −2.04 | 24.00 | −9.67 |
| Cyclopentane | | | | | |
| Enlargement of ring | − 9.3 | 0.7 | −1.04 | 19.30 | −5.79 |
| First substitution | − 5.2 | 11.5 | −0.07 | 18.57 | −5.77 |
| Second substitution: | | | | | |
| *ortho* | −12.2 | | | | |
| *meta* | − 8.4 | | −0.24 | 16.56 | −5.05 |
| *para* | − 7.1 | | | | |
| Third substitution | − 7.0 | | | | |
| Benzene and naphthalene | | | | | |
| First substitution | − 4.5 | 12.0 | 0.36 | 17.65 | −5.88 |
| Second substitution: | | | | | |
| *ortho* | − 6.3 | 8.1 | 5.20 | 6.02 | 1.18 |
| *meta* | − 6.5 | 9.2 | 1.72 | 14.18 | −3.76 |
| *para* | − 8.0 | 7.8 | 1.28 | 14.57 | −3.98 |
| Third substitution (*sym*) | | 8.0 | 0.57 | 16.51 | −5.19 |
| Methylamine | − 5.7 | | | | |
| Dimethylamine | − 6.3 | | −0.10 | 17.52 | −5.35 |
| Trimethylamine | − 4.1 | | | | |
| Formamide | | | | | |
| Substitution on C atom | − 9.0 | | 6.11 | −1.75 | 4.75 |

carbons on the nucleus, *meta* to carbon atoms separated by a (minimum of a) single carbon within the ring. In the naphthenes formed by enlargement of the cyclopentane ring, we may also refer to a *para* substitution when the second replacement is on a carbon atom in the ring separated by (a minimum of) two carbons from the atom on which the first substitution was made.

Attention may be turned now to the effects of a second substitution on a single carbon atom of one of the base groups. These secondary replacements have to be treated in more detail because the changes in thermodynamic properties depend upon the nature of the carbon atom on which the replacement is being made, as well as upon that of the adjacent carbon atom. For this reason, these carbon atoms are characterized by "type numbers," as shown in Table 12-5. The thermodynamic changes associated with secondary methyl substitutions then may be tabulated as in Table 12-6. The number in the column headed "A" is the type number of the carbon atom on which the second methyl substitution is made, and that in the column headed "B" is the highest type number of an adjacent carbon atom, each number referring to the status of the carbon atom before the substitution is made.

In connection with these secondary methyl substitutions in Table 12-6, it is necessary to introduce two special categories for use in estimating changes in thermodynamic properties for esters and ethers. The last entry

**Table 12-5**

*Type numbers of different carbon atoms*

| *Type number* | *Nature* |
|---|---|
| 1 | $—CH_3$ |
| 2 | $—\overset{\mid}{C}H_2$ |
| 3 | $—\overset{\mid}{\underset{\mid}{C}}H$ |
| 4 | $—\overset{\mid}{\underset{\mid}{C}}—$ |
| 5 | C in benzene or naphthalene ring |

in Table 12-6 gives the changes accompanying the replacement of the H atom in the OH of a carboxyl group by a $CH_3$ group to form a methyl-ester. Similarly, the next to the last entry refers to the replacement of an H atom on the methyl group of an $OCH_3$ group in either an ether or an ester to form the corresponding ethyl ether or ester, as the case may be.

The effect of introducing multiple bonds in a molecule are treated in a category by themselves. The appropriate corrections have been assembled in Table 12-7 and require no special comments, except perhaps an emphasis upon the *additional* contribution which must be introduced every time a pair of conjugated double bonds is formed by any of the preceding substitutions in this table.

Finally we shall consider the changes in properties accompanying the introduction of various functional groups in place of one or two of the

**Table 12-6**

*Secondary methyl substitutions replacing hydrogen*

| A | B | $\Delta(\Delta Hf^\circ_{298.1})$ (g), kcal mole$^{-1}$ | $\Delta S^\circ_{298.1}$ (g), cal mole$^{-1}$ deg$^{-1}$ | Heat-capacity constants for ideal gas at $T$°K: $\Delta a$ | $\Delta b(10^3)$ | $\Delta c(10^6)$ |
|---|---|---|---|---|---|---|
| 1 | 1 | −4.5 | 9.8 | −0.97 | 22.86 | − 8.75 |
| 1 | 2 | −5.2 | 9.2 | 1.11 | 18.47 | − 6.85 |
| 1 | 3 | −5.5 | 9.5 | 1.00 | 19.88 | − 8.03 |
| 1 | 4 | −5.0 | 11.0 | 1.39 | 17.12 | − 5.88 |
| 1 | 5 | −6.1 | 10.0 | 0.10 | 17.18 | − 5.20 |
| 2 | 1 | −6.6 | 5.8 | 1.89 | 17.60 | − 6.21 |
| 2 | 2 | −6.8 | 7.0 | 1.52 | 19.95 | − 8.57 |
| 2 | 3 | −6.8 | 6.3 | 1.01 | 19.69 | − 7.83 |
| 2 | 4 | −5.1 | 6.0 | 2.52 | 16.11 | − 5.88 |
| 2 | 5 | −5.8 | 2.7 | 0.01 | 17.42 | − 5.33 |
| 3 | 1 | −8.1 | 2.7 | −0.96 | 27.47 | −12.38 |
| 3 | 2 | −8.0 | 4.8 | −1.19 | 28.77 | −12.71 |
| 3 | 3 | −6.9 | 5.8 | −3.27 | 30.96 | −14.06 |
| 3 | 4 | −5.7 | 1.7 | −0.14 | 24.57 | −10.27 |
| 3 | 5 | −9.2 | 1.3 | 0.42 | 16.20 | − 4.68 |
| 1 —O— in ester or ether | | −7.0 | 14.4 | −0.01 | 17.58 | − 5.33 |
| Substitution of H of an OH group to form ester | | +9.5 | 16.7 | 0.44 | 16.63 | − 4.95 |

methyl groups on a given carbon atom. These are listed in Table 12-8. The only likely source of confusion is perhaps in the formation of aldehydes or ketones. The figures given in the table refer to the changes accompanying the replacement of *two* methyl groups by a =O. Thus, when such a substitution leads to the formation of an aldehyde, the entropy change is $-12.3$ cal mole$^{-1}$ deg$^{-1}$. Similarly, a loss of two methyl groups and gain of a =O to give a ketone is accompanied by a change of $-2.4$ eu.

The procedure followed in the use of the tables of Andersen, Beyer, and Watson has been described for the estimation of standard entropies. These tables also include columns of base structure and group contributions for estimating $\Delta Hf^\circ_{298.1}$, the standard heat of formation of a compound, as well as $\Delta a$, $\Delta b$, and $\Delta c$, the constants in the heat-capacity equations described in Chapter 8, p. 157. Thus it is possible to estimate $\Delta G_{298.1}$ by appropriate summations of group contributions to $\Delta H^\circ_{298.1}$ and $\Delta S^\circ_{298.1}$. Then, if information is required at some other temperature, the constants of the heat-capacity equations may be inserted into the appropriate equations for $\Delta G^\circ$ as a

***Table 12-7***

*Multiple-bond contributions replacing single bonds*

| A | Type of bond | B | $\Delta(\Delta Hf^\circ_{298.1})$ (*g*), kcal mole$^{-1}$ | $\Delta S^\circ_{298.1}$ (*g*), cal mole$^{-1}$ deg$^{-1}$ | Heat-capacity constants for ideal gas at $T$°K | | |
|---|---|---|---|---|---|---|---|
| | | | | | $\Delta a$ | $\Delta b(10^3)$ | $\Delta c(10^6)$ |
| 1 | = | 1 | 32.8 | $-$ 2.1 | 1.33 | $-12.69$ | $+$ 4.77 |
| 1 | = | 2 | 30.0 | 0.8 | 1.56 | $-14.87$ | $+$ 5.57 |
| 1 | = | 3 | 28.2 | 2.2 | 0.63 | $-23.65$ | $+13.10$ |
| 2 | = | 2 | 28.0 | $-$ 0.9 | 0.40 | $-18.87$ | $+$ 9.89 |
| 2 | = | 2 *cis* | 28.4 | $-$ 0.6 | 0.40 | $-18.87$ | $+$ 9.89 |
| 2 | = | 2 *trans* | 27.5 | $-$ 1.2 | 0.40 | $-18.87$ | $+$ 9.89 |
| 2 | = | 3 | 26.7 | 1.6 | 0.63 | $-23.65$ | $+13.10$ |
| 3 | = | 3 | 25.5 | | $-4.63$ | $-17.84$ | $+11.88$ |
| Additional correction for each pair of conjugated double bonds | | | $-3.8$ | $-10.4$ | Approximately zero | | |
| 1 | ≡ | 1 | 74.4 | $-$ 6.8 | 5.58 | $-31.19$ | $+11.19$ |
| 1 | ≡ | 2 | 69.1 | $-$ 7.8 | 6.42 | $-36.41$ | $+14.53$ |
| 2 | ≡ | 2 | 65.1 | $-$ 6.3 | 4.66 | $-36.10$ | $+15.28$ |
| Correction for double bond adjacent to aromatic ring | | | $-5.1$ | $-$ 4.3 | Approximately zero | | |

*Table 12-8*

*Substitution group contributions replacing $CH_3$ group*

| Group | $\Delta(\Delta Hf^{\circ}_{298.1})$ (*g*), kcal mole$^{-1}$ | $\Delta S^{\circ}_{298.1}$ (*g*), cal mole$^{-1}$ deg$^{-1}$ | Heat-capacity constants for ideal gas at $T°K$ | | |
|---|---|---|---|---|---|
| | | | $\Delta a$ | $\Delta b(10^3)$ | $\Delta c(10^6)$ |
| —OH (aliphatic, *meta, para*) | −32.7 | 2.6 | 3.17 | −14.86 | 5.59 |
| —OH *ortho* | −47.7 | | | | |
| $—NO_2$ | 1.2 | 2.0 | 6.3 | −19.53 | 10.36 |
| —CN | 39.0 | 13.1 | 3.64 | −13.92 | 4.53 |
| —Cl | 0 for first Cl on a carbon; 4.5 for each additional | 0 | 2.19 | −18.85 | 6.26 |
| —Br | 10.0 | 3.0[a] | 2.81 | −19.41 | 6.33 |
| —F | −35.0 | − 1.0[a] | 2.24 | −23.61 | 11.79 |
| —I | 24.8 | 5.0[a] | 2.73 | −17.37 | 4.09 |
| =O aldehyde | −12.9 | −12.3 | 3.61 | −55.72 | 22.72 |
| =O ketone | −13.2 | − 2.4 | 5.02 | −66.08 | 30.21 |
| —COOH | −87.0 | 15.4 | 8.50 | −15.07 | 7.94 |
| —SH | 15.8 | 5.2 | 4.07 | −24.96 | 12.37 |
| $—C_6H_5$ | 32.3 | 21.7 | −0.79 | 53.63 | −19.21 |
| $—NH_2$ | 12.3 | − 4.7 | 1.26 | − 7.32 | 2.23 |

[a] Add 1.0 to the calculated entropy contributions of halides for methyl derivatives; for example, methyl chloride = 44.4 (base) + 10.4 (primary $CH_3$) − 0.0 (Cl substitution) + 1.0.

function of temperature, and $\Delta G^{\circ}$ may be evaluated at any desired temperature. The details of this procedure have been described adequately in Chapter 8 and hence will not be repeated at this point.

## Typical Problems in Estimation of Entropies

The use of these tables is illustrated best by consideration of several specific examples.

*Example* 1. Estimate the entropy, $S^{\circ}_{298.1}$, of *trans*-2-pentene(*g*).

```
              H
              |
Base group, H—C—H                    44.5
              |
              H
```

| | | |
|---|---|---|
| Primary $CH_3$ substitution → $CH_3—CH_3$ | | 10.4 |
| Secondary $CH_3$ substitutions → $CH_3—CH_2—CH_2—CH_2—CH_3$ | | |
| *Type numbers* | | |
| Carbon A | Carbon B | $\Delta S^\circ_{298.1}$ |
| 1 | 1 | 9.8 |
| 1 | 2 | 9.2 |
| 1 | 2 | 9.2 |
| Introduction of double bond at 2-position | | |
| 2 | 2 *trans* | −1.2 |
| Summation of group contributions | | 81.9 eu |
| Experimental value (NBS tables) | | 81.81 eu |

*Example* 2. Estimate the entropy, $S^\circ_{298.1}$, of acetaldehyde($g$).

```
                 H
                 |
Base group,  H—C—H                                44.5
                 |
                 H
```

Primary $CH_3$ substitution → $CH_3—CH_3$ 10.4

```
                                   CH3
                                   |
Secondary CH3 substitutions → CH3—CH
                                   |
                                   CH3
```

| *Type numbers* | | |
|---|---|---|
| Carbon A | Carbon B | $\Delta S^\circ_{298.1}$ |
| 1 | 1 | 9.8 |
| 2 | 1 | 5.8 |

Substitution of =O replacing 2 —$CH_3$

```
            H
            |
  → CH3—C=O                       −12.3
```

| | |
|---|---|
| Summation of group contributions | 58.2 eu |
| Experimental value (NBS tables) | 63.5 eu |

These examples illustrate the procedure used in the Andersen–Beyer–Watson method. The first is one with unusually good agreement, the second an example of an uncommonly poor case. In general it is preferable to consider the group substitutions in the same order as has been used in the presentation of the tables. Experience shows that when more than one base group is possible, the one with the largest entropy should be chosen. Also, best agreement with experimental values, when they have been known, has been obtained by the use of the minimum number of substitutions necessary to construct the molecule. In cases where several alternate routes with the minimum number of substitutions are possible, the average of the different results should be used.

## Other Methods

Although the tables proposed by Parks and Huffman[5] are based on older data, they are often more convenient to use, since they are simpler and also because they have been worked out for the liquid and solid states, as well as for the gaseous phase. A very complete survey and analysis of methods of estimation of thermodynamic properties is available[6] in Janz' monograph. The practicing chemist should have a general acquaintance with more than one method of estimating entropies, if he expects a high degree of success in predictions of the feasibility of new reactions.

## Accuracy of the Approximate Methods

Free-energy changes and equilibrium constants calculated from the enthalpy and entropy values estimated by the group-contribution method are generally reliable only as to order of magnitude. Andersen, Beyer, and Watson, for example, have found that their estimated enthalpies and entropies usually differ from experimental values, when known, by less than 4.0 kcal $mole^{-1}$ and 2.0 cal $mole^{-1}$ $deg^{-1}$, respectively. If errors of this magnitude occurred cumulatively, the free-energy change would be incorrect by approximately 4.6 kcal $mole^{-1}$ near 25°C. Such an error in the free energy corresponds to an uncertainty of several powers of 10 in an equilibrium constant. With few exceptions, such an error is an upper limit. Nevertheless, it must be emphasized that approximate methods of calculating these thermodynamic properties are reliable for estimating the feasibility of a projected reaction but are not adequate for calculating equilibrium compositions to better than the order of magnitude.

## Exercises

**1.** The following problem illustrates the application of calculations involving the third law to a specific organic compound, *n*-heptane. The necessary data may be

[5] G. S. Parks and H. M. Huffman, *The Free Energies of Some Organic Compounds*, Reinhold, New York, 1932.

[6] G. J. Janz, *Estimation of Thermodynamic Properties of Organic Compounds*, Academic Press, New York, 1958.

*Table 12-9*

| Temperature, °K | $C_p$, cal mole$^{-1}$ deg$^{-1}$ |
|---|---|
| 194.60 | 48.07 |
| 218.73 | 48.49 |
| 243.25 | 49.77 |
| 268.40 | 51.71 |
| 296.51 | 53.68 |

obtained from sources mentioned in the footnotes of Tables 12-1 and 12-2 of this chapter, or in Section 11-4, p. 216.

(a) From published tables of the enthalpy function, $H^\circ - H_0^\circ$, find $\Delta H^\circ$ for the reaction (at 298.16°K)

$$7C\ (\text{graphite}) + 8H_2\ (\text{hypothetical ideal gas}) = n\text{-}C_7H_{16}\ (\text{hypothetical ideal gas}) \quad (12\text{-}17)$$

(b) The following equation can be derived for the pressure coefficient of the enthalpy[7]:

$$\left(\frac{\partial H}{\partial P}\right)_T = V - T\left(\frac{\partial V}{\partial T}\right)_P \quad (12\text{-}18)$$

Using the Berthelot equation of state, derive an expression to evaluate $(H_{\text{ideal}} - H_{\text{real}})$, that is, the correction in enthalpy for deviations from ideal behavior, at any pressure, $P$ [analogous to Eq. (11-67) for $S_{\text{ideal}} - S_{\text{real}}$].

(c) Find the critical constants for $n$-heptane in the *International Critical Tables*, and its vapor pressure at 298.16°K in the tables of the American Petroleum Institute Research Project 44. Calculate the change in enthalpy for the transformation (at 298.16°K)

$$n\text{-}C_7H_{16}\ (\text{hypothetical ideal gas}, P = 1\ \text{atm}) = n\text{-}C_7H_{16}\ (\text{real gas}, P = p_{\text{vap}}) \quad (12\text{-}19)$$

where $p_{\text{vap}}$ represents the pressure of the vapor in equilibrium with liquid $n$-heptane.

(d) With the aid of data for the vaporization of $n$-heptane, find $\Delta H^\circ_{298.16}$ for the reaction

$$7C\ (\text{graphite}) + 8H_2\ (g) = n\text{-}C_7H_{16}(l) \quad (12\text{-}20)$$

(e) Calculate $S^\circ_{298.16}$ for liquid $n$-heptane from the heat-capacity data in Table 12-9 and from those for solid $n$-heptane given in Table 2-4. Integrate by means of the Debye equation to obtain the entropy up to 15.14°K and carry out a graphical

[7] See Exercise 3 at end of Chapter 8.

integration ($C_p/T$ vs. $T$) thereafter. Obtain $\Delta H°$ of fusion from American Petroleum Institute Tables.

(f) Calculate $\Delta S°$ for reaction (12-20) at 298.16°K. Use National Bureau of Standards data on graphite and hydrogen.

(g) Calculate the entropy of vaporization of liquid *n*-heptane at 298.16°K.

(h) Find the entropy change for the following transformation at 298.16°K:

$$n\text{-}C_7H_{16} \text{ (real gas, } P = p_{\text{vap}}) = n\text{-}C_7H_{16} \text{ (hypothetical ideal gas, } P = 1) \qquad (12\text{-}21)$$

(i) By appropriate summation of the results of Parts (f), (g), and (h), calculate $\Delta S°$ for reaction (12-17) at 298.16°K.

(j) Calculate $\Delta Gf^\circ_{298.16}$ for liquid *n*-heptane.

(k) Calculate $\Delta Gf^\circ_{298.16}$ for gaseous *n*-heptane in the (hypothetical ideal gas) standard state.

(l) From tables of the free-energy function $(G° - H^\circ_0)/T$, calculate $\Delta Gf^\circ_{298.16}$ for gaseous *n*-heptane in the (hypothetical ideal gas) standard state. Compare with the value obtained in (k).

(m) Estimate $S^\circ_{298.16}$ for *n*-heptane (gas) by the group-contribution method of Andersen, Beyer, and Watson. Compare with the result obtainable from the information in parts (f) and (i).

(n) Estimate $S^\circ_{298.16}$ for liquid *n*-heptane from the rules of Parks and Huffman. Compare with the result obtained in part (e).

**2.** (a) Using the group contribution method of Andersen, Beyer, and Watson estimate $S^\circ_{298.1}$ for 1,2-dibromoethane(*g*).

(b) Calculate the entropy change when gaseous 1,2-dibromoethane is expanded from 1 atm to its vapor pressure in equilibrium with the liquid phase at 298.1°K. Neglect any deviations of the gas from ideal behavior. Appropriate data on vapor pressures have been assembled conveniently by D. R. Stull, *Ind. Eng. Chem.*, **39**, 517 (1947).

(c) Using the data in Stull's publication, find the heat of vaporization of 1,2-dibromoethane at 298.1°K.

(d) Find the entropy, $S^\circ_{298.1}$, for liquid 1,2-dibromoethane.

(e) Compare the estimate obtained in part (d) with that obtainable from the rules of G. S. Parks and H. M. Huffman in *The Free Energies of Some Organic Compounds*, Reinhold, New York, 1932.

(f) Compare the estimates of parts (d) and (e) with the value found by K. S. Pitzer, *J. Am. Chem. Soc.*, **62**, 331 (1940).

**3.** Recent precision measurements of heats of formation and entropies are probably accurate to perhaps 60 cal mole$^{-1}$ and 0.2 cal mole$^{-1}$ deg$^{-1}$, respectively. Show that either one of these uncertainties corresponds to a change of 10 per cent in an equilibrium constant at 25°C.

**4.** It has been suggested [G. J. Janz, *Can. J. Res.*, **25B**, 331 (1947)] that 1,4-dicyano-2-butene might be prepared in the vapor phase from the reaction of cyanogen with butadiene.

(a) Estimate $\Delta Hf°$ and $S°$ for the dicyanobutene at 25°C by the group contribution method.

(b) With the aid of the following additional information, calculate the equilibrium constant for the suggested reaction:

| Substance | $\Delta Hf^{\circ}_{298.16}$, cal mole$^{-1}$ | $S^{\circ}_{298.16}$, cal mole$^{-1}$ deg$^{-1}$ |
|---|---|---|
| Butadiene(*g*) | 26,748 | 66.42 |
| Cyanogen(*g*) | 71,820 | 57.64 |

**5.** (a) Estimate $\Delta Hf^{\circ}$ and $S^{\circ}$ for benzonitrile, $C_6H_5CN(g)$, at 750°C by the group-contribution method, using toluene as the parent compound.

(b) Combining the result of (a) with published tables, estimate $\Delta G^{\circ}$ at 750°C for the reaction:

$$C_6H_6(g) + (CN)_2(g) = C_6H_5CN(g) + HCN(g)$$

An estimate of −18.4 kcal has been reported by G. J. Janz, *J. Am. Chem. Soc.*, **74**, 4529 (1952).

# Index